BIOLOGICAL STRUCTURE AND FUNCTION
VOLUME I

Biological Structure and Function

Proceedings of the First IUB/IUBS International Symposium Held in Stockholm, September 12–17, 1960

Edited by

T. W. GOODWIN

Department of Agricultural Biochemistry
Institute of Rural Science
Penglais, Wales

O. LINDBERG

The Wenner-Gren Institute for
Experimental Biology, University
of Stockholm, Sweden

Volume I

Withdrawn from UF. Surveyed to Internet Archive

1961

ACADEMIC PRESS · LONDON · NEW YORK

ACADEMIC PRESS INC. (LONDON) LTD.
BERKELEY SQUARE HOUSE,
BERKELEY SQUARE, LONDON, W.1

U.S. edition published by

ACADEMIC PRESS INC.
111 FIFTH AVENUE
NEW YORK 3, NEW YORK

Copyright © 1961, by Academic Press Inc. (London) Ltd.

Library of Congress Catalog Card Number: 61-17329

PRINTED IN GREAT BRITAIN BY
SPOTTISWOODE, BALLANTYNE & CO. LTD.,
LONDON AND COLCHESTER

Col. 416

Contributors to Volume I

PER-ÅKE ALBERTSSON, *Institute of Biochemistry, Uppsala, Sweden.*

VINCENT G. ALLFREY, *The Rockefeller Institute, New York, N.Y., U.S.A.*

ERIK ARRHENIUS, *The Wenner-Gren Institute for Experimental Biology, University of Stockholm, Sweden.*

KÅRE ASPBERG, *Research Laboratory, AB Pharmacia and the Institute of Biochemistry, Uppsala, Sweden.*

GUNNAR BLIX, *Medicinsk-kemiska Institutionen, Uppsala, Sweden.*

H. G. BOMAN, *The Institute of Biochemistry, Uppsala, Sweden.*

I. A. BOMAN, *The Institute of Biochemistry, Uppsala, Sweden.*

P. N. CAMPBELL, *Courtauld Institute, Middlesex Hospital, London, England.*

E. S. CANELLAKIS, *Department of Pharmacology, Yale University Medical School, New Haven, Connecticut, U.S.A.*

H. CHANTRENNE, *Laboratory of Biological Chemistry, Faculty of Sciences, University of Brussels, Belgium.*

ERWIN CHARGAFF, *Department of Biochemistry, Columbia University, New York, N.Y., U.S.A.*

J. N. DAVIDSON, *Department of Biochemistry, University of Glasgow, Scotland.*

ALBERT DORFMAN, *The LaRabida-University of Chicago Institute and the Departments of Pediatrics and Biochemistry, University of Chicago, Chicago, Illinois, U.S.A.*

PER FLODIN, *Research Laboratory, AB Pharmacia and the Institute of Biochemistry, Uppsala, Sweden.*

F. HAGUENAU, *Laboratoire de Médecine Expérimentale du Collège de France, Paris, France.*

MIRJAM HALMANN, *Department of Biology, Brookhaven National Laboratory, Upton, Long Island, N.Y., U.S.A.*

EDWARD HERBERT, *Department of Biology, Massachusetts Institute of Technology, Cambridge, Massachusetts, U.S.A.*

SHLOMO HESTRIN, *Department of Biological Chemistry, The Hebrew University, Jerusalem, Israel.*

C. H. W. HIRS, *Department of Biology, Brookhaven National Laboratory, Upton, Long Island, N.Y., U.S.A.*

GOTTWALT CHRISTIAN HIRSCH, *Zoologisches Institut, Göttingen, Germany.*

K. H. HOLLMANN, *Laboratoire de Médecine Expérimentale du Collège de France, Paris, France.*

H. HOLTER, *Carlsberg Laboratory, Copenhagen, Denmark.*

TORE HULTIN, *The Wenner-Gren Institute for Experimental Biology, University of Stockholm, Sweden.*

J. C. KENDREW, *MRC Unit for Molecular Biology, Cavendish Laboratory, Cambridge, England.*

JADWIGA H. KYCIA, *Department of Biology, Brookhaven National Laboratory, Upton, Long Island, N.Y., U.S.A.*

W. K. MAAS, *New York University School of Medicine, New York, N.Y., U.S.A.*

WINFIELD S. MORGAN, *Department of Pathology, Massachusetts General Hospital, Boston, Massachusetts, U.S.A.*

H. R. PERKINS, *National Institute for Medical Research, Mill Hill, London, England.*

GERTRUDE E. PERLMANN, *The Rockefeller Institute, New York, N.Y., U.S.A.*

PETER PERLMANN, *The Wenner-Gren Institute for Experimental Biology, University of Stockholm, Sweden.*

KEITH R. PORTER, *The Rockefeller Institute, New York, N.Y., U.S.A.*

PETER REICHARD, *Department of Chemistry I, Karolinska Institutet, Stockholm, Sweden.*

H. J. ROGERS, *National Institute for Medical Research, Mill Hill, London, England.*

SARA SCHILLER, *The LaRabida-University of Chicago Institute and the Departments of Pediatrics and Biochemistry, University of Chicago, Chicago, Illinois, U.S.A.*

PHILIP SIEKEVITZ, *The Rockefeller Institute, New York, N.Y., U.S.A.*

A. TISELIUS, *Institute of Biochemistry, Uppsala, Sweden.*

ALEXANDRA VON DER DECKEN, *The Wenner-Gren Institute for Experimental Biology, University of Stockholm, Sweden.*

M. H. F. WILKINS, *Physics Department, King's College, London, England.*

Preface

In 1956 The International Union of Biological Sciences (IUBS) decided to set up a Biochemistry Section Committee, which would be a Co-ordinating Committee between IUBS and the International Union of Biochemistry (IUB) and, through a Co-ordinating Committee of IUB and the International Union of Pure and Applied Chemistry (IUPAC), would also have contact with IUPAC. It was considered that the Committee would be specifically concerned with *chemical biology* within the framework of the Unions federated to the Councils of Scientific Unions (ICSU). The members of the Biochemistry Section Committee are at present: R. Brunel (Toulouse) and O. Lindberg (Stockholm) (appointed by IUBS), M. Florkin (Liège) and T. W. Goodwin (Aberystwyth) (appointed by IUB), and P. Boyer (Minneapolis) and F. Lynen (Munich) (co-opted members). Florkin and Goodwin were elected Chairman and Secretary respectively.

The first Committee meeting was held in 1958 during the 4th International Congress of Biochemistry in Vienna. It had been visualized throughout the discussions that an important function of the Committee would be to make suggestions for various International Symposia to both IUBS and IUB. It was agreed that subjects would be appropriate only if both biochemistry and the biological sciences were combining to produce a rapidly expanding sphere of knowledge. A number of possibilities were considered at Vienna and it was eventually decided that "Biological Structure and Function" was most appropriate at this time. This idea was accepted by the two International Unions and plans began to be formulated. It was readily agreed that the most suitable centre in Europe for such a symposium was the Wenner-Gren Institute, with its well-established, international reputation in this field and, furthermore, the project had the blessing and support of Dr. Axel Wenner-Gren himself, who honoured the Symposium by agreeing to act as Patron of Honour and by attending the Inaugural Session to deliver the opening address.

The IUB and IUBS have supported this Symposium financially but the realization of the Symposium would not have been possible without the generous aid of the Wenner-Gren Foundation, and of the various bodies in different countries which support the attendance of scientists at important international meetings. It was extremely satisfying to the organizers to know that these official bodies considered this First IUB/IUBS Joint Symposium worthy of support, and mention should be made of the National Science Foundation which supported so many of our U.S. participants; furthermore, in this connection the work done on our behalf by Dr. Elmer Stotz, the treasurer of IUB, should not be forgotten.

The organizers hope that this Symposium will be the forerunner of a long line of similar international symposia based on fruitful co-operation between biochemists and biologists from all nations.

The organizers are most grateful to the Institute of Physics, University of Stockholm, for their generosity in putting their attractive new lecture theatre at the disposal of the Symposium.

In preparing the proceedings for the press the organizers have been greatly helped by Miss J. T. Peel, who transcribed the recorded discussions, and by Mr. D. J. Howells, who prepared the subject index.

April, 1961   T. W. GOODWIN
O. LINDBERG

Contents of Volume I

Contents of Volume II

INTACT CELLULAR STRUCTURE AND FUNCTION

SPECIFIC MEMBRANE TRANSPORT AND ITS ADAPTATION

MACROMOLECULAR STRUCTURE AND FUNCTION

Introduction

A. Tiselius

Biochemical Institute, The University of Uppsala, Sweden

I think it is very interesting and significant that at this first joint Symposium of the International Union of Biochemistry and the International Union of Biology you have asked an ex-president of the International Union of Pure and Applied Chemistry to be in the chair during the first day's discussion of macromolecular structure and function. I have ventured to interpret this as signifying that these problems, so fundamental in biochemistry and biology, can now be discussed also in strictly chemical terms, and it is very gratifying that the host Unions in their activities do not feel themselves limited by barriers between different disciplines, barriers which no longer have any meaning.

It is very gratifying that among our speakers today we have several to whom we owe some of the most fundamental recent discoveries in this field which have made a symposium with today's subject possible and worth while for discussion.

Macromolecular substances in biochemistry were until not very long ago confined to what one might call "pre-structural" chemistry. That is to say, one had to content oneself with isolation and characterization, perhaps involving also one or two essential structure details. This is still a very important field of biochemistry, but it is a great advance that today we know that an almost complete structure analysis, also in a strictly chemical sense, can now be made on some typical and particularly important substances of this category. The methods of approach to such structural problems have proved of such general applicability that we have the right to be optimistic about further advances in the near future. It is particularly important just now to observe how different modes and ways of attacking problems of structure among biochemically important macromolecules at last merge together so that information of different kinds can be utilized in the final attempt to unveil a structure. This is, I understand, what is now happening in the field of protein structure, when X-ray crystallographic analysis data can now be combined with amino acid sequence determinations to work out the details of the structure (e.g. the position of the side chains). Something similar is happening in the nucleic acid field, although the advance there has naturally been slower.

When discussing biochemical *function* in relation to structure on a molecular level we are thus now gradually approaching the state in which we can say that we share the problems and the difficulties in some of the most advanced fields of physics and chemistry. The situation makes me recall a conversation I had with a distinguished elderly professor of organic chemistry when I was a young man and found myself gradually drifting from physical chemistry into biochemistry. "Be careful," he said, "this is a dangerous subject, and you will never become a good biochemist anyhow. What is the use of studying enzymes and the mechanism of their action until the phenomena of catalysis have been analyzed and elucidated by the physical chemists?" I have always doubted whether he was right in this, and today I doubt it still more. I do not propose to say that the biochemists can get much further than the physical chemists in providing the ultimate explanation for these and similar phenomena, but I do believe that they have brought to light a number of observations which must be of fundamental importance in any attempt to work out a general theory of catalytic function in the inorganic world. Thus the study of the functions of substances of complicated structure—such as we find in biological materials—may contribute just as much, or even more, to our basic knowledge in the field in general as a study confined only to the very simplest inorganic reactions. It would appear natural that this should be so: the phenomena of catalysis which we meet in biological matter are among the most striking and most specific found in Nature. Thus, quite aside from their interest *per se*, it must be worth while to study them from a very general and advanced point of view.

Discussion of function on a molecular level usually involves mechanisms of activation and the structural background of highly specific affinities. This is of course the case when we deal with reactions between, for example, a macromolecular enzyme and substrate molecule of smaller size. But it is also true when we deal with those specific interactions between different kinds of macromolecules which appear to play such an important role in the organized chemical reactions characteristic of life. Here also, structural aspects come into the picture and we then gradually find ourselves discussing organization rather than intermolecular structures without being able to define a borderline in the application of these terms. This is also reflected in the methods used, where electron microscopy goes hand in hand with methods of structure analysis such as X-ray crystallography and organic chemistry have provided. I shall not dwell upon this interesting field of "molecular biology", as this rather belongs to the programme of the following days—especially the forthcoming discussion about structure and function of certain submicroscopic particles. But I wish to emphasize that here again we have a field which is yielding much new information of a very general importance—also to the chemists. The elusiveness of the structures and functions involved in this highly organized matter is of a kind where biologists and biochemists with their gentle methods and somewhat greater reverence for Nature in its intact forms are more likely to succeed than the chemists.

The Structure of Globular Proteins

J. C. KENDREW

MRC Unit for Molecular Biology,
Cavendish Laboratory,
Cambridge, England

Proteins have probably been more intensively studied than any other class of molecule. Not only have they been subjected to exhaustive investigation by the classical techniques of organic chemistry, culminating in the determination of the complete amino acid sequence of insulin (by Sanger) and later of several other proteins; but also a whole armoury of physicochemical methods has been used to interpret the behaviour of proteins in solution and, finally, the kinetics and specificity of enzyme reactions have been investigated in great detail. All this work has had the object of understanding the function and biosynthesis of proteins in living organisms. Hitherto the chief obstacle in the way of applying the results of these researches to biological problems has been our ignorance of the *structure* of proteins, that is to say, of the three-dimensional arrangement of the atoms of which they are composed. The amino acid sequence is in effect a topological description; but in a molecule as complex as a protein topography is much more important than topology, because it is the spatial relations between the side-chains which determine the chemical behaviour of the molecule, and these relations cannot be determined, except in a fragmentary manner, by chemical methods.

We are now for the first time in a position to appreciate the general principles of protein architecture, indeed in one or two cases to understand their application in some detail. If we work upwards in the hierarchy of organization of protein molecules we find a remarkable alternation between the simple and the complex in structural arrangement. At the lowest level, the polypeptide chain itself is of the utmost simplicity, having the same backbone structure of repeated peptide groups whatever the side-chains attached to them (with proline as the only exception). When we examine the amino acid sequence, however—the so-called primary structure—we find a bewildering irregularity; there are no discernible periodicities in the sequence, which in some places seems to be entirely random and in others highly non-random, several identical side-chains being grouped closely together. At the next level, the spatial configuration of the polypeptide chain (the secondary structure), we find simplicity and regularity once more. This regularity was first appreciated by Astbury in his classical studies of fibrous proteins, resulting in his classification of polypeptide chain configurations into three main types, to one of which almost all known fibrous proteins conform. The most important of these is the so-called α-configuration, and its structural basis was revealed by

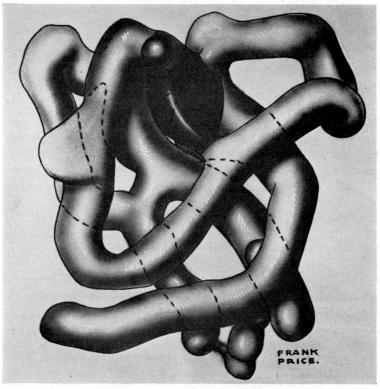

FIG. 1. Model of myoglobin based on the three-dimensional Fourier synthesis at a resolution of 6 Å, showing the general arrangement of the polypeptide chain and the position of the haem group.

Pauling and Corey [1] when they discovered the α-helix. For some time indirect evidence has been accumulating that the α-helix is a structural element in the globular as well as in the fibrous proteins, but definite proof of this has only recently been obtained, in the structure analysis of myoglobin.

The first stage of the X-ray analysis of myoglobin [2] gave a three-dimensional picture of the molecule at a resolution of 6 Å (Fig. 1), revealing the general arrangement of the polypeptide chain and of the haem group, in other words of the tertiary structure of the molecule. The tertiary structure is highly irregular and complex, in sharp contradiction to the simplicity of the secondary structure. More recently [3] the resolution of the analysis has been increased to 2 Å (Fig. 2). Although neighbouring covalently bonded atoms are still not resolved, it is now possible to separate atoms which are hydrogen bonded or in Van der Waals contact, with the result that the atomic arrangement of most of the molecule can

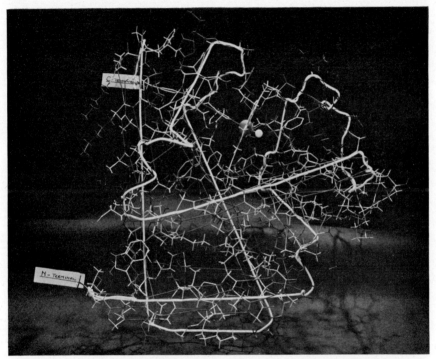

FIG. 2. Model of myoglobin based on the three-dimensional Fourier synthesis at a resolution of 2 Å. The model is seen from the same point of view as that of Fig. 1. The course of the main-chain is indicated by a white cord: side-chains have been inserted wherever possible.

be inferred. It turns out that all the straight regions of polypeptide chain are in the α-helical configuration; in fact the molecule consists of eight segments of α-helix joined by irregular regions of varying length; the helical segments comprise 75% of the amino acid residues, in agreement with estimates made on the basis of optical rotation and deuterium exchange studies. The appearance of the haem group corresponds closely with theoretical expectation, and it can be seen that the iron atom is attached to a neighbouring α-helix by means of a group which is almost certainly the imidazole ring of a histidine residue.

In the Fourier synthesis the side-chains can be seen as dense regions emerging from the helical main chain at intervals corresponding to the parameters of the α-helix. A close examination of these regions often makes it possible to identify a side-chain with certainty; in other cases some ambiguity remains but the choice of side-chain can be reduced to two or three. At the present resolution about one-third of the side-chains can be identified with certainty, and another third with fairly high probability. It now becomes possible to correlate these X-ray results with the preliminary data obtained by Dr. A. Edmundson who is engaged in working out the amino acid sequence of myoglobin by chemical methods. He has broken down the molecule into short peptides by tryptic digestion, and has determined the composition, and in a few cases the internal sequence, of these peptides. By comparing his results with our own it has proved possible to place almost all the tryptic peptides along the polypeptide chain, and the order of peptides thus ascribed corresponds with the order which has in a few cases been suggested by Edmundson on the basis of a preliminary examination of the chymotryptic digest. A few discrepancies remain, but although the amino acid sequence has not yet been completely determined, its main features are now beyond doubt. We are now engaged in an attempt to increase the resolution of the X-ray results still further, and we hope that the remaining ambiguities will then be removed.

Large molecules are often built up of sub-units, whose spatial arrangement may be called the quaternary structure. At this level of organization we return once more to simplicity and symmetry. Thus recent X-ray studies of haemoglobin by Perutz and his collaborators [4], resulting in a three-dimensional Fourier synthesis with a resolution of 5.5 Å, have shown that in this protein the four sub-units are arranged in the most symmetrical manner possible, namely at the vertices of a tetrahedron. Another very remarkable result has also emerged, namely that each of the four sub-units, consisting of a single polypeptide chain together with a haem group, very closely resembles the molecule of myoglobin in tertiary structure.

In still bigger molecules, such as the viruses, the number of sub-units may be very large, nevertheless their arrangement is highly regular. For example in tobacco mosaic virus there are about 2000 sub-units arranged in the form of a helix; in the spherical viruses the sub-units are arranged on the surface of regular or semi-regular polyhedra.

Thus we are now beginning to get a first glance at the general nature of protein structure at all levels of complexity. It seems certain that during the next 4 years these preliminary glimpses will lead to a detailed picture of the structure of proteins which will give an immense impetus to biochemistry generally, and indeed in many respects transform it.

References

1. Pauling, L., Corey, R. B., and Branson, H. R., *Proc. nat. Acad. Sci., Wash.* **37,** 205 (1951).
2. Bodo, G., Dintzis, H. M., Kendrew, J. C., and Wyckoff, H. W., *Proc. roy. Soc.* A **253,** 70 (1959).
3. Kendrew, J. C., Dickerson, R. E., Strandberg, B. E., Hart, R. G., Davies, D. R., Phillips, D. C., and Shore, V. C., *Nature, Lond.* **185,** 422 (1960).
4. Perutz, M. F., Rossmann, M. G., Cullis, A. F., Muirhead, H., Will, G., and North, A. C. T., *Nature, Lond.* **185,** 416 (1960).

Discussion

Tiselius: Is it possible by comparing the structure, derived by your crystallographic methods, of reduced and oxidized haemoglobin or myoglobin to get any hints about any structural changes which would accompany the combination with oxygen ?

Kendrew: A crystal of met-myoglobin can very easily be converted into the reduced form by diffusing into it a solution of sodium dithionite and watching the colour change. The crystal is quite unharmed by this procedure, and its X-ray pattern is virtually identical with that of met-myoglobin. If the same experiment is performed with haemoglobin, the result is quite different; haemoglobin crystals on reduction fall to pieces, and if one begins with a solution of reduced haemoglobin and adds salt the crystals which are formed are quite different from those of met-haemoglobin. The simplest hypothesis which would explain these results is that during oxygenation the haemoglobin molecule changes shape, the sub-units moving relative to one another: in myoglobin no such change could occur because there are no sub-units. This idea is purely speculative at present, but my colleague Dr. Perutz is now beginning a study of crystals of reduced haemoglobin with the object of discovering exactly what differences there are between its structure and that of met-haemoglobin.

Chance: It is obvious that Dr. Kendrew's results are important not only for those interested in the mechanism of oxygenation but also for those interested in the mechanism of haemoprotein action where the histidine group connected to the iron is of special importance. I have one question which is prompted by Philip George, as to how certain one may be that this link is histidine; how well does histidine fit the electron densities near the iron atom ? A second question is the interesting electron-dense material on the other side of the water molecule, which leads one to wonder in the reactions of the ferrimyoglobin which is really what we are talking about, the way which you would speculate that this material will interfere with ligands for the oxygen atom ?

Kendrew: At the present resolution of our Fourier synthesis of myoglobin, namely 2 Å, it is not possible to be absolutely certain of the identity of the haem-linked side chain in myoglobin, but it is very probably histidine. As an alternative we have tried to build a model of lysine into the electron density, but for several reasons this solution seems very unsatisfactory.

With regard to the group on the other side of the haem group, we are in more difficulty. We think it probable that this residue also is histidine, but there is a

B*

definite possibility that it is glutamic acid. It is probable that we shall have to wait for a more highly resolved Fourier synthesis before this question can be answered definitely.

There are indeed serious problems about the attachment of large ligand groups. We have found that p-iodophenyl isocyanide can be diffused into a crystal of myoglobin and that it combines at the haem group, producing the characteristic change in spectrum. When one looks at the model of the myoglobin molecule, and notes how closely the side chains are packed together, it is hard to understand how a ligand as large as this can approach the iron atom without a major disturbance in the structure. It may indeed be that some disturbance does take place, because we find that the p-iodophenyl isocyanide derivative of myoglobin crystallizes with slightly different cell dimensions from the normal crystal, and on some occasions assumes a totally new crystal form, which suggests that the overall shape of the molecule may have been slightly changed. In this connexion we are contemplating the possibility of making comparative studies of the detailed structure of myoglobin with different ligands attached to the haem group.

THEORELL: Of course, this change in shape of haemoglobin molecule on oxygenation is very interesting indeed, as it has been since the observation over 30 years ago of the strictly hyperbolic oxygenation curve of the myoglobin. Do you think the S shape could be a consequence of the change in shape of the molecule ? Could it explain why the introduction of the first oxygen for instance is so difficult and the latter ones so much easier ?

KENDREW: I agree that it is quite possible to imagine that the first oxygen becoming attached to haemoglobin in some way alters the relative position of the sub-units, so that subsequent oxygens can enter more readily. This idea, however, is purely speculative at present.

THEORELL: It would be very interesting to know if under low oxygen tension the whole change occurs at the introduction of the first oxygen molecule.

KENDREW: It would be very difficult to study this question experimentally unless somebody could discover a method of preparing crystals of haemoglobin in the partly oxygenated state.

HIRS: In applying the method of isomorphous replacement to myoglobin you prepared several heavy atom derivatives with reagents such as mercury diammine, aurichloride, etc., in which you were subsequently able to locate the position of the heavy atoms in regard to the 6 Å resolution structure. Can you now tell us with which residues these derivatives are formed ? I believe the information would be of interest to some of us.

KENDREW: The heavy atom groups which we used for working out the structure of myoglobin undoubtedly cause local disturbances on the side chains in their immediate neighbourhood. These disturbances mean that it is particularly difficult to identify just those side chains which are of most interest in the present context. In succeeding stages of the analysis we propose to use conventional refinement methods which do not involve the introduction of heavy atoms at all; if these methods are successful the problem of local disturbances will not arise and we shall then be in a position to identify the important side chains. Our impression is that in most cases the heavy atom groups do not combine in a strictly chemical fashion with the myoglobin molecule, but that they lodge in interstices in the lattice. This means that if the same molecule is crystallized in a new form, with a different packing arrangement, it reacts quite differently with heavy-atom ligands. Thus sperm whale myoglobin crystallizes in a monoclinic form from ammonium sulphate, and in an orthorhombic form from phosphate. In the former, p-chloromercuribenzene sulphonate enters the lattice at one place on the molecule and indeed proved to be one of our most useful heavy atoms. In the latter, the behaviour is entirely different; the group becomes attached at four different sites on the molecule and is really of little use for analytical purposes.

Molecular Configuration of Nucleic Acids

M. H. F. WILKINS

MRC Biophysics Research Unit,
Physics Department, King's College,
London, England

Need for certainty in the structure determination of DNA

Molecular theory of replication of genetic material and of mutation is based on the structure of DNA. Since the ideas of Watson and Crick concerning DNA are so aesthetically attractive and are now being extended in many ways to create almost a whole subject of nucleic acid biology (e.g. the structures of RNA's with various functions in protein synthesis are being derived by analogy with DNA), it is important that these ideas do not become a dogma and that alternatives are not ignored. It is also desirable that a stage be reached where the structure of DNA can no longer be regarded as hypothetical. It is essential therefore that the structure be placed on a sound basis of experimental fact.

It is generally agreed that DNA consists of two polynucleotide chains linked together by hydrogen bonds between adenine and thymine and between guanine and cytosine. It is, however, still a somewhat open question whether the hydrogen bonding scheme in the base pairs is that proposed by Watson and Crick or has some other form. Valuable evidence supporting the Watson–Crick scheme is supplied by the studies of enzymic synthesis of DNA (e.g. Josse and Kornberg [1]) and evidence in favour is also given by studies of complexes of synthetic polyribonucleotides [2]. I wish to discuss here, however, X-ray diffraction data on DNA itself and the extent to which these data provide an exact structure for DNA and give a unique solution.

Difficulties in the X-ray structure analysis of DNA

There are two main difficulties in studying DNA by means of X-ray diffraction. First, DNA, like other chain polymer molecules, does not form single crystals. The advantage of single crystals is that they enable diffraction to be separated in all directions in three dimensions. Second, the resolving power of the data has until very recently been insufficient to show individual atoms in the structure. The first difficulty has to a large extent been overcome: the DNA molecule is highly regular and fibres may be prepared which consist of aggregates of parallel microcrystals. With care in producing the DNA (by Dr. L. D. Hamilton of the Sloan-Kettering Institute, New York) and by taking pains with the diffraction

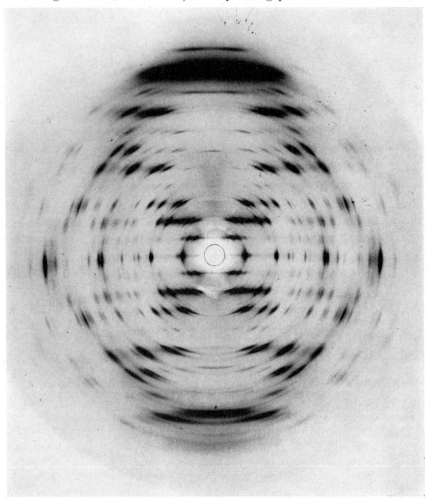

FIG. 1. X-ray diffraction photograph of microcrystalline fibres of the lithium salt of DNA.

technique we have gradually improved our fibre diffraction photographs, and such is their sharpness now that overlapping of reflections is to a large extent avoided (Fig. 1.) As a result we are able to separate a large proportion of several hundred reflections in three dimensions and obtain a reasonably accurate set of intensities. We have also reduced the difficulty of limited resolving power of the data. We have recently increased the resolving power by recording diffraction at angles corresponding to spacings as small as $1 \cdot 1$ Å. As mentioned later, we have not yet analyzed these new data but expect that they will improve considerably the results described here.

In our earlier work we had in the main analyzed the diffraction data in two dimensions and by trial had adjusted a molecular model until it was in agreement with the diffraction data in two dimensions [3, 4]. We have now used the three-dimensional data to check the accuracy of the model and to find the extent to which it is a unique solution. The Fourier synthesis method is convenient for this purpose. The syntheses which I will describe have been obtained by Dr. D. A. Marvin (aided by a computer programme written by Dr. O. S. Mills).

Principles of the Fourier synthesis method of structure analysis

The Fourier synthesis method [5] may in simple terms be described as follows. The diffracted X-rays have three characteristics:

1. Direction of diffraction.
2. Amplitude (given by the measured intensities).
3. Phase.

The direction of diffraction corresponds to the spacing of the electron density in the structure. A Fourier synthesis is produced if the various spacings, with correct amplitudes, are added together or subtracted. The result is that one obtains directly a picture of the structure. The phases of the diffracted beams, roughly speaking, tell one which amplitudes are to be added and which subtracted. Without knowledge of the phases the structure cannot be derived. The main difficulty with the X-ray diffraction method is that the phases are not given directly by the X-ray photograph. In favourable cases, phases can be derived by measuring intensities with and without a heavy atom placed in the molecule. This method has been used in the remarkably successful structure analysis of myoglobin [6].

Another approach is as follows. If one has already a roughly correct idea of the structure or of an appreciable part of it, one can obtain a complete and exact structure, provided that the X-ray intensity data are complete and exact. The procedure is to calculate the phases from the rough structure, in this case our molecular model, and perform a Fourier synthesis using the experimentally determined amplitudes and the calculated phases. The picture given by this synthesis has the following characteristics:

1. If the model is correct the picture is like the model (except that the limited resolving power may not enable all the detail of the model to be seen.)
2. If the model requires modification the picture is intermediate between the model and the correct structure. As a result one can see how to adjust the model to make it more nearly correct.

3. Parts of the structure not included in the model appear roughly in the picture, i.e. approximately half-height on the electron density contour map. For example the positions of water molecules in crystals of vitamin B_{12} have been determined ([7] and private communication) when phases were calculated from the vitamin molecule alone.

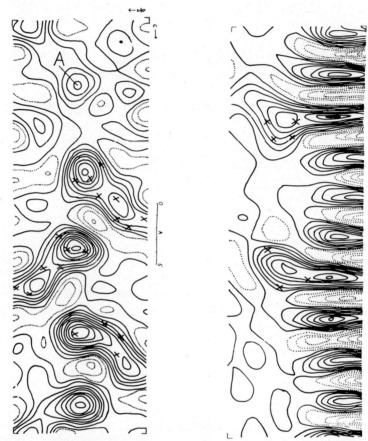

FIG. 2. (*Right*). Fourier synthesis of section through DNA molecule. The helix axis is vertical, approximately in the plane of the section, and on the right-hand side of the diagram. (*Left*). Section through phosphate groups of two neighbouring DNA molecules. *A* marks a peak that may correspond to a chloride ion. Two smaller peaks lie to the right of *A* and probably correspond to water molecules. The *X* marks show positions of atoms in the molecular model.

Fourier syntheses for DNA

Fourier syntheses of sections through the structure of the lithium salt of DNA are shown in Fig. 2. The model used for calculating the phases was the final model (Model 3) described in Langridge *et al.* [3, 4]. The section on the right in Fig. 2 is along the helix axis of a DNA molecule and shows the bases stacked on one another and confined to the central part of the molecule. Parts of the deoxyribose sugar ring are shown where the section passes through them. The section on the left is parallel to the helix axis but removed from it and passes through various phosphate groups. Some of the phosphate groups belong to one molecule and others

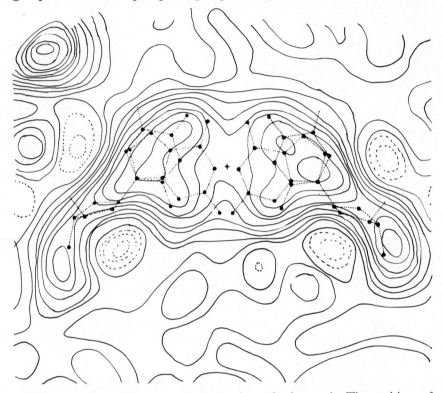

FIG. 3. Typical Fourier synthesis in plane of a base-pair. The positions of atoms in the model are shown. + marks the position of the helix axis. The base-pairs and deoxyribose rings show clearly in the synthesis.

to an adjacent molecule in the crystal. The resolution is insufficient to show separately the oxygen atoms of the phosphate groups. The main interest of this section is that in the region occupied by water and between the DNA molecules, several peaks appear on the contour map. Possibly several of these peaks correspond to water molecules and they do in fact occur in stereochemically likely positions. One peak at *A* is higher than the others and might be due to a chloride ion, for it is necessary that chloride be present in the DNA for the crystalline structure to form.

Figure 3 shows a section at right angles to the helix axis and in the plane of a base-pair. The position of the atoms in the model are marked. Since the sequence of bases along a polynucleotide chain is not periodic, the

FIG. 4. Fourier difference synthesis through same section as Fig. 3. The space between DNA molecules has been treated approximately as uniformly filled with water. There is almost no indication that the separation of the glycosidic links needs to be altered. If the Watson–Crick pairs were incorrect and the Hoogsteen scheme correct, the region near *AA* should be positive and that at *BB* negative. In fact the signs are the reverse.

X-ray diffraction method shows an average base. It may be seen that regions of high electron density correspond to the positions of atoms in the base and deoxyribose parts of the molecule. The distance between the glycosidic links appears somewhat larger on the Fourier section than on the model. However, the synthesis was performed without taking account of the presence of water in the structure. When the DNA molecule is treated as being immersed in water of uniform electron density [3, 4] this discrepancy largely disappears (Fig. 4).

Preliminary study of sections through all parts of the molecule indicates that the model requires little or no adjustment. This result is not surprising if we assume the water molecule peaks are not spurious, for unless the

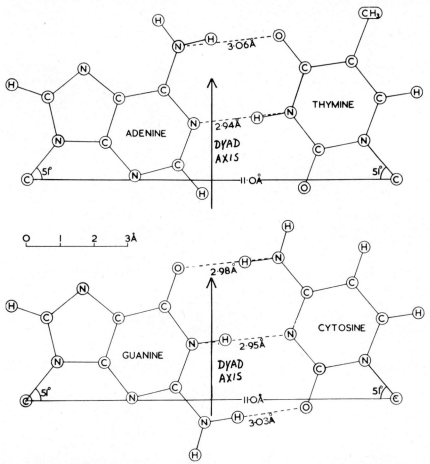

FIG. 5. Scale drawing of Watson–Crick base-pairs [10]. The glycosidic links all make an angle of 38° with the dyad axis and are equally distant from it.

positions of the DNA atoms were fairly accurate the synthesis would not have shown these molecules. It is clear, however, that the limited resolving power of the data so far used does not enable the positions of atoms in the base-pair to be distinguished. Therefore the question arises as to whether the atoms in the base-pair might be arranged in some other way which would also correspond with the observed data.

The Watson–Crick base-pairing schemes and possible alternatives

The Watson–Crick scheme [8, 9, 10] is shown in Fig. 5. It should be noted that the glycosidic links in both base-pairs are arranged symmetrically about a line (dyad axis) in the plane of the diagram and passing

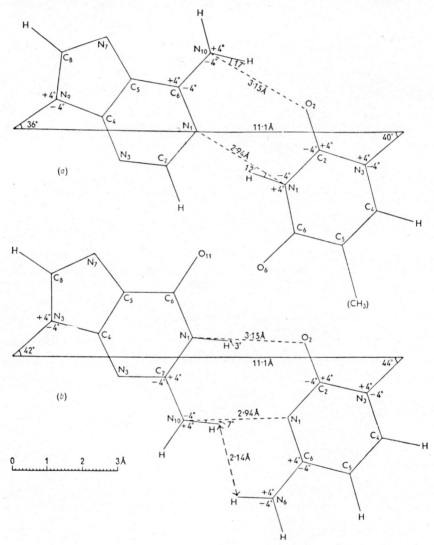

FIG. 6.   The Donohue base-pairs [10].

through the helix axis. As a result the molecule has the same appearance (apart from the sequence of bases) when turned upside down, i.e. when rotated 180° about the dyad axis. In both pairs the separation of the glycosidic links is the same. Attractive features of the base-pairing are that the hydrogen bonds are reasonable lengths [11] and almost linear, and that the positions and directions of the glycosidic links in all four

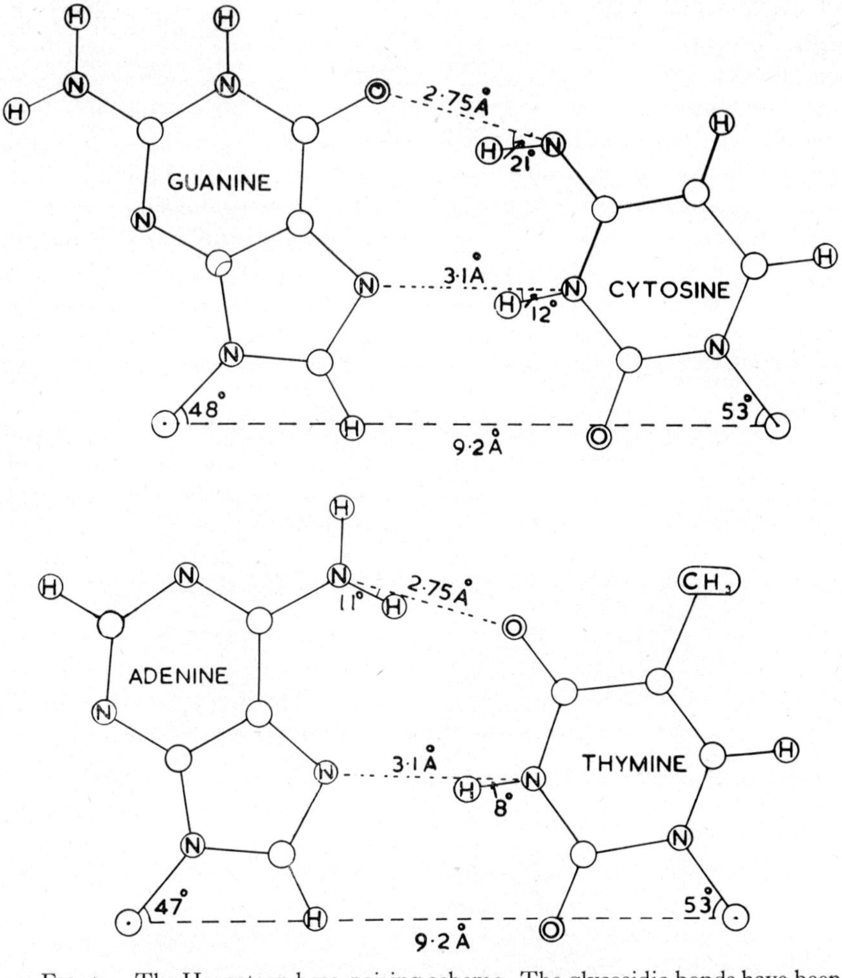

FIG. 7. The Hoogsteen base-pairing scheme. The glycosidic bonds have been placed as far apart as seems reasonable. (I am indebted to Dr. M. Spencer for this diagram.)

nucleotides can be made exactly the same [10]. This equivalence of glycosidic links enables the arrangement of the deoxyribose and phosphate atoms to be made identical in every nucleotide in the helical molecule.

As alternatives to the Watson–Crick scheme, two schemes are worth considering. The first is the Donohue pairing [12, 10, 13] shown in Fig. 6.

Although the two pairs give almost the same separation of the glycosidic bonds, the direction of the bonds cannot be made exactly the same. Some of the hydrogen bonds deviate appreciably from linearity. However, the stereochemical shortcomings are not so great that, considered from this viewpoint alone, the scheme would appear unlikely to apply to DNA. Other somewhat unfavourable features of the Donohue scheme have been discussed [10] e.g. considerations of the directions of atomic sequence in the two phosphate-ester chains in the molecule. The main difference between the Donohue and Watson–Crick schemes lies in the symmetrical relationship of the glycosidic links. In the Donohue scheme these bonds are not symmetrical with respect to a dyad axis perpendicular to the helix axis: as a result a double helix molecule with a structure of this kind will appear different when turned upside down, i.e. rotated 180° about a line at right angles to the helix axis. In other words a Donohue-type molecule may be specified with respect to a direction along the helix axis while Watson–Crick molecules are symmetrical and are the same in both directions.

The second scheme (Fig. 7) involves a hydrogen bond arrangement found between adenine and thymine [14, 15] and derives from a suggestion made by Professor Linus Pauling. We will refer to the scheme as the Hoogsteen scheme. The base-pairing is symmetrical as in the Watson–Crick scheme. The scheme requires cytosine to have a not very probable tautomeric form in which a hydrogen atom is moved from an amino group to a ring nitrogen atom.

Possible ways of constructing DNA models incorporating base-pairs alternative to those of Watson and Crick

In considering molecular models of DNA involving base-pairing schemes other than that of Watson and Crick, it is necessary that the position of the base, sugar, and phosphate parts of the molecule be placed in approximately the same position as in the Watson–Crick type model we have described [3, 4]. I think we can safely assume that no other arrangement would be compatible with the X-ray data. The idea that our model is at least in this sense unique is confirmed by comparison of the B and C configurations of DNA. We have shown that a small change in the configuration (mainly a displacement of the nucleotide position in the helical structure) causes the B diffraction pattern to change into the C pattern [16, 17].

Let us attempt to build, with Donohue pairs, a DNA model as required with the phosphate group positions related by the dyad axis referred to above. The glycosidic links will not be related by the dyad axis. Hence the base pair and the sugar groups will both be placed asymmetrically in

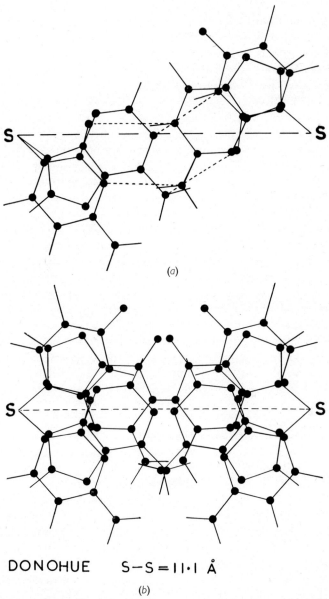

(a)

DONOHUE   S—S = 11·1 Å

(b)

FIG. 8.   (a) Donohue base-pairs arranged asymmetrically with respect to the line joining the points of attachment of glycosidic links to the deoxyribose rings in DNA. (b) Symmetrical arrangement of "average base-pair".

relation to the dyad. In each nucleotide pair the base-pair will be arranged lop-sided. There will be two arrangements: with base-pair extending as in Fig. 8(*a*) from bottom left to top right, or from top left to bottom right. If every base-pair is arranged in the same way, a regular helical model will be built. If this model is turned upside down the lopsided arrangement of the base-pairs will appear to have changed—the helical system of base-pairs will have rotated relative to the phosphate groups. If the model is viewed as a simple helix, the rotation is equivalent to a displacement in the helix axis direction. In a fibre of DNA there will on the average be an equal number of molecules up one way or the other. If one molecule passes through the repeat unit in the structure, as in the *A* structure [18], each repeat unit will at random contain base-pairs in one position or the other. This random arrangement will give rise to continuous diffraction along the layer lines on the diffraction pattern. The *A* type diffraction patterns of DNA give no trace of this continuous diffraction (Fig. 9). The possibility that the molecule contains an appreciable degree of asymmetry, as is required by the Donohue scheme, is therefore excluded.

There may be a possible way out of this difficulty. If the model were not built in a regular helical fashion but if successive base-pairs in a molecule were placed at random lopsided one way or the other, the base-pairs would on the average be symmetrical. The shape of the resultant average base-pair, consisting of two lopsided base-pairs lying criss-cross (Fig. 8(*b*)), would be extended considerably in the plane of the base-pairs. Such a model is unattractive because of its considerable irregularity (probably it would not be possible to form the phosphate-ester chains) and because the base-pairs would be stacked on one another only to a small extent and as a result their hydrophobic surfaces would be largely exposed.

The Hoogsteen base-pairs have the desirable feature, like those of Watson and Crick, of symmetrically-placed glycosidic links. The distance between the glycosidic links is smaller than in the Watson–Crick scheme by about 2 Å. (This difference could be larger—we have used a minimum value estimated by Dr. M. Spencer.) The other main difference in the base-pairs is that the six-membered ring in purines is placed, in the Hoogsteen scheme, to one side of the pair of hydrogen bonds (at *X* in Fig. 10), whereas in the Watson–Crick scheme this ring is at *Y* in line with the bonds.

A molecular model resembling DNA has been built consisting of adenine-thymine pairs of Hoogsteen type [19]. The diffraction pattern of the model resembles that of DNA but the agreement between calculated and observed intensities is not so good as that obtained with Watson-Crick pairing. However, the best way of comparing the agreement between calculated and observed intensities for different models is to use the Fourier

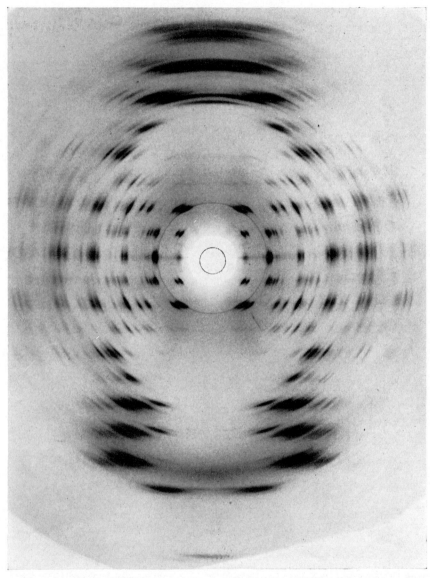

FIG. 9. X-ray diffraction pattern of sodium salt of DNA in *A* configuration. Clearly defined spots are seen and there is no sign of diffraction streaks along the layer lines.

synthesis method as described below. Stereochemical difficulty has been found in placing guanine-cytosine pairs in the model [19] but these difficulties may not be insurmountable.

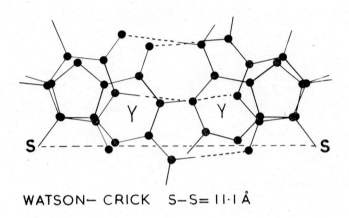

WATSON– CRICK   S–S= 11·1 Å

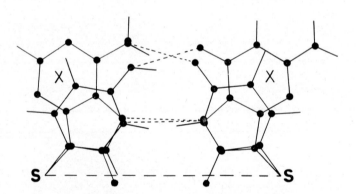

HOOGSTEEN S–S=9·2 Å MAXIMUM

FIG. 10. Comparison of the Watson–Crick and Hoogsteen base-pairing arrangements. The hexagonal purine ring is at X and Y in the two schemes.

Use of the Fourier synthesis method to assess the probability that base-pairs in DNA are not of the Watson–Crick type

We have built complete molecular models of DNA with Watson–Crick base-pairs [3, 4]. The Fourier synthesis method enables us to assess the probability that the base pairs are of a different type without constructing molecular models with alternative base-pairs or calculating diffraction from the models. If the base-pairs in the DNA model require modification, the nature of the modification should appear when the Fourier synthesis is examined.

Consider first the Donohue scheme. There is no indication in the syntheses in Figs. 3 and 4 that the average base-pair should be made larger, in the plane of the base-pair, than the average Watson–Crick pair. Therefore it is unlikely that the Donohue scheme exists in DNA. We may note, however, that a double-helix structure with glycosidic links arranged as in the Donohue scheme has been established for the two-chain complex of polyriboadenylic acid ([2] and private communication). The structure is clearly distinguishable from that of DNA, and the sequences of atoms in the two phosphate-ester chains run in the same direction and not in the opposite direction as experimental evidence (other than that obtained from X-ray diffraction) indicates is the case for DNA [1].

Examination of the Fourier syntheses also shows that the Hoogsteen scheme almost certainly cannot exist in DNA. First, it seems most un-likely that, as required in the Hoogsteen scheme, the distance between glycosidic links could be 2 Å less than in our model: if any alteration is required it is that the distance should be increased slightly. Second, there is no indication that the position of the purines in the base-pairs should be altered to that in the Hoogsteen pairs. This is shown most clearly in the Fourier difference synthesis (Fig. 4). Such a synthesis corresponds roughly to the difference between the real structure and the model used in the synthesis. If the real structure contained Hoogsteen pairs, the difference synthesis would have positive sign at AA Fig. 4, where the six-membered purine ring occurs in the Hoogsteen scheme, and negative at BB, where the ring occurs in the average Watson–Crick pair. The observed signs are opposite to those expected if the Hoogsteen scheme were correct. Hence, once more, the existence of the Hoogsteen scheme appears unlikely. We hope to confirm this conclusion by calculating a Fourier difference synthesis for the Langridge–Rich model containing Hoogsteen adenine-thymine pairs. If our approach is correct the synthesis will indicate that the Hoogsteen base-pair in the model should be replaced by the Watson–Crick pair.

It might be thought that because the X-ray data cannot resolve spacings less than 3 Å and as a result show individual atoms, the data could not be used to distinguish between two types of base-pairing in which the positions of the atoms differed in the main by less than 3 Å. This, however, is not so: the data can be used to distinguish between a structure that is nearly correct and one in which the atoms are displaced by 1 Å or even less. In the case of well-defined groups, such as the phos-phate group, the position may be determined to within 0·5 Å. We are, however, not satisfied with the present state of the X-ray analysis. The difference synthesis should have almost zero amplitude whereas in fact appreciable amplitudes are present. These are presumably due to errors in X-ray intensity measurements and errors in estimating the position of

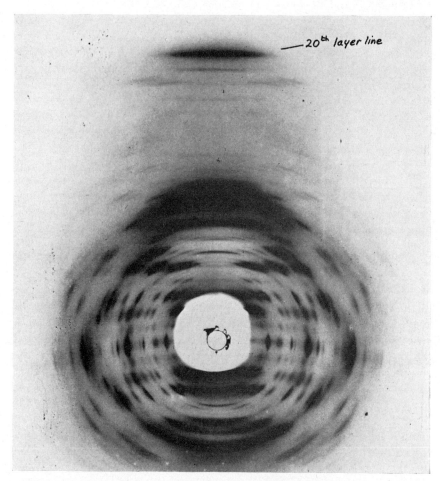

FIG. 11. X-ray diffraction photograph (with Mr. N. E. Chard) of lithium salt of DNA showing layer lines to the 20th. The diffraction corresponds to spacings extending down to 1·7 Å.

water molecules in the structure. Use of X-ray data of higher resolution would make the errors less important and give further confirmation of the correctness of the structure. Fortunately we have recently been able to obtain data of higher resolution, all layer lines to the 20th (1·7 Å) being observed (Fig. 11) and also an isolated reflection on the 30th layer line

(1·1 Å) (Fig. 12). We intend to use these data in future Fourier analysis. Another means of confirming the correctness of our analysis is to substitute bromide for chloride in the structure and show that the height of the supposed halide peak increases in the expected manner. We are at present obtaining intensity data from bromide-containing DNA.

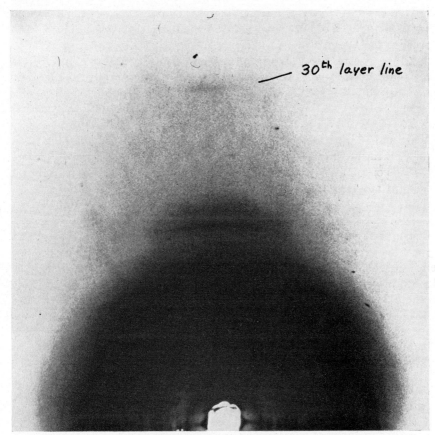

FIG. 12.   X-ray diffraction photograph (with Mr. N. E. Chard) of lithium salt of DNA showing 1·1 Å reflection on the 30th layer line.

Notes on the molecular configuration of RNA

Improved methods of preparing RNA and the separation of various types of RNA have helped to clarify X-ray diffraction studies of RNA. Soluble RNA (transfer RNA with amino acids attached) can be oriented in sheets and gives diffraction patterns which, though rather diffuse, are clearly similar to those of DNA [20]. It is fairly certain that these RNA molecules have a DNA type structure because other types of double-helix structure formed by synthetic polyribonucleotides [2] give recognizable and distinctly different patterns. Moreover the molar proportion of adenine and uracil and of guanine and cytosine are almost equal in this RNA. Mr. W. Fuller has modified the DNA structure and built a molecular model of RNA. The hydroxyl group of the ribose is accommodated in the structure by means of various slight distortions. The molecule is stabilized by a hydrogen bond between the hydroxyl oxygen atom and an atom of the adjacent phosphate group.

This type of structure appears to hold also for ribosomal RNA from *Escherichia coli* [21]. It has not been found possible to orient the double-helices in this RNA. It appears likely therefore that double helical regions of the molecule are linked together by non-helical parts to form a cluster of short helical regions. This is probably the structure within the ribosomes because the diffraction pattern of ribosomes is the same as that of the RNA mixed with protein.

It is of interest that earlier preparations of RNA, e.g. from liver, yeast, tobacco mosaic virus, etc., always gave a double helical pattern which, though having a general resemblance to that of DNA, showed distinct differences [22]. It has been noted [21] that this RNA pattern resembles that of a mixture of DNA and double-helix polyriboadenylic acid [2]. Presumably some of these RNA specimens consisted largely of ribosome material. It may be that the earlier methods of preparation caused the RNA molecule to be extended into a filamentous form capable of being oriented and that parts of the molecule had approximately DNA-like base-sequences and that other parts contained more predominantly adenine and formed anti-parallel double-helix structures. This problem is being investigated further. In all cases, however, the length of regular DNA-like regions in RNA is restricted and the diffraction patterns are not well defined. The relation of structure to function in RNA is not yet clear, it has been found, for instance, that the original intact double-helix structure is not required in soluble RNA for amino acid-binding activity to be present [20].

Acknowledgments

In this brief space I will not attempt to acknowledge all those who have contributed to this work but I wish to mention specially Drs. D. A. Marvin and M. Spencer, Mr. W. Fuller, and the University of London Computer Unit.

References

1. Josse, J. and Kornberg, A., *Fed. Proc.* **19,** 305 (1960).
2. Rich A., *in* "A Symposium on Molecular Biology", ed. R. E. Zirkle, University of Chicago Press (1959).

3. Langridge, R., Marvin, D. A., Seeds, W. E., Wilson, H. R., Hooper, C. W., Wilkins, M. H. F., and Hamilton, L. D., *J. mol. Biol.* **2**, 38 (1960).
4. Langridge, R., Wilson, H. R., Hooper, C. W., Wilkins, M. H. F., and Hamilton, L. D., *J. mol. Biol.* **2**, 19 (1960).
5. Lipson, H., and Cochran, W., "The Determination of Crystal Structures", G. Bell, London (1957).
6. Kendrew, J. C., Dickerson, R. E., Strandberg, B. E., Hart, R. G., Davies, D. R., Phillips, D. C., and Shore, V. C., *Nature, Lond.* **185**, 422 (1960).
7. Hodgkin, D. C., Pickworth, J., Robertson, J. H., Prosen, R. J., Sparks, R. A., and Trueblood, K. N., *Proc. roy. Soc.* A **251**, 306 (1959).
8. Crick, F. H. C., and Watson, J. D., *Proc. roy. Soc.* A **223**, 80 (1954).
9. Pauling, L., and Corey, R. B. *Arch. Biochem. Biophys.* **65**, 164 (1956).
10. Spencer, M., *Acta Cryst.* **12**, 60 (1959).
11. Fuller, W., *J. phys. Chem.* **63**, 1705 (1959).
12. Donohue, J., *Proc. nat. Acad. Sci., Wash.* **42**, 60 (1956).
13. Donohue, J., and Trueblood, K. N., *J. mol. Biol.* **2**, 363 (1960).
14. Hoogsteen, K., *Acta Cryst.* **12**, 822 (1959).
15. Pauling, L., "The Nature of the Chemical Bond", 3rd Edn. Cornell Univ. Press, Ithaca, N.Y., 504 (1960).
16. Marvin, D. A., Spencer, M., Wilkins, M. H. F., and Hamilton, L. D., *Nature, Lond.* **182**, 387 (1958).
17. Marvin, D. A., Spencer, M., Wilkins, M. H. F., Hamilton, L. D., *J. mol. Biol.* in press (1961).
18. Langridge, R., Seeds, W. E., Wilson, H. R., Hooper, C. W., Wilkins, M. H. F., and Hamilton, L. D., *J. biophys. biochem. Cytol.* **3**, 767 (1957).
19. Langridge, R., and Rich, A. *Int. Union of Crystallography Fifth International Congress*, abstracts 78 (1960).
20. Brown, G. L., and Zubay, G., *J. mol. Biol.* **2**, 287 (1960).
21. Zubay, G., and Wilkins, M. H. F., *J. mol. Biol.* **2**, 105 (1960).
22. Rich, A., and Watson, J. D., *Proc. nat. Acad. Sci., Wash.* **40**, 759 (1954).

Discussion

CHARGAFF: I want to ask Dr. Wilkins a question concerning the nucleoproteins. There is some evidence I believe that the nucleic acids in the cell are mostly present as complicated nucleoproteins, nucleoprotamines and nucleohistones. I believe that Dr. Wilkins has published some evidence about nucleoprotamines which seems to indicate that the structure of DNA is maintained in these protamine complexes. However, there are much more complicated nucleoproteins found, for instance, in bacteria. We have described a deoxyribonucleoprotein from tubercle bacilli which seems to contain one amino acid equivalent per two nucleotides. It is a very peculiar and stable nucleoprotein which cannot be dissociated by strong salt concentrations; and I am wondering whether anything is known of the X-ray structure of these more highly organized nucleoproteins or, for that matter, whether anything is known about the X-ray structure of the single strand DNA as isolated from a small virus.

WILKINS: I did not attempt in this talk to get on to the subject of nucleoproteins which is a big and very interesting subject. There is, as Dr. Chargaff points out, good evidence that the nucleic acids do on the whole retain their double helical configuration in nucleoproteins. The diffraction diagram of nucleoprotamine is very similar to that of DNA and it is clear that the DNA retains its configuration when combined with protamine. Nucleohistone in the chromosomes of somatic cells of higher organisms again gives an X-ray diffraction diagram which is characteristic of the double helix of DNA; it appears that the protein is rather loosely bound and fills the space between the DNA molecules. In the case of bacteria we have so far only looked at one nucleoprotein which Dr. G. Zubay in our laboratory prepared from *E. coli*. In that case the X-ray diffraction diagram, which we published, shows that much of the DNA is in the double-helix form. It also shows that the DNA is largely free from protein. We cannot be certain that some of this free DNA might not be an artifact of the extraction procedure. Dr. Kellenberger has evidence from electron microscope studies on *E. coli* that the chromosomes in these bacteria may not consist of nucleoprotein, but might consist of DNA itself. One can see the individual threads of the DNA molecules passing through the nucleus. In the case of RNA the same also appears roughly to be true and the diffraction pattern from ribosomes of *E. coli* is essentially the same as that from a mixture of protein and double-helix RNA. These results have been confirmed by Dr. Klug and his colleagues at Birkbeck College. In many nucleoproteins, and *in vivo*, both the RNA and DNA have a double helical configuration and the protein is somehow built around them and does not alter that configuration very much. There certainly are exceptions to this rule and there is no double helix, for instance, in tobacco mosaic virus; there the RNA is a single chain molecule and does not have a configuration at all resembling that of the DNA double helix; it may be that other exceptions will be found and that the interesting nucleoprotein from tubercle bacilli, referred to by Dr. Chargaff has a special structure. We do know, however, that the tubercle DNA after separation from the protein has the usual double-helix structure.

Partition of Macromolecules in Aqueous Two-Phase Systems

PER-ÅKE ALBERTSSON

Institute of Biochemistry, Uppsala, Sweden

Separation of substances by partition between two immiscible solvents is one of the most frequently used methods in organic chemistry; in inorganic chemistry, partition has also been widely used both for preparative and analytical purposes. Many biochemical substances, such as polypeptides and even proteins, have also been studied by partition methods, for example countercurrent distribution [1, 2].

One of the advantages of partition between two liquid phases is that there is generally a greater possibility of obtaining a state of equilibrium between two liquid phases than between a solid and a liquid phase. This is particularly so when macromolecules are involved. It would be of great value if partition methods could also be applied to very high molecular weight macromolecules of biological origin such as proteins, highly polymerized nucleic acids, viruses, and cell particles. In recent years we have studied this possibility in Uppsala and the present paper will describe some experiments and a summary of the results obtained. A monograph [3] dealing with the theoretical background and experimental details has recently been published.

Polymer two-phase systems

In order to partition successfully biochemical macromolecules one cannot usually use conventional two-phase systems containing an organic solvent since this may cause denaturation. Instead a number of polymer two-phase systems, obtained by mixing aqueous solution of two different polymers, have been used. It is a general phenomenon [4] that when polymer solutions are mixed they give rise to two liquid phases, one phase containing one polymer and the other phase the other polymer; both phases have a high water content (85–99%). Two aqueous phases in equilibrium are thus obtained. The difference in composition between the phases is comparatively small; the interfacial tension, the differences between the refractive indices and the densities of the two phases are therefore much smaller for polymer phase systems than for conventional,

c

low molecular weight phase systems. Due to the presence of the polymers in the phases, their viscosities are relatively high. The time of phase separation is comparatively long for polymer two-phase systems; varying from about 5 minutes to 1 day. Both non-ionic polymers and poly-electrolytes may be used for the construction of a two-phase system [3]. By varying the molecular weight, the number of non-polar groups, or the number of charged groups on the polymers, a large number of phase systems having highly diversified properties may be obtained. The phase systems may be complemented by adding low molecular weight sub-stances, such as sucrose or electrolytes, to achieve a suitable environment for biological material.

Partition of proteins, nucleic acids, and viruses

The partitioning of a particle in a two-phase system depends mainly on its surface properties including the area and the chemical properties of the outer layer of the particle.

The partition coefficients of some proteins and viruses have been measured in a two-phase system of dextran and methylcellulose [3, 5] and

TABLE I

THE PARTITION COEFFICIENT, K, AND THE SURFACE AREA OF A NUMBER OF VIRUS PARTICLES AND PROTEIN MOLECULES IN A TWO-PHASE SYSTEM OF DEXTRAN AND METHYLCELLULOSE AT $4°$.*

Data from refs. [3] and [5].

Particle	K	Surface area $(m\mu)^2$
Phycoerythrin	0·95	0·3
Haemocyanin "eighth"	0·62	0·86
Haemocyanin whole	0·25	3·5
Echo virus	0·2–0·3	1·3
Polio virus	0·2	2·3
Phage T3	$2·3 \times 10^{-2}$	8·7
Tobacco mosaic virus	$(1–2) \times 10^{-2}$	14·4
Phage T2	$(6–10) \times 10^{-4}$	25·5
Phage T4	$(3–5) \times 10^{-4}$	25·5
Vaccinia	$(4–12) \times 10^{-5}$	220

the results are given in Table I together with the surface areas of the partitioned particles, calculated from their form and dimensions as determined with the electron microscope. As may be seen in Table I, all particles favour the bottom phase and the partition coefficient becomes smaller the larger the particle size. In Fig. 1, the log K values are plotted against the particle surface area; it can be seen that the points lie around a

* (K = concentration in top phase/concentration in bottom phase.)

straight line indicating that in this phase system it is mainly the surface area which determines the K value. An upper limit of the K value is obtained which is probably due to incomplete separation of the phases. No K value less than 10^{-4} has been observed even for very large particles.

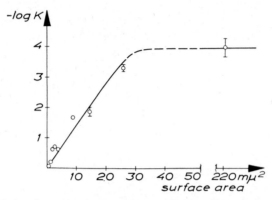

FIG. 1.   Relation between the partition coefficient, K, and the surface area of virus particles and protein molecules. The data of Table I are plotted in this figure.

The fact that the virus concentration is 1000 to 10 000 times higher in one phase than in the other, may be utilized for the concentration and purification of viruses [3, 6, 7, 8, 9, 10].

TABLE II

DISTRIBUTION OF SOME NUCLEIC ACID PREPARATIONS IN A NA DEXTRAN SULPHATE– METHYLCELLULOSE SYSTEM

C_t = concentration in top phase, C_b = concentration in bottom phase, V_b = volume of bottom phase, a = amount of nucleic acid collected at the interface (Lif *et al.* to be published; for experimental details see ref. [3]).

Nucleic acid	$S_{20,w}$	$K_i = \dfrac{C_t}{C_b + a/V_b}$
RNA from yeast	3·5	0·67
DNA from calf thymus (I)	20·4	0·17
DNA from calf thymus (II)	21·8	0·14
DNA from calf thymus (III)	22·5	0·12
DNA from phage T2 (I)	31·1	0·012
DNA from phage T2 (II)	31·5	0·08
DNA from phage T2 (III)	33·0	0·02

Partition of some nucleic acid preparations has recently been studied [11] in a dextran sulphate–methylcellulose system. Preliminary results are shown in Table II and Fig. 2. In this phase system a major part of the nucleic acids collected at the interface. This part was included in the bottom phase and thus the K_i values given in Table II are not strictly partition coefficients. As may be seen in Table II, the larger the sedimentation constant the smaller the tendency for the nucleic acids to partition in favour of the top phase.

Most proteins in the native state partition in favour of the lower phase of the dextran–methylcellulose system and the partition coefficient is

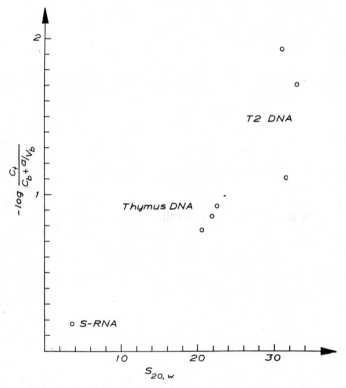

FIG. 2. Relation between the "partition coefficient", K_i, and the sedimentation constant, S_{20}, for a number of nucleic acid preparations. The data of Table II are plotted in this figure.

little influenced by the electrolyte composition. Thus, if the partition is carried out in the presence of a 0·01 M buffer and an excess (0·1 M) of NaCl, the partition coefficient is constant over a wide pH range; see Fig. 3, where an experiment with human serum albumin is recorded [3]. Below pH 4–5, however, the K value increases and even becomes greater than unity, indicating that the protein has more affinity for the top phase at acid pH values. It is interesting to compare this result with the viscosity and optical rotation of serum albumin as a function of pH. Thus there is

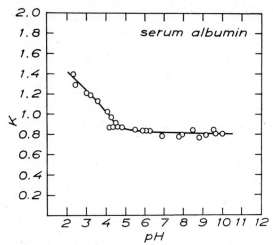

FIG. 3.   Partition coefficient, K, of serum albumin as a function of pH in a dextran–methylcellulose system. From ref. [3].

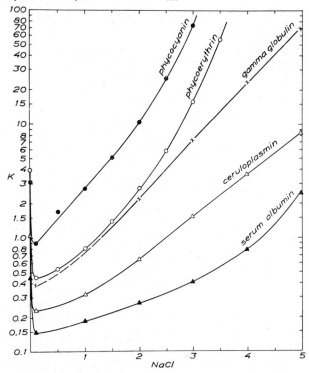

FIG. 4.   Partition coefficient, K, of a number of proteins in a dextran–poly-ethylene glycol system with 0·005 M KH_2PO_4 and increasing concentrations of NaCl; the latter is expressed as moles NaCl added to 1 kg of phase system. For experimental details see ref. [3].

an increase in the limiting viscosity number [12, 13] and in the laevorotation [14] at low pH values indicating a change in the structure of the protein. It has also been reported [15] that there is an increase in the number of hydrophobic groups on the protein surface at low pH values which could explain why the protein at these pH values favours the top phase containing more methyl groups than the bottom phase. If this explanation is correct it means that partition provides a method for the determination of the "hydrophobicity" of proteins and particles.

It was mentioned above that the partition in the dextran–methylcellulose system is only influenced to a small degree by the electrolyte composition. In contrast, the dextran–polyethylene glycol system shows many

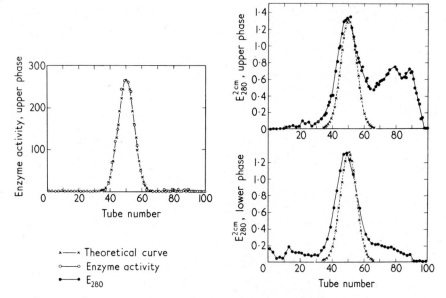

FIG. 5. Countercurrent distribution of partly purified ceruloplasmin in a dextran–polyethylene glycol system. From refs. [3] and [18].

striking salt effects [3, 16]. Thus, a protein or particle may be transferred almost entirely from one phase to the other by changing the salt content. As may be seen in Fig. 4, where the partition coefficients of a number of proteins in a dextran–polyethylene glycol system are recorded, phycoerythrin is in the top phase $(K=5)$ with o·o1 M phosphate buffer pH = 6·8. If NaCl is added up to o·1 M, the protein is transferred to the bottom phase $(K=0·3)$; further additions of NaCl increase the K value so that the proteins again partitions in favour of the top phase. When the concentration of NaCl is increased from 1 to 5 M, all proteins studied transfer to the top phase. Further information on the partition of proteins in the dextran–polyethylene glycol system may be found in refs. [3] and [16]. The dextran–polyethylene glycol system is useful in the countercurrent distribution of proteins [17, 18]. The settling time of this system may be as short as 5–10 minutes. A countercurrent distribution experiment [18] with a partly purified preparation of ceruloplasmin is recorded in Fig. 5. The enzyme activity curve is almost identical with the theoretical curve indicating that the enzyme activity is associated with a single component. Most experiments indicate that proteins partition according to the Nernst partition law in the dextran–polyethylene glycol system, that is, the value of the partition coefficient is independent of the protein concentration and the presence of other proteins. This phase system may therefore be used for characterization and fractionation of proteins.

References

1. Tavel, P., and Signer, R., "Advances in Protein Chemistry" **11**, 237 Academic Press, New York (1956).
2. Craig, L. C., *in* "A Laboratory Manual of Analytical Methods of Protein Chemistry", Vol. 1, ed. P. Alexander and K. J. Block. Pergamon Press, Oxford, 121 (1960).
3. Albertsson, P.-Å., "Partition of Cell Particles and Macromolecules". Almqvist & Wiksell, Stockholm; John Wiley & Sons, Inc., New York (1960).
4. Dobry, A., and Boyer-Kawenoki, F., *J. Polym. Sci.* **2,** 90 (1947).
5. Albertsson, P.-Å., and Frick, G., *Biochim. biophys. Acta* **37,** 230 (1960).
6. Frick, G., and Albertsson, P.-Å., *Nature, Lond.* **183,** 1070 (1959).
7. Wesslén, T., Albertsson, P.-Å., and Philipson, L., *Arch. Virusforsch.* **9,** 510 (1959).
8. Philipson, L., Albertsson, P.-Å., and Frick, G., *Virology* **11,** 553 (1960).
9. Norrby, E., and Albertsson, P.-Å., *Nature, Lond.* **188,** 1047 (1960).
10. Frick, G., *Exp. Cell Res.* (in press).
11. Lif, T., Frick, G., and Albertsson, P.-Å., to be published.
12. Tanford, C., "Symposium on Protein Structure", ed. A. Neuberger. Methuen & Co. Ltd., London; John Wiley & Sons, Inc., New York, 35 (1958).
13. Yang, J. T., and Foster, J. F., *J. Amer. chem. Soc.* **76,** 1588 (1954).
14. Sterman, M., and Foster, J. F., *J. Amer. chem. Soc.* **78,** 3652 (1956).
15. Foster, J. F., in Putnam, F. W., "The Plasma Proteins", Vol. 1. Academic Press, New York, 1 (1960).
16. Albertsson, P.-Å., and Nyns, E. J., *Ark. Kemi* **17,** 197 (1961).
17. Albertsson, P.-Å., and Nyns, E. J., *Nature, Lond.* **184,** 1465 (1959).
18. Broman, L., and Albertsson, P.-Å., to be published.

Discussion

HIRS: Have there been any studies on the rate at which equilibrium has been obtained with some of these systems?

ALBERTSSON: We haven't studied this systematically but it appears that just a few inversions are enough to get an equilibrium.

THEORELL: How is the separation of these materials from the polymers achieved?

ALBERTSSON: There is not one general method, of course; different methods are used for different materials. One way, for example, is to use adsorption. In the case of the proteins, we have adsorbed the protein on a column of calcium phosphate and the polymers, being non-ionic, pass through and may be washed away. This is a convenient method and a concentration of the proteins is obtained at the same time. Another way is to transfer the substance from a polymer phase to a polymer-free phase. If we are using the dextran–polyethylene glycol system we can, by adding salt, transfer the protein to the top phase which contains polyethylene glycol as the only polymer. This top phase can then be transferred to another tube and mixed with ammonium sulphate (or potassium phosphate) when we get a new phase system consisting of a polyethylene glycol phase in equilibrium with an ammonium sulphate phase, this latter phase containing almost no polyethylene glycol. If one is lucky, the protein is transferred to the ammonium sulphate phase under these circumstances. This method works for some of the serum proteins, for example ceruloplasmins. It is possible to adjust the volumes of the phases so that a concentration of the protein is obtained at the same time.

The Reactivity of Certain Functional Groups in Ribonuclease A towards Substitution by 1-Fluoro-2,4-dinitrobenzene. Inactivation of the Enzyme by Substitution at the Lysine Residue in Position 41

C. H. W. Hirs, Mirjam Halmann,* and Jadwiga H. Kycia

Department of Biology, Brookhaven National Laboratory, Upton, L.I., N.Y., U.S.A.

Introduction

In this communication some of the initial results obtained in a study of the dinitrophenylation of ribonuclease A will be presented. Publication of the preliminary findings is warranted because some new information has been brought to light concerning the manner in which ribonuclease A interacts with its substrate.

While the reactivity of the functional groups in proteins has continued to be the subject of comprehensive study, a more extensive development of knowledge in this area of interest will have to await the elucidation of the structures of the macromolecules involved. When it became possible to put forward a primary structural formula for ribonuclease A [1, 2] studies of the reactivity of certain functional groups in this protein became of interest as a means with which to probe the secondary and tertiary structure of the ribonuclease A molecule in solution. It was hoped that information about the secondary and tertiary structure made available in this way would also prove useful in delineating some of the structural features associated with the catalytic activity of this protein.

It has become common practice to attribute variations in the reactivity of the amino acid side-chains in proteins to their degree of accessibility to reagents. Residues reacting more slowly than others of the same type are considered to be "masked" or "buried". When the reactivity of such residues returns to the anticipated level through exposure of the protein to agents such as extremes of pH, urea in high concentrations, etc., capable of causing the disruption of the secondary and tertiary structure, it is usual to attribute the effect to "unmasking". While emphasizing the importance of steric effects such views tend to draw attention away from the possibility

* Present address: *Israel Institute for Biological Sciences, Nes Ziona, Israel.*

c*

that in some cases large effects on reactivity may also be the consequence of neighbouring group participation, or the influence of electrostatic interactions in the vicinity of the reacting groups. A further factor of importance may be the ability of the protein molecule to absorb the reagent specifically and thereby to facilitate the reaction of a proximally located functional group by overcoming the usual entropy factor. Finally, the introduction of modified amino acid residues into the protein fabric may of itself induce variations in the reactivity of the as yet unsubstituted residues, either by direct steric interference or by alteration of the tertiary structure. In general, therefore, unless it becomes possible to locate a number of the functional groups with unusual reactivity by direct reference to the primary structure, there is little chance that observations on reactivity alone can be of value in revealing specific aspects of the secondary and tertiary structure.

1-Fluoro-2,4-dinitrobenzene (FDNB) has a number of properties desirable in a reagent that is to be used in studying the reactivity of functional groups in a protein. It behaves in the manner of a typical reactive alkyl halide* and is capable of reacting with unprotonated α-amino, ε-amino, and imidazole groups, as well as with thiol and phenolic hydroxyl groups in the form of their conjugate bases. Introduction of the dinitrophenyl group into the protein confers the characteristic spectral properties of this chromophore to the new compound, a feature of value in analysis, and excess reagent and dinitrophenol, formed from the reagent by hydrolysis, are readily removed from the reaction mixture by extraction.

The groups potentially sensitive to fluorodinitrobenzene in ribonuclease A comprise the single α-amino group of the lysine residue at the amino–terminal end of the peptide chain, the 10 ε-amino groups of the lysine residues at positions 1, 7, 31, 37, 41, 61, 66, 91, 98, and 104, the imidazole groups of the four histidine residues at positions 16, 48, 105, and 119, and the phenolic hydroxyl groups of the six tyrosine residues at positions 25, 73, 76, 92, 97, and 115. Under the conditions examined thus far, fluorodinitrobenzene does not readily form sulphonium derivatives with the thioether function of the methionine residues, nor is reaction with the hydroxyl functions of the serine and threonine residues in ribonuclease A appreciable.

Analytical

In the present studies the extent of substitution on dinitrophenylation of the enzyme has been followed by quantitative amino acid analysis with the method of Moore et al. [3] in conjunction with an automatic analyzer

---

*Because of this similarity, we have elected to call substitution reactions involving the introduction of the dinitrophenyl group alkylations, even though it would be more accurate to use the term *arylation*.

of the type described by Spackman *et al.* [4]. It should be emphasized that this approach is limited in its application, in the ideal case, to the study of substitutions that lead to the formation of derivatives capable of withstanding the customary acid hydrolysis necessary for the breakdown of the protein to amino acids. Moreover, in using acid hydrolysis the possibility must be recognized that the appearance of a stable derivative on hydrolysis may in itself constitute an artifact reflecting the consequences of an acid-catalyzed rearrangement in which migration of the dinitro-phenyl group from the functional group of original substitution is in-volved. When substitution takes place with the formation of derivatives unstable to acid hydrolysis, two broad alternatives are possible: the derivative may decompose by reversal of its formation and thereby re-generate the amino acid, or decomposition may take place into other products without regeneration of the amino acid. The first of these alternatives makes it essential that the degree of substitution of the protein be checked prior to hydrolysis by means of absorption measurements in the ultra-violet; the second requires that the degree of substitution be measured by difference analysis after hydrolysis.

Substitution on the amino–terminal lysine residue in ribonuclease A may result in the formation of three products: α-dinitrophenyl-lysine, ϵ-dinitrophenyl-lysine, and α,ϵ-bis-dinitrophenyl-lysine. ϵ-Dinitrophenyl-lysine is an α-amino acid and reacts with ninhydrin under the conditions that obtain in the automatic amino acid analyzer to give a blue product in approximately the same yield as typical α-amino acids. In our hands it has proved to be stable (loss less than 5 % after 22 hours at 110° in constant boiling HCl) to the usual conditions of hydrolysis routinely employed as a preliminary to quantitative amino acid analysis. α-Dinitrophenyl-lysine contains a free ϵ-amino group with the characteristics towards ninhydrin of the amino group in γ-aminobutyric acid. The relatively greater basicity of the amino group in γ-aminobutyric acid causes the compound to be more strongly retained than α-aminobutyric acid upon chromatography over columns of sulphonated polystyrene resins. Similarly, α-dinitro-phenyl-lysine is more strongly retained by these resins than the ϵ-isomer. The presence of a dinitrophenyl radical in both derivatives confers on them an enhanced affinity for the matrix of polystyrene based ion-exchangers. Thus, when a mixture of the common protein amino acids and ϵ-dinitro-phenyl-lysine is chromatographed on the 15 cm. column of Amberlite IR-120, normally used for the separation of the basic amino acids on the automatic analyzer, the dinitrophenyl derivative emerges 35 effluent ml. after arginine. α-Dinitrophenyl-lysine is even more strongly retained and is not eluted satisfactorily from the column under the same conditions. α,ϵ-Bis-dinitrophenyl-lysine does not react with ninhydrin and is so firmly bound by Amberlite IR-120 that only drastic conditions will serve to remove it from the resin. Both α-dinitrophenyl-lysine and α,ε-bis-dinitro-phenyl-lysine undergo decomposition during acid hydrolysis prior to amino acid analysis to varying extents up to 30% in 22 hours, but lysine is not regenerated in the process.

The histidine residues in ribonuclease A react with fluorodinitro-benzene to form *imidazole*-dinitrophenyl derivatives. The tautomerism of the imidazole nucleus makes it possible for two dinitrophenyl derivatives to be formed at each histidine residue. On hydrolysis in acid these deriva-tives appear as the *im*-dinitrophenylhistidines, unstable compounds that break down into an as yet unidentified substance, with the properties of an amino acid, that persists as the stable end-product of the acid hydrolysis. Free histidine is not regenerated. The unidentified substance is eluted more rapidly than histidine on the 15 cm. column used for the analysis of the basic amino acids with the automatic analyzer, at a position 12 effluent ml. before lysine.

Tyrosine residues in ribonuclease A become modified at the phenolic hydroxyl group by fluorodinitrobenzene. The resulting tyrosine ether residues may be measured as *o*-dinitrophenyltyrosine subsequent to hydrolysis. Under the conditions of acid hydrolysis used in the present work, *o*-dinitrophenyltyrosine has proved to be a stable compound. It is bound strongly by Amberlite IR-120 and is not eluted from the resin under the conditions used in the automatic analyzer.

These observations on the dinitrophenyl derivatives of lysine, histidine, and tyrosine have permitted the use of difference analysis to estimate the extent of substitution of the ribonuclease A molecule on dinitrophenylation.

Completely dinitrophenylated ribonuclease A on hydrolysis yields nine equivalents of ε-dinitrophenyl-lysine and one equivalent of α,ε-bis-dinitrophenyl-lysine per molecule. At intermediate stages of substitution, blocking of the α-amino group of lysine at the amino terminus of the peptide chain in ribonuclease A is revealed by the inequality between ten equiva-lents (the total lysine available) and the sum of the equivalents of unreacted lysine and ε-dinitrophenyl-lysine.

With histidine an independent check on the values obtained by dif-ference is provided by the quantity of the unidentified degradation product of *im*-dinitrophenylhistidine formed during acid hydrolysis. Free tyrosine, unlike histidine and lysine, undergoes destruction during the acid hydrolysis normally used for amino acid analysis to the extent of 5 to 8 %. Difference analysis as a measure of substitution of the six tyrosine residues in ribonuclease A is therefore rendered uncertain to the extent of the slight variations normally observed in the destruction of this amino acid. For more reliable values, particularly at low degrees of sub-stitution, it would be preferable to determine the *o*-dinitrophenyltyrosine in the hydrolysates directly.

Dinitrophenylation of ribonuclease A

In view of the strong affinity of ribonuclease for polyvalent anions (cf. discussion by Stein [5]) and the possibility that interaction with such ions might modify the reactivity of some of the histidine and lysine side chains, the ribonuclease A used in the present studies was subjected to a preliminary ion-exchange step in which conversion to the acetate of the protein was achieved.

The reaction between the protein and fluorodinitrobenzene was carried out in aqueous solution at a constant pH, maintained with a pH-stat. A large excess of reagent was used, and the solution was kept saturated with reagent by vigorous stirring. As pointed out by Levy [6], under these conditions the kinetics of the reaction with a particular functional group become pseudo first-order in nature. The reaction may be stopped by acidification to a pH of about 2, whereupon excess reagent and dinitrophenol may be removed by extraction.

Ribonuclease A can be completely dinitrophenylated. There are no residues inaccessible to fluorodinitrobenzene, though it is evident that wide variations in reactivity are to be found among the groups undergoing substitution. At pH 10, and at 40°, for example, approximately 30 hours are required for complete dinitrophenylation. After this time, some 0·3 residues of lysine remain unsubstituted, while free histidine and tyrosine are absent from hydrolysates of the modified protein. After 15 hours under the same conditions, the equivalent of one lysine residue remains unsubstituted, while reaction with histidine and tyrosine is complete. It is therefore clear that a number (possibly one or two) of the ε-amino groups in the protein have decreased reactivity even at pH 10. The property is probably dependent on some feature of the primary structure, because performic acid-oxidized ribonuclease A exhibits similar behaviour on dinitrophenylation.

It is noteworthy that completely dinitrophenylated ribonuclease A is a soluble protein in the pH range from 2 to 10. This rather unusual property is of value in handling the partly substituted derivatives of ribonuclease A, for it permits the facile separation of excess fluorodinitrobenzene from the protein.

Of more immediate interest in the present contribution are the residues in ribonuclease A that are most reactive towards substitution by fluorodinitrobenzene. At pH 8 analysis indicates that certain ε-amino groups are substituted more rapidly than any other functional groups, including the α-amino group. This will be apparent from Table I, in which are given the results obtained upon quantitative amino acid analysis of aliquots removed after successive time intervals from a reaction mixture at pH 8 and at 15°. The values for all the residues in ribonuclease are shown, and in each case represent the results of single determinations. The agreement shown for the residues not affected by dinitrophenylation will serve to give an impression of the degree of reproducibility attainable by this approach.

TABLE I

The Dinitrophenylation of Ribonuclease A at pH 8·0, 15°

An aqueous $0·7 \times 10^{-3}$ M solution of ribonuclease A (acetate) at pH 8·0 and at 15° was stirred vigorously with 20 times the quantity of 1-fluoro-2,4-dinitrobenzene required for the substitution of all the potentially available functional groups in the protein. The initial volume was 13·6 ml. and the pH was maintained at a value of $8·0 \pm 0·1$ with 0·2 N NaOH added with the aid of a pH-stat. Before addition of the reagent an aliquot of the protein solution was removed, acidified to pH 1·8 with 0·06 N HCl, and the solution extracted 6 times with 20 volumes of benzene. The protein was subjected to hydrolysis with constant boiling HCl in an evacuated, sealed tube for 22 hours at 110°, after which the hydrolysate was concentrated to remove excess acid, and the amino acid composition of the sample determined by the method of Spackman et al. [4]. In a similar manner, aliquots of the reaction mixture following the addition of FDNB were removed at successive intervals of time, and the reaction in each case terminated by the addition of acid to pH 1·8. Thereafter, excess FDNB was removed by extraction, and the protein subjected to quantitative amino acid analysis by the same procedure. The results are expressed in terms of molar ratios of the constituent amino acids. Other aliquots of the acidified, extracted reaction mixture were kept for determinations of ribonuclease activity.

Amino acid	Time of reaction (minutes)								
	0	3	6	20	40	60	90	180	240
Aspartic acid	15·0	15·3	15·1	15·1	15·0	15·1	14·9	15·1	15·1
Glutamic acid	12·0	12·0	12·0	11·9	11·9	12·1	11·9	12·0	12·0
Glycine	3·04	3·13	3·14	3·01	3·07	3·00	3·02	3·03	3·32
Alanine	11·9	11·9	11·9	11·9	11·9	11·8	12·0	11·9	12·0
Valine	8·82	8·77	8·82	8·86	8·89	8·76	8·94	8·87	9·28
Leucine	1·95	1·99	2·01	2·03	2·06	2·06	2·00	1·96	2·01
Isoleucine*	2·35	2·34	2·50	2·36	2·57	2·53	2·74	2·42	2·53
Serine†	13·3	13·4	13·3	13·5	12·9	13·6	12·9	13·3	13·6
Threonine†	9·46	9·52	9·50	9·61	9·43	9·74	9·51	9·54	9·68
Cystine (half)†	7·24	7·51	6·86	6·31	7·09	5·99	6·60	7·42	6·92
Methionine†	2·49	2·77	1·42	1·87	2·39	1·30	1·45	2·57	1·46
Methionine Sulphoxides	0·86	0·51	1·34	1·29	0·86	1·45	1·22	0·71	1·27
Proline	3·9	4·1	3·8	4·0	4·4	3·9	4·2	3·9	4·3
Phenylalanine	2·97	2·96	2·98	2·94	3·08	3·00	3·08	2·96	3·07
Tyrosine†	5·68	5·78	5·55	5·78	5·72	5·53	5·35	5·58	5·24
Histidine	4·00	4·04	3·99	3·99	4·07	3·83	3·86	3·64	3·42
Lysine	10·1	10·0	9·86	9·35	8·85	8·09	7·69	6·69	6·33
Arginine	4·00	4·00	3·95	4·04	4·00	4·00	4·00	4·00	4·00
ε-DNP-lysine	—	0·0	0·2	0·53	1·04	1·40	1·97	2·06	2·54
Lysine+ε-DNP-lysine	—	10·0	10·1	9·88	9·89	9·49	9·66	8·75	8·87
Unknown from histidine	—	0·0	0·0	0·0	0·0	0·01	0·08	0·29	0·42
,, + Histidine	—	4·04	3·99	3·99	4·07	3·84	3·94	3·93	3·84

* Incompletely liberated after hydrolysis for 22 hours.
† Correction for destruction on hydrolysis not applied.

Examination of Table I reveals that the only values altering significantly with time are those for lysine, histidine, and tyrosine. Methionine recovery was poor throughout, but the values for the sum of free methionine and the methionine sulphoxides remained satisfactorily constant.

Had there been alkylation at the thioether sulphur of this amino acid, it is likely that the acid decomposition products of the alkyl derivative (cf. Gundlach *et al.* [7]), particularly homoserine lactone, would have been formed and detected. The analyses for the hydroxyamino acids are also satisfactorily constant in the series, though it is clear that for an amino acid like serine, of which there are fifteen residues in ribonuclease A, the precision attainable by difference analysis would make it impossible to detect a change of half a residue.

Comparison of the values for lysine, histidine, and tyrosine in Table I shows that substitution on lysine is clearly the most rapid reaction. Substitution on histidine does not become detectable before the 60-minute point, while reaction at tyrosine is not evident until the 240-minute point (analyses of the products obtained at longer time intervals are not included in Table I). A further breakdown of the results of the lysine analyses is possible. The values for ϵ-dinitrophenyl-lysine show that this derivative appears to the extent of $1\cdot04$ equivalents in 40 minutes, at which time the sum of the equivalents of unsubstituted lysine and ϵ-dinitrophenyl-lysine is equal (within the combined errors involved) to the total available lysine. This sum becomes significantly less than 10 at 60 minutes, with ϵ-dinitrophenyl-lysine at $1\cdot4$ equivalents, and falls to a value of 9 at 180 minutes, at which time the value for ϵ-dinitrophenyl-lysine has reached $2\cdot1$ equivalents. A value of 9 equivalents for the sum of free lysine and ϵ-dinitrophenyl-lysine is the value to be expected of a protein in which the terminal α-amino group has been completely substituted. Since determinations of α,ϵ-bis-dinitrophenyl-lysine were not carried out, an estimate of double substitution at the terminal lysine residue in ribonuclease A could not be made. Thus the values for ϵ-dinitrophenyl-lysine represent minimum estimates of the extent of substitution of the ϵ-amino groups. Nonetheless, the results in Table I demonstrate that at least two ϵ-amino groups in ribonuclease A may react faster with fluorodinitrobenzene than the α-amino group under these conditions.

Further progress in interpreting these observations depends on the isolation and characterization of the partly substituted protein derivatives. Moreover, without further information about the initial steps, it would be impossible to investigate the kinetics of subsequent substitutions in the molecule. As will be seen some success in the direction of isolating the initial reaction products at pH 8 has been attained. Before considering the isolation work, the effect of dinitrophenylation on the activity of the enzyme will be described.

Loss of enzymic activity on dinitrophenylation

Ribonuclease A (acetate) is rapidly inactivated by dinitrophenylation at pH 8. After an initial lag phase (also obvious from the results in Table I), probably associated mainly with the process of saturating the solution with fluorodinitrobenzene, the inactivation follows pseudo first-order kinetics in the range from zero to about 95% inactivation. Representative kinetic runs at three temperatures are shown in Fig. 1. Ribonuclease activity was measured with the aid of a pH-stat by the method of Gundlach *et al.* [8] using cyclic cytidylic acid as the substrate. In the initial phases of the work measurements of depolymerase activity were also effected. The spectrophotometric method of Kunitz [9] with purified yeast ribonucleic acid as substrate was employed with modifications to permit the use of a Cary recording spectrophotometer. The results obtained with this method, though less precise than those obtained with the nucleotide substrate, gave the same kinetic constants.

Determinations of the pseudo first-order constant at 15° gave values ranging from 0·010 to 0·020 min.$^{-1}$ (based on decimal logarithms). The same sample of ribonuclease A (acetate) gave values that agreed within 10%, but different samples of ribonuclease A (acetate) gave significantly different values for "k". A possible explanation for this variation became apparent subsequently when it was found that the inactivation of ribonuclease A by dinitrophenylation was strongly inhibited by pyrophosphate ion. A quantity of pyrophosphate equivalent to that of ribonuclease A in an experiment of the type shown in Fig. 1 was sufficient to decrease the rate of inactivation one-fifth. It is possible that the reaction would also be inhibited by other polyvalent anions, such as phosphate and sulphate, just as the inactivation of the enzyme by carboxymethylation on histidine is inhibited by such ions [5]. Because of the methods of preparation different samples of ribonuclease A (acetate) could well be contaminated to varying extents by orthophosphate ions.

The inactivation reaction at pH 8 is also inhibited by adenylate, cytidylate, and uridylate. Inhibition by the pyrimidine nucleotides, which are well known competitive inhibitors of ribonuclease, has been found to be particularly effective. Cytidylate at equal concentration to ribonuclease in an experiment of the kind shown in Fig. 1 caused the rate of inactivation to be slowed to approximately one-quarter of the rate in the absence of the inhibitor. At a ratio of 10 equivalents of cytidylate to 1 of ribonuclease A inhibition was essentially complete. Adenylate was approximately half as effective as cytidylate at the same concentration.

While the inactivation of the enzyme by dinitrophenylation was inhibited by these anions, the over-all reaction with fluorodinitrobenzene, as measured by alkali uptake in the pH-stat, was not detectably slowed down. Thus far a detailed analysis of the kinetics of the reaction as measured with the pH-stat has not been attempted, but it is likely that, with improved technique and working on a larger scale, a difference of rate in the initial stages in the presence and absence of inhibitor will be detected. At present, however, it is evident that the presence of inhibitor serves to slow the reaction down at relatively few of the available functional groups on the protein molecule.

Examination of the values in Table I suggested that the inactivation reaction was primarily due to substitution at an ε-amino group. Ray and Koshland have recently developed a treatment for dealing with the results

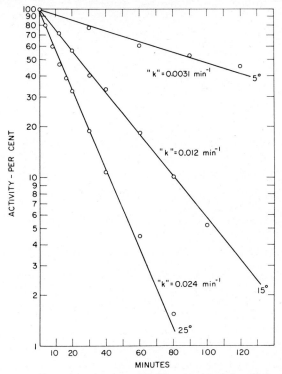

FIG. 1. Kinetics of inactivation of ribonuclease A by dinitrophenylation. An initial lag phase in the reaction is not shown. The conditions of dinitrophenylation were the same as those described in Table I. The points represent the average of two determinations at different concentrations of the remaining ribonuclease activity. The procedure of Gundlach *et al.* [8] was used with cyclic cytidylic acid as the substrate.

obtained by kinetic analysis of modification reactions with proteins [10]. With this approach, and on the assumption that during the initial stages of dinitrophenylation (up to 40 minutes in Table I) the drop in the total lysine value is due exclusively to reaction of fluorodinitrobenzene at but two ε-amino groups, a pseudo first-order reaction rate constant for these two groups of 0·010 min.$^{-1}$ was calculated. Determination of the remaining ribonuclease activity in the reaction products during the same experiment permitted the evaluation of a pseudo first-order rate constant of 0·010 min.$^{-1}$ (on the basis of decimal logarithms) for the inactivation reaction. The results are represented graphically in Fig. 2, in which the difference in time scale for the lysine and activity values are occasioned by the difference of 2 minutes in the lag phases observed for the dinitrophenylation and inactivation reactions. The agreement in the values is probably to some extent fortuitous in view of the usual errors that obtain in the

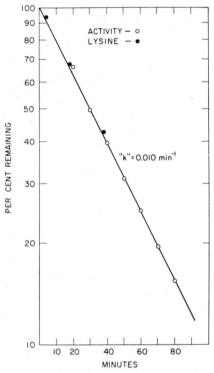

FIG. 2. Kinetics of inactivation of ribonuclease A by dinitrophenylation. Conditions were the same as described in Table I. For the significance of the lysine values, see the text.

determination of lysine and the problems involved in removing excess reagent before undertaking the measurement of ribonuclease activity. The values for the constant nevertheless furnish quantitative evidence that the substitution of a single ε-amino group is capable of inactivating the enzyme. The powerful inhibition effected by the nucleotides and pyrophosphate ion suggest that the ε-amino group in question is located at either the binding or catalytic site of the molecule.

It is likely that other groups essential to the activity of the enzyme are among those that become substituted much more slowly at pH 8 through the action of fluorodinitrobenzene. Their detection by kinetic methods would demand a greater degree of refinement in the analytical work than has been attained thus far. On the other hand, reaction of fluorodinitrobenzene at these more slowly reacting groups may not be inhibited as effectively by the agents already discussed, and their detection might therefore be facilitated by the study of the consequences of dinitrophenylation in the presence of the competitive inhibitor of the enzyme.

Isolation of inactivated mono-ε-dinitrophenylaminoribonuclease A

In an experiment similar to that described in Table I, aliquots of the reaction mixture of ribonuclease A (acetate) and fluorodinitrobenzene at pH 8 were chromatographed on an analytical scale on columns of the sodium form of IRC-50 equilibrated with 0·2 M sodium phosphate buffer at pH 6·47 [11]. The chromatograms showed that the reaction mixture rapidly becomes complex. At higher degrees of substitution, the products present could not be eluted satisfactorily from the resin.

When the products formed from 100 mg. of ribonuclease A (acetate) inactivated to the extent of 20% were chromatographed on a larger scale the result shown in Fig. 3 was obtained. The elution diagram shows a simultaneous plot of the absorbance, determined at 360 mμ, and of the ninhydrin colour value developed by aliquots of the effluent fractions. The values for the absorbance at 360 mμ and for the ninhydrin colour value are normalized at the maximum of the elution peak at 350 effluent ml. As expected, the peak at 435 effluent ml. was found to represent unchanged ribonuclease A. The trailing shoulder of the peak at 350 ml. exhibits an esentially constant ratio of the ninhydrin colour value to absorbance at 360 mμ, suggesting the presence of material of a constant degree of substitution. Aliquots of the fractions in this portion of the chromatogram when subjected to ribonuclease activity determinations were found to be devoid of activity. As little as 0·2% of the original specific activity could have been detected by the procedure used. Partly overlapping the peak at 350 ml. on the chromatogram is a smaller peak at 325 ml., exhibiting a variable ninhydrin colour value to absorbance at 360 mμ ratio. Material corresponding to the fractions in this peak was enzymically active, as was the protein in the fractions corresponding to the relatively unretarded peaks, with varying ninhydrin colour value to absorbance at 360 mμ ratios, between 250 and 300 effluent ml. The latter evidently represent a mixture of different partly substituted proteins with ribonuclease activity.

A cut was made of the yellow protein represented by the trailing shoulder of the peak at 350 ml., and the resulting solution was freed of buffer salts by gel filtration over a column of Sephadex G-25 [12]. On rechromatography under identical conditions of elution the inactive dinitrophenylated ribonuclease A was eluted as a symmetrical peak at the same position. A mixture of ribonuclease A and the inactivated protein separated in the manner to be expected from Fig. 3. When the inactive protein was rechromatographed on IRC-50 in 0·2 M sodium phosphate buffer at pH 6·02 [13] a single, symmetrical peak was again obtained on

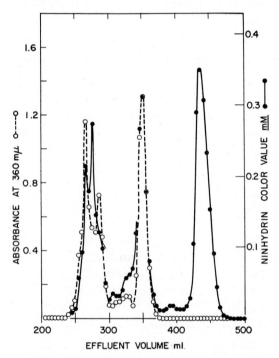

FIG. 3.   Chromatography of the reaction mixture from ribonuclease A (acetate) and dinitrofluorobenzene at pH 8 and 15° after the attainment of 20% inactivation. Conditions for the reaction were the same as described in Table I. The IRC-50 column measured 37 × 330 mm. and was equilibrated with 0·2 M sodium phosphate buffer at pH 6·47. The rate of elution was 15 ml./hour and the effluent was collected in 5 ml. fractions. The absorbance of the effluent fractions was measured at 360 mμ with a Beckman DU spectrophotometer. Aliquots of the fractions were also subjected to ninhydrin analysis (cf. [11]), and to ribonuclease activity determinations by the procedure described in Fig. 1.

the elution curve with a maximum at 3·6 times the effluent volume of the maximum observed at pH 6·47.

On quantitative amino acid analysis the protein from the 350 ml. elution peak in Fig. 3 gave the results shown in Table II. For comparison, the results obtained on analysis of the ribonuclease A (acetate) used in this experiment are also included. The values for all the residues agree satisfactorily with the exception of those for lysine. The analysis makes it clear that the inactive protein contains a single residue of ϵ-dinitrophenyl-lysine. The ultra-violet absorption spectrum of the inactive derivative was typical of the spectrum to be expected of an ϵ-dinitrophenylamino derivative of ribonuclease. The analysis in Table II permitted the evaluation of a molar extinction coefficient at the 365 mμ maximum of $1\cdot51 \times 10^4$, a value in the range usually observed [14] for the extinction coefficient of amino-substituted dinitrophenyl derivatives of amino acids.

Degradation of inactive mono-ϵ-dinitrophenylribonuclease A

The kinetic analysis in Fig. 2, the analytical values of Table II, and the chromatographic results described in the previous section, strongly

TABLE II

AMINO ACID COMPOSITION OF RIBONUCLEASE A (ACETATE) AND OF INACTIVE DINITROPHENYLATED RIBONUCLEASE A

For procedure of analysis, see Table I. The results are expressed in terms of molar ratios of the constituent amino acids.

Amino acid	Ribonuclease A	DNP— derivative†
Aspartic acid . . .	15·0	14·8
Glutamic acid . . .	12·0	12·0
Glycine	3·05	2·99
Alanine	12·0	11·8
Valine	8·62	8·95
Leucine	1·98	1·94
Isoleucine . . .	2·31*	2·24*
Half cystine . . .	6·32	7·13
Methionine	3·51	3·57
Serine	13·3	12·7
Threonine	9·35	9·33
Proline	4·4	4·0
Tyrosine	5·57	5·46
Phenylalanine . . .	3·07	2·92
Histidine	3·92	3·96
Arginine	4·02	4·04
Lysine	*10·0*	*9·18*
ϵ-DNP-lysine . . .		*0·94*

* Incompletely liberated after hydrolysis for 22 hours.
† Molar extinction coefficient at 365 mμ = $1\cdot51 \times 10^4$.

implied that a single inactive protein was responsible for the peak at 350 effluent ml. in Fig. 3. In order to shed further light on this question some 120 mg. of the inactive dinitrophenylated protein were prepared by repeating an experiment of the kind illustrated in Fig. 3 a sufficient number of times. The protein was freed from contaminating chloride ion and subsequently oxidized with performic acid under conditions identical to those used in structural work with ribonuclease A [15]. The performic acid-oxidized ribonuclease A derivative was subjected to quantitative amino acid analysis, the results of which demonstrated that complete oxidation of the disulphide bonds had occurred, that methionine had been quantitatively converted to the sulphone, and that there had been no destruction or alteration [15] of tyrosine during the oxidation. The oxidized protein derivative was submitted to tryptic hydrolysis at pH 7 in the presence of catalytic quantities of trypsin prepared by the activation of chromatographically purified [16] chymotrypsinogen-free trypsinogen. The conditions were similar to those already described for the tryptic hydrolysis of performic acid-oxidized ribonuclease A [17]. The mixture of peptides formed after 24 hours of hydrolysis was fractionated on Dowex 50-X2 columns in the sodium form by procedures very similar to those described for the tryptic peptides from oxidized ribonuclease A [17]. Formate and acetate buffers were used to facilitate quantitative amino acid analysis of the peptide fractions (cf. [18]).

All the peptides found in a tryptic hydrolysate of oxidized ribonuclease A [17] were present in the hydrolysate with the exception of peptides O-Tryp 9 and O-Tryp 14. Identification of the peptide fractions was in each instance confirmed by quantitative amino acid analysis. In order to make certain that ninhydrin-negative peptides were not being overlooked, the aliquots removed from the effluent fractions were subjected to alkaline hydrolysis [17] prior to ninhydrin analysis. Within the precision attainable by quantitative analysis of appropriate cuts from the peptide zones on the chromatogram it was clear that the peptides in the hydrolysate of the oxidized, inactive derivative were formed in the same yields as they are from oxidized ribonuclease A. It was not possible to detect any dinitrophenyl peptides present in the tryptic hydrolysate in the effluent from the Dowex 50-X2 column. Moreover, since subsequent extraction with $0 \cdot 1$ N NaOH failed to remove any significant quantities of material absorbing at 360 mμ from the resin, it is possible that severe "tailing" was responsible for the loss of the dinitrophenyl peptides. The high affinity of dinitrophenyl derivatives of amino acids for the polystyrene matrix of the resin has already been described.

Peptides O-Tryp 9 and O-Tryp 14 are related [19] in the amino acid sequence of ribonuclease. Peptide O-Tryp 14 is an intermediate in the tryptic hydrolysis of oxidized ribonuclease A. On further hydrolysis it breaks down into peptides O-Tryp 9 and O-Tryp 7 (Asp.Arg) by cleavage at the carbonyl bond of the arginine residue of peptide O-Tryp 7. The absence of peptides O-Tryp 9 and O-Tryp 14 in the Dowex 50-X2 eluate thus reveals that modification of a lysine residue in O-Tryp 9 must have taken place as the only consequence of dinitrophenylation. There are two lysine residues in peptide O-Tryp 9. Since the peptide following O-Tryp 9 in the amino acid sequence is O-Tryp 5, had dinitrophenylation taken place at the carboxyl-terminal lysine residue of peptide O-Tryp 9, tryptic hydrolysis at this residue would have been blocked and O-Tryp 5 could not have formed. Since peptide O-Tryp 5 was present in the tryptic hydrolysate, the dinitrophenylated lysine residue in O-Tryp 9 must have been the lysine residue near the amino-terminal end of this peptide. Examination of the amino acid sequence [1] shows that this is the lysine residue at position 41 along the chain. Experiments on the further characterization of the inactive protein, and on the isolation of dinitrophenylated peptide derivatives are now in progress.

Conclusions

These preliminary studies have revealed that amino groups are the most reactive functional groups in ribonuclease towards substitution by dinitrofluorobenzene at pH 8. Two ε-amino groups react faster than the α-amino group of the lysine residue at the amino-terminal end of the peptide chain. The substitution of one of the rapidly reacting ε-amino groups is accompanied by the inactivation of the enzyme. This group is the ε-amino group of the lysine residue at position 41.

The ease of substitution of the ε-amino group of the lysine residue at position 41 is of interest in relation to the primary structure of the protein. One of the relatively few unique features of the amino acid sequence is the accumulation of basic amino acid residues in the region between residues 31 and 41. As pointed out elsewhere [1], there are five residues capable of conferring a positive charge in these 11 residues, and only one carboxyl group. A further structural feature of significance is that lysine residue 41 is preceded by half-cystine residue 40 and followed by proline residue 42. The combined influence of charge repulsion at pH 8 among the cationic centres and the influence of the adjoining cystine and proline residues would be factors adversely affecting the stability of an α-helix formed in this part of the molecule. An additional feature of note is that half-cystine 40 is the first half-cystine of the II-VII disulphide bond [2]. Examination of the primary structural formula will reveal that the II-VII disulphide bond is a fulcrum about which any folding of the ribonuclease molecule must hinge. The ease of substitution of lysine residue 41 may therefore indeed reflect a greater degree of accessibility of this residue because of less compact folding of the structure in this region.

The inhibition of dinitrophenylation at lysine residue 41 by cytidylate and pyrophosphate is extremely effective even when only one equivalent of inhibitor is present per molecule of enzyme. This makes it likely that the ε-amino group of this residue is closely related to the catalytic function of the protein. Substitution on lysine may, because of the size of the substituent, locally distort the tertiary structure, or prevent the formation of a critical hydrogen bond required to maintain the configuration of the active site during catalysis. Substitution may also, by removing a potential positive charge, cause a collapse of an electrostatically maintained configuration, or prevent electrostatic interaction with the substrate. Finally, the introduced dinitrophenyl group may be effective in preventing bound substrate from interaction with the catalytically essential, bond-breaking amino acids. Further work will permit a narrowing down of the possible alternatives. In the meantime, it is worth recalling that in our earlier work, the speculation was made [1] that the residues between positions 31 and 41 might constitute a binding site for anions. A similar idea was recently expressed by Parks [20], who has proposed a model for the tertiary structure and the mechanism of action of ribonuclease.

Inactivation of ribonuclease by modification of lysine residues has been observed previously. Gundlach et al. [8] have shown that carboxymethylation of ribonuclease A at pH 8 is accompanied by the inactivation of the enzyme, and that, under these conditions, the reaction is limited to the lysine residues in the protein. Taborsky has phosphorylated ribonuclease A [21] with imidazole phosphate and has isolated an inactive monophospho ribonuclease in which the introduced phospho group is on a lysine residue. Carboxymethylation and phosphorylation on ε-amino groups results in a charge reversal, whereas introduction of a dinitrophenyl group makes the lysine residue neutral. If, as seems likely, the same lysine residue is involved in the inactivation reaction with iodoacetate, imidazole phosphate, and fluorodinitrobenzene, it is possible that the groups introduced effect inactivation by different mechanisms.

In conclusion we may briefly list the structural features in ribonuclease A now known to be important in the catalytic action of the protein. Studies on ribonuclease S (for summary, cf. Richards [22]) have demonstrated that the binding of S-peptide (residues 1–20 in the original protein) is essential to the maintenance of activity in ribonuclease S. Carboxymethylation at pH 5 results in inactivation of ribonuclease A [8] by reaction of the histidine residue at position 119 [23]. Limited pepsin degradation has revealed that aspartic acid residue 121 is required for the maintenance of activity in ribonuclease A [24]. With the implication of the lysine residue at position 41, it is becoming increasingly clear that for the maintenance of the configuration of the catalytic and binding sites of the molecule, the co-operative interaction of many functional groups, located at widely separated points in the primary structural formula, is required.

Acknowledgments

This research at Brookhaven National Laboratory has been performed under the auspices of the United States Atomic Energy Commission. The participation of one of us (C. H. W. H.) at the Symposium was made possible by the combined support of the National Science Foundation (grant No. NSF-G-12926) and the United States Atomic Energy Commission. We wish to thank Mrs. B. M. Floyd for her assistance in the performance of the amino acid analyses.

References

1. Hirs, C. H. W., Moore, S., and Stein, W. H., *J. biol. Chem.* **235,** 633 (1960).
2. Spackman, D. H., Stein, W. H., and Moore, S., *J. biol. Chem.* **235,** 648 (1960).
3. Moore, S., Spackman, D. H., and Stein, W. H., *Analyt. Chem.* **30,** 1185 (1958).
4. Spackman, D. H., Stein, W. H., and Moore, S., *Analyt. Chem.* **30,** 1190 (1958).
5. Stein, W. H., *in* Brookhaven Symposia in Biology 13, "Protein Structure and Function", Upton, N.Y., 104 (1960).
6. Levy, A. L., *Nature, Lond.* **174,** 126 (1954).
7. Gundlach, H. G., Moore, S., and Stein, W. H., *J. biol. Chem.* **234,** 1761 (1959).
8. Gundlach, H. G., Stein, W. H., and Moore, S., *J. biol. Chem.* **234,** 1754 (1959)
9. Kunitz, M., *J. biol. Chem.* **164,** 563 (1946).
10. Ray, W. J., Jr., and Koshland, D. E., Jr., *in* Brookhaven Symposia in Biology 13, "Protein Structure and Function", Upton, N.Y., 135 (1960).
11. Hirs, C. H. W., Moore, S., and Stein, W. H., *J. biol. Chem.* **200,** 493 (1953).
12. Porath, J., and Flodin, P., *Nature, Lond.* **183,** 1657 (1959).
13. Hirs, C. H. W., *J. biol. Chem.* **205,** 93 (1953).
14. Fraenkel-Conrat, H., Harris, J. I., and Levy, A. L., *in* "Methods of Biochemical Analysis", ed. D. Glick. New York, **2** (1955).
15. Hirs, C. H. W., *J. biol. Chem.* **219,** 611 (1956).
16. Keller, P. J., Cohen, E., and Neurath, H., *J. biol. Chem.* **233,** 457 (1958).
17. Hirs, C. H. W., Moore, S., and Stein, W. H., *J biol. Chem.* **219,** 623 (1956).
18. Hirs, C. H. W., *J. biol. Chem.* **235,** 625 (1960).
19. Hirs, C. H. W., Stein, W. H., and Moore, S., *J. biol. Chem.* **221,** 151 (1956).
20. Parks, J. M., *in* Brookhaven Symposia in Biology 13, "Protein Structure and Function", Upton, N.Y., 132 (1960).
21. Taborsky, G., *J. biol. Chem.* **234,** 2915 (1959).
22. Richards, F. M., *in* Brookhaven Symposia in Biology 13, "Protein Structure and Function", Upton, N.Y., 115 (1960).
23. Barnard, E. A., and Stein, D. W., *J. mol. Biol.* **1,** 339 (1960).
24. Anfinsen, C. B., *J. biol. Chem.* **221,** 405 (1956).

The Relation of the Secondary Structure of Pepsin to Its Biological Activity

GERTRUDE E. PERLMANN

The Rockefeller Institute,
New York, U.S.A.

Two decisive advances in the understanding of protein structure are the elucidation by Sanger of the amino acid sequence of insulin [1] and the more recently completed investigations on pancreatic ribonuclease by Hirs, Moore, and Stein [2]. The biological activity of a protein, however, depends not only on the amino acid sequence but also on the folding of the peptide chains, their arrangement in space and how they are packed into the protein molecule. The only technique available for obtaining detailed and precise information about the folding is undoubtedly the X-ray method which has been demonstrated so clearly by the work of Kendrew and his collaborators on myoglobin [3]. In the studies on pepsin which I shall report, more indirect methods have been used. Nevertheless, such methods may help in defining the conformation of the peptide chain segment necessary for the biological activity of the enzyme, as well as the type of forces responsible for maintaining the "native" configuration.

Thus far, amino acid sequence work on pepsin has not been attempted, which may partly be attributed to the size of the molecule. Pepsin is a protein with a molecular weight of 35 000 and has only one peptide chain which is cross-linked by three disulphide bonds. Examination of the amino acid distribution, as given in Table I, reveals that the protein has 71 acidic residues (44 aspartic acids and 27 glutamic acids) and only four basic ones (1 histidine, 1 lysine, 2 arginines). Moreover, pepsin has a high content of non-polar and hydroxyamino acids and 15 prolines [4]. It is, therefore, not unlikely that such an unusual amino acid distribution influences the secondary structure of the protein.

It is well established that in most globular proteins a certain fraction of the amino acid residues is in the α-helical configuration. Whenever a helical structure is present, hydrogen bonds between the oxygen atoms of the carbonyl groups and the imino group of the peptide linkages play an essential role in determining the folding of the polypeptide chain. However, hydrophobic bonds may also be important in maintaining the secondary structure.

TABLE I

Amino Acid Composition of Crystalline Pepsin [4]

Nature of amino acid	No. of residues per molecule	Per cent of total
Acidic: (Asp,Glu)	71	20·7
Basic: (His,Lys,Arg)	4	1·2
Non-polar: (Gly,Val,Leu,Ileu,Ala,Met) .	137	40·0
Hydroxy: (Ser,Thr)	72	20·9
Aromatic: (Tyr,Try,Phe) . . .	38	11·1
Proline	15	4·4
1/2 Cys (–S–S–)	6	1·7
Total	343	100·0

That pepsin is a tightly folded molecule is indicated by its low intrinsic viscosity. The question arose, therefore, as to whether or not reagents could be found that would unfold the polypeptide chain and if unfolding

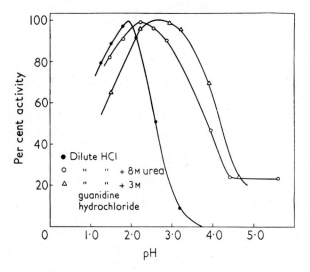

Fig. 1.   pH dependence of the activity of pepsin for the hydrolysis of haemoglobin.

occurred, how certain properties, such as viscosity, optical rotation and the biological activity of the enzyme, would be affected.

The first two reagents which were investigated for their effect on pepsin were urea and guanidine hydrochloride which are known to have a profound influence on the biological activity of enzymes, e.g. ribonuclease [5], chymotrypsin [6] and trypsin [7]. In contrast to the enzymes, which are readily inactivated if brought into contact with these reagents, pepsin remains active after short exposure to urea and guanidine hydrochloride. However, as illustrated with the aid of Fig. 1, the pH of maximum hydrolysis, which in aqueous solutions is at pH 1·8, is shifted to an apparent pH of 2·3 in 8·0 M urea and to pH 3·0 in 3·0 M guanidine hydrochloride.

Further investigation of the effect of urea and guanidine hydrochloride on pepsin has revealed that the enzymic activity in the presence of these hydrogen-bond breaking reagents depends on a variety of factors: (1) concentration of the reagent, (2) time of exposure, (3) temperature, and (4) pH.

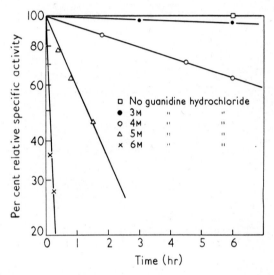

FIG. 2.   Dependence of pepsin activity on time of exposure to guanidine hydrochloride at 37°.

In Fig. 2, are shown the results of measurements in which the concentration of guanidine hydrochloride was varied but the pH of the reaction mixture maintained at 3·4. In 3·0 M guanidine hydrochloride, pepsin is almost as active as in buffer, whereas in 6·0 M guanidine hydrochloride complete inactivation occurs within 30 minutes of contact with the reagent [8]. A similar behaviour of the protein is observed in experiments in which the urea concentration is varied from 2·0 M to 8·0 M [9].

The second factor mentioned is temperature. If, at a constant concentration of 4·0 M guanidine hydrochloride of pH 3·4, the temperature is lowered, the rate of inactivation decreases. Thus at 37°, the first-order rate constant, k, is $1·53 \times 10^{-3}$, at 30°, $k = 3·06 \times 10^{-4}$ and at 25°, $k = 1·5 \times 10^{-4} \times$ min.$^{-1}$ (8).

The next point to be discussed is the effect of pH on the rate of in-activation. In Fig. 3, is given a comparison of the effect of 8·0 M urea and 4·0 M guanidine hydrochloride if pepsin is exposed to the reagent for 1 hour at 37°. Three points become apparent: (1) The range of maximum stability of pepsin, which in aqueous solution extends to pH 5·5, is narrowed to pH 3·0 to 3·5 in 4·0 M guanidine hydrochloride and to pH 3·3 to 4·3 in 8·0 M urea, respectively. (2) Although denaturation of pepsin at low pH values, i.e. 1·5, has been reported by Northrop [10], the loss of activity in the presence of hydrogen-bond breaking reagents proceeds rapidly below pH 3·0, and the formation of low molecular weight

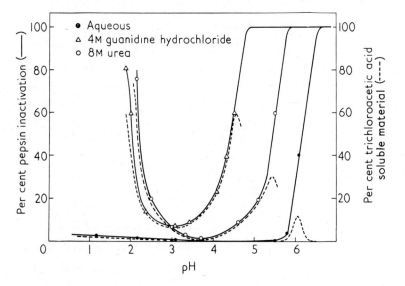

FIG. 3. Effect of various solvents on pepsin. Time of incubation: 1 hour at 37°.

peptides, resulting from the action of intact pepsin on the denatured material, closely parallels the rate of inactivation. (3) At pH values more alkaline than 6·0, pepsin loses its activity spontaneously without the forma-tion of non-protein material. In the presence of guanidinium ions or urea, this rapid loss occurs at more acid pH values. Moreover, it is of interest to note that although the pH zone in which inactivation takes place depends on the reagent and its concentration, the maximum rate of inactivation, within a small pH interval is *independent* of the nature of the solvent. One may, therefore, conclude that intramolecular bonds of the same nature are sensitive to the hydroxyl ions of the medium. Thus, in the pH range of 3·5 to 5·5 the main effect of the hydrogen-bond breaking reagents consists in loosening the secondary structure of the pepsin molecule.

Consequently, some of the bonds that are necessary for maintenance of the enzymically active configuration are broken at lower pH values than in aqueous solution.

That the loosening of the configuration is a slight one and not similar to the unfolding that is observed if other proteins are brought into contact with hydrogen-bond breaking reagents is apparent from the intrinsic viscosity given in Table II. Thus the intrinsic viscosity changes only from

TABLE II

INTRINSIC VISCOSITY, SPECIFIC OPTICAL ROTATION, $[\alpha]$, AND ROTATORY DISPERSION CONSTANT, λ_c, OF PEPSIN IN VARIOUS SOLVENTS AT 25°

Composition of solvent	pH*	$[\eta]$ (g/ml)$^{-1}$	$-[\alpha]$ 600 mμ	400 mμ	λ_c
0·1 M Acetate buffer . . .	4·6$_4$	3·0$_9$	63·4	178	216
8 M Urea-acetate . . .	5·3$_5$	3·5$_7$	64·1	179	218
3 M Guanidine hydrochloride .	3·4$_0$	3·5$_4$	62·1	173	217
4 M Guanidine hydrochloride .	3·4$_0$	3·4$_7$	62·1	173	217

* Apparent pH.

3·09 to 3·54 (g/ml)$^{-1}$ if 8·0 M urea or 3·0 to 4·0 M guanidine hydrochloride is present in the reaction mixture. Moreover, as also shown in Table II, the specific optical rotation, $[\alpha]$, and the rotatory dispersion constant, λ_c, remain completely unaltered [11]. This behaviour is in contrast to that found in the case of many proteins where the values of the specific rotation, $[\alpha]_D$, of the native protein decreases by 20 to 60° upon denaturation [12]. Likewise, the dispersion constant, λ_c, is lowered from the range of 230–270 mμ to 210 mμ upon contact with hydrogen-bond breaking reagents [13]. These changes usually reflect a major unfolding of the polypeptide chain or a transition from an α-helical structure to a random coil. Thus, the results obtained with pepsin further support the view that no major change is brought about after short exposure to urea or guanidine salts.

If, however, as shown in Table III, the optical rotation, $[\alpha]$, and the rotatory dispersion constant, λ_c, are measured at 55°, λ_c increases from 216 to 230 mμ. As illustrated in Fig. 4, the increase of the rotatory dispersion constant occurs above 45°, but, as indicated by the dashed lines, the loss of activity accompanies or precedes the changes of λ_c. It appears, therefore, that certain amino acid residues, e.g., proline or serine, lock the peptide chain into a configuration which confers considerable stability upon the protein. At higher temperatures, however, transition to a less stable configuration takes place. It is clear that in this case the chain

TABLE III

ROTATORY DISPERSION CONSTANT, λ_c, AND SPECIFIC ACTIVITY OF PEPSIN IN VARIOUS
SOLVENTS AS FUNCTION OF TEMPERATURE

Composition of solvent	pH*	Temperature	λ_c	Relative specific activity per unit nitrogen in per cent†
0·1 M Acetate buffer	4·3₄	23	216	100
		55	227	99
8·0 M Urea-acetate	5·3₅	23	218	95
		55	229	5
5·0 M Guanidine hydrochloride	3·5₀	23	217	100
		55	226	4

* Apparent pH.
† The relative specific activity of a freshly prepared pepsin solution in 0·1 M
acetate buffer of pH 4·6 is taken as 100.

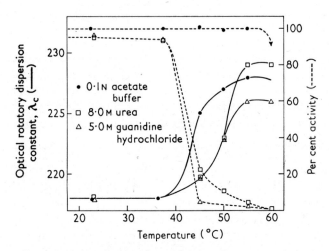

FIG. 4. Dependence of temperature of the optical rotatory dispersion constant,
λ_c, and enzymic activity of pepsin in various solvents.

segment necessary for the biological activity of the enzyme has been
affected.

From the results presented here, one can conclude:

1. Although hydrogen bonds undoubtedly exist in pepsin, they are
relatively unimportant in maintaining the configuration of the protein
essential for its enzymic action.

2. Pepsin does not contain large helical regions but has essentially a "random coil" configuration. This lack of any repeating or periodically organized structure as a helical conformation represents, however, does not exclude that each amino acid residue is in a specific or unique location.

3. We should like to propose that in the case of pepsin hydrophobic bonds play a considerable role in determining the secondary structure of this enzyme.

Acknowledgment

This work was supported in part by Grant A2449 of the United States Public Health Service.

References

1. Sanger, F., and Tuppy, H., *Biochem. J.* **49,** 463, 481 (1951); Sanger, F., and Thompson, E. O. P., *Biochem. J.* **53,** 353 (1953); Ryle, A. P., and Sanger, F., *Biochem. J.* **60,** 535 (1955); Ryle, A. P., Sanger, F., Smith, L. F., and Kitai, R., *Biochem. J.* **60,** 541 (1955).
2. Hirs, C. H. W., Moore, S., and Stein, W. H., *J. biol. Chem.* **235,** 633 (1960).
3. Kendrew, J. C., Davies, D. R., Phillips, D. C., and Shore, V. C., *Nature, Lond.* **185,** 422 (1960); Kendrew, J. C., Bodo, G., Dintzis, H. M., Parrish, R. G., Wyckoff, H., and Phillips, D. C., *Nature, Lond.* **181,** 662 (1958); Bluhm, M. M., Bodo, G., Dintzis, H. M., and Kendrew, J. C., *Proc. roy. Soc.* A **246,** 369 (1958).
4. Blumenfeld, O. O., and Perlmann, G. E., *J. gen. Physiol.* **42,** 553 (1959).
5. Sela, M., and Anfinsen, C. B., *Biochim. biophys. Acta* **24,** 229 (1957).
6. Neurath, H., Rupley, J. A., and Dreyer, W. J., *Arch. Biochem. Biophys.* **65,** 243 (1956).
7. Harris, J. I., *Nature, Lond.* **177,** 471 (1956)
8. Blumenfeld, O. O., Leonis, J., and Perlmann, G. E., *J. biol. Chem.* **235,** 379 (1960).
9. Perlmann, G. E., *Arch. Biochem. Biophys.* **65,** 210 (1956).
10. Northrop, J. H., *J. gen. Physiol.* **16,** 33 (1932).
11. Perlmann, G. E., *Proc. nat. Acad. Sci., Wash.* **45,** 915 (1959).
12. Simpson, R. B., and Kauzmann, W., *J. Amer. chem. Soc.* **75,** 5139 (1953).
13. Linderstrøm-Lang, K., and Schellman, J. A. *Biochim. biophys. Acta* **15,** 203 (1955).

The Problem of Nucleotide Sequence in Deoxyribonucleic Acids

ERWIN CHARGAFF

Columbia University, New York, N.Y., U.S.A.

Introduction

Now that some of the most tremendous problems in biochemistry have, it is said, been solved successfully—such as the nature of the genetic material, its structure and mode of replication, and even its biosynthesis— our time, tired of so much exertion, may take a deep breath and then, perhaps, decide that it all has to be done over again. I should not dare contradict, for I have always been more impressed by the enormity of the gap between claim and achievement than by the magnitude of the former.

In any event, we have set ourselves a much more modest, but by no means easy, task, namely, the elucidation of some of the aspects of the primary structure of deoxyribonucleic acids, especially in regard to the arrangement of the nucleotide constituents. In this connection, and since this talk is given in Stockholm, I may be permitted to recall that it was here, and also in Uppsala, that I had the first opportunity to review our original observations on deoxyribonucleic acid. This is what I said in 1949 and what was printed a few months later [1].

"The desoxypentose nucleic acids extracted from different species thus appear to be different substances or mixtures of closely related substances of a composition constant for different organs of the same species and characteristic of the species.

"The results serve to disprove the tetranucleotide hypothesis. It is, however, noteworthy—whether this is more than accidental, cannot yet be said—that in all desoxypentose nucleic acids examined thus far the molar ratios of total purines to total pyrimidines, and also of adenine to thymine and of guanine to cytosine, were not far from 1."

You will recognize here, among other things, the first statement of the well-known pairing principles.

Even the earliest observations on the nucleic acids, which showed the existence of remarkable similarities and, at the same time, of outstanding differences in the distribution and, therefore, the sequence of the con- stituent monomers, the nucleotides, made it appear of great interest to learn something about the structural principles that came into play. I shall first discuss some of the basic concepts that must be considered.

Remarks on the conceptual basis of sequence analysis

THE PROBLEM OF HOMOGENEITY

What determines the composition of a given biological polymer has been much discussed in the recent past, at any rate in regard to proteins and nucleic acids. Almost no attention has been paid, as has been pointed out recently [2], to the presumably equally rigid control of the composition of other cell-specific polymers, such as the polysaccharides or even certain macromolecular lipids. The usual expedient, in which I wish I could concur with greater enthusiasm [3], has been the formulation of some sort of template which obviously makes up in versitility for what it lacks in concreteness. This Disneyland of templates and pools and feedbacks, presided over by never-smiling ogres, will make us the laughing stock of later times.

What determines the size of a given biological polymer has, on the other hand, been neither determined nor even much discussed. The cell will in many instances contain, or at least it will be made to yield, compounds belonging to the same class, but very much different in size. Proteins, the best investigated group of cellular macromolecules, vary in size over a considerable range, from something like 12 000 to many millions [4]. Deoxyribonucleic acid preparations appear, in contrast, to fall into two principal groups of molecular weight: (a) of 6 to 8 million; (b) of 12 to 16 million [5].* Such distinctions are probably not of great heuristic value, since the cell, which is not simply a bag containing many chemicals of different size and quality, must impress on its components a pattern of multiple associations which it is not possible even to define at present.

Dissimilarity in size is, however, less of a problem for the student of the chemistry of deoxyribonucleic acids than is the possible heterogeneity of his specimens as regards their composition and sequence characteristics. It is, in fact, possible to divide a preparation of total deoxyribonucleic acid into a series of fractions of graded composition (starting with a, sometimes extreme, GC-type [7] and going to a very marked AT-type) which, however, all still exhibit the pairing regularities [8]; but the real meaning of such a fractionation is far from clear. It could be, as was pointed out by us [9], that these fractionated preparations actually represent some form of sub-units of a large aggregate, though it is not easy to describe the nature

---

* An interesting exception—a polydeoxyribonucleotide of mol. wt. 10 000 to 12 000—has been described recently as a component of crystalline cytochrome b_2 [6]. It is noteworthy that this small polymer of only about 40 nucleotides still exhibits the pairing principles [1] mentioned above.

of the links that are disrupted *repeatably* during the mild fractionation procedure. In this view, in its extreme form, the nucleus of a given species
could conceivably contain only one type of deoxyribonucleic acid. At the
other extreme would have to be placed the view that a given nucleic acid
preparation may comprise an entire spectrum of differently constituted
individuals so that no two nucleic acid molecules within the same nucleus
would be entirely identical [10]. That neither of these opposite extremes can
as yet be disavowed entirely demonstrates the deep cleft that still exists
between metabiological assertions and scientific facts.

THE PROBLEM OF MACROMOLECULAR STRUCTURE

It would, of course, be good if the investigator of the structure of a
deoxyribonucleic acid knew whether he was dealing with one chain or
with two [11] or even more [12] complementary chains; but at the present,
little advanced, state of our knowledge of the nucleic acids this is not
essential. The value of any information on the sequential characteristics
of the nucleic acid is not diminished if the complementary chains are
considered to be joined at one end or even at both ends, as may well be
the case, so as to constitute an uninterrupted sequential progression. I
am not aware of the demonstration of distinct end groups in undegraded
deoxyribonucleic acid.

The maintenance of sequence integrity of the preparations to be
examined is, on the other hand, a problem of great importance. If—quite
apart from the secondary valence forces supporting the architecture of
the secondary or tertiary structures of the deoxyribonucleic acids—there
really exist weak links in their primary structure [13], it may be essential
to avoid the rupture of the latter, since otherwise valuable features of
sequential arrangement may be lost. This applies, of course, even more to
the avoidance of chemical or enzymic degradation during the isolation.

It is quite likely that very few of the deoxyribonucleic acid preparations
described so far, and none of the models proposed to describe their structure, are representative of the native state. The actual operative entity—
though not necessarily amenable to biological testing *in vitro*—possibly is
an aggregate of very long polynucleotide chains linked to each other,
perhaps by oligopeptide bridges, and bonded to proteins in a spatially
unique configuration. If this is so, the problem of heterogeneity, mentioned in the preceding section, is ostensible rather than actual, having
been introduced as a necessary, but strictly non-biological, artifact of
purification. By this token, a preferred isolation method for deoxyribonucleic acid would be one that avoided, as far as possible, denaturation by
chemical or physical means. Nearest to these requirements is perhaps
the procedure described on p. 326 of a previous survey [7] and applied

by us to preparations from calf thymus [14] and *Escherichia coli* protoplasts [15].

THE PROBLEM OF STATISTICAL SEQUENCE ANALYSIS

The possibility that no two nucleic acid molecules within the same nucleus are entirely identical offers "a prospect that would seem to condemn us to forced statistics for life" [16]. It is this more than anything else that has made work on the nucleotide sequence in nucleic acids appear so unattractive. Who would, after all, undertake to read a book that has been passed through a grinder? Nevertheless, being rather modest in what I expected to gain from a perusal of the nucleic acid text, I have never been able to share these apprehensions completely. I knew that a great deal can be learned about an unknown language through a study of its phonemes, their frequency, distribution density, and allophonic relationships.

If the total deoxyribonucleic acid of a given species represents a text, it is made up of "words"—the individual molecules—that are composed of a singularly meagre alphabet: four or five letters. But the words so spelled out are 10 000-letter words, each of which could occur in a fantastically great number of positional isomers: between 10^{2000} and 10^{8000}, according to how many restrictions on neighbours are admitted [3]. The situation facing us in examining a nucleic acid preparation comprising a large number of isomers or homologues would, then, be comparable to one in which all the words in a dictionary are lined up end to end in a continuous, and essentially arrhythmic and aperiodic, sequence.

It is quite clear that the first attempt at unravelling such a clutter will have to be based on statistics and that it must limit itself to the description of tendencies or trends of arrangement. To give an example: running together the thirteen words making up the first sentence of *King Lear* I obtain a monster word of fifty-seven letters of which twenty-one are vowels. On this word a number of determinations can be made: (*a*) the ratio of consonants to vowels; (*b*) the nature of the individual consonants and vowels; (*c*) the relative frequency of each constituent. If I have a way of removing the vowels without disturbing the rest of the arrangement, I shall isolate six solitary consonants, eight pairs of consonants, three bunches of triple consonants and one cluster of five consonants in a row. Each of these units, I would conclude, was originally flanked on both sides by vowels. Other words would yield other combinations, with the unambiguity of distinction increasing with the length of the consonant clusters. In very long words composed of only two vowels and two or three consonants, unique clusters can be expected only very rarely; but the relative frequency of the various combinations of consonants (runs of 1, 2, 3, etc.) will be a means of unique differentiation, even though it will not yet make it possible to reconstruct the entire text.

This is what we have been doing with many deoxyribonucleic acid preparations.

Remarks on nomenclature

DEFINITION OF THE TERM "HOMOTOPE"

If one monomeric constituent can take the position of another in a definable segment of a polymer, we propose to designate it as a *homotope* (from the Greek for occupying the same place). If in the A-chain of insulin positions 8 to 10 are occupied by Ala.Ser.Val in the ox [17], but by Ala.Gly.Val in the sheep [18], I would say that serine and glycine are homotopic with respect to this sequence. The importance of this term for a consideration of nucleic acid structure will become clear presently.

DEFINITION OF THE TERM "PLEROMER"

If in the total composition of polymers that are characterized by balances such as the well-known pairing principles in deoxyribonucleic acid [1, 7], and in a more limited way in ribonucleic acids [19], one constituent can ostensibly replace another in respect to these balances, we propose to designate it as a *pleromer* (from the Greek for filling up the measure). Thus, if in the deoxyribonucleic acid of wheat germ [20] the molar quantity of guanine equals that of the sum of cytosine and 5-methyl-cytosine, I would say that these two 6-amino pyrimidines are pleromeric.

SOLITARY AND BUNCHED NUCLEOTIDES

A pyrimidine nucleotide that, within the polynucleotide chain of a nucleic acid, is contiguous only to purine nucleotides, will be referred to as "solitary"; pyrimidine nucleotides that occur in tracts of two or more, flanked on both sides by purine nucleotides, will be designated as "bunched" [21]. In the diagram shown in Fig. 1, solitary thymidylic acid, for instance, appears in positions 3, 9 and 8′, bunched pyrimidine nucleotides are seen in positions 5 to 7.

Early attempts at sequence investigation

Since 1947, when in an early review on deoxyribonucleic acids (p. 32 of ref. [22]), I first discussed the possible importance of variations in the nucleotide sequence for the biological specificity of a deoxyribonucleic acid, this problem has remained among the interests of my laboratory. Our first chemical evidence on the existence of different deoxyribonucleic acids [23, 24] made it clear that whatever "code" was carried by the

nucleic acids must be imprinted on the sequential arrangement of the
monomeric constituents and prompted us to search for ways to approach
this difficult task.

The general problem is similar to that of the structure of proteins, but
immensely more forbidding. The very great length of the chains composed
of a much smaller number of different monomers raises obstacles that
render improbable an unambiguous solution by existing methods. Moreover, the available procedures are not yet as refined as in the case of the
proteins: few specific enzymes, no generally applicable method for marking
the end groups. On the other hand, the remarkable difference in the stability

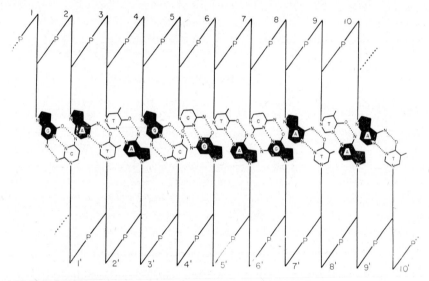

FIG. 1. Schematic representation of a fragment of a double strand of a deoxyribonucleic acid. The purines (A, adenine; G, guanine) are depicted in black, the
pyrimidines (C, cytosine; T, thymine) in white.

of the glycosidic bonds holding the purines and the pyrimidines offered a
novel possibility that we have exploited fully.

Our first attempts in the direction of utilizing a specific enzyme were
concerned with the problem of a recognizable repeating unit.

STEPWISE DEGRADATION BY DEOXYRIBONUCLEASE

When crystalline pancreatic deoxyribonuclease acts on a highly polymerized preparation of a deoxyribonucleic acid, it is possible to conduct
the experiment in such a manner as to collect the products detached
gradually in a dialyzable form and to separate them from the enzyme-
resistant core [7, 25]. The latter is characteristically different in composition

from the intact polymer; there is, moreover, a significant trend in the composition of the products produced by the stepwise enzymic digestion. No indications of any regularity in the release or the composition of fragments were observed; no sub-units of recognizably recurrent structure were seen: deoxyribonucleic acids apparently exhibit a largely arrhythmic nucleotide sequence.

APURINIC ACID

This has proved a very useful compound; it is, in fact, the first intermediate product in all procedures involving acid degradation [26]. When a deoxyribonucleic acid is exposed to mildly acidic conditions (pH 1·6 at 37°) all the purines are cleaved off gradually, leaving behind a polymer representing the original polynucleotide, but composed of deoxyribophosphate units, at the places of the previous purine nucleotides, and of the pyrimidine nucleotides in unchanged ratio and at the same position as in the native starting material. For instance, in the segment represented in Fig. 1, positions 3, 5–7, 9, 1′, 2′, 4′, 8′, 10′ would remain unchanged, whereas in the remaining places the purines would now have made room for the reactive aldehydo groups of the deoxy sugar. The presence of the aldehydo group [27] and, therefore, of a free hydroxyl at 4′ brings about a remarkable labilization of the polymer: it is broken not only by alkali, but even by buffers (pH 8·6) containing primary amino groups [28]. It is likely that this susceptibility of the poly-sugar-phosphate backbone of apurinic acid to amines is involved in the degradation reactions employing diphenylamine under acidic conditions [29].

Studies on the arrangement of the pyrimidine nucleotides in apurinic acid [28] were, in fact, the first that made possible an approach to the problem of nucleotide sequence in deoxyribonucleic acid. The information so obtained was limited, since it was only qualitative, but it showed that a considerable portion of the pyrimidine nucleotides, and therefore also of the purine nucleotides, was arranged in the form of tracts of several nucleotides of one kind.

Sequence studies through differential distribution analysis

MECHANISM

The important discovery that among the fragments produced by the acid degradation of deoxyribonucleic acids there are found the 3′, 5′-diphosphates of deoxycytidine and thymidine is due to the work of Levene, Thannhauser and their collaborators [30–33]. A more recent re-investigation [34] by improved techniques, which confirmed the occurrence of these diphosphates, prompted a discussion of the possible bearing of this

D*

finding on the problem of nucleic acid structure (p. 366 of ref. [7]). It was clear that for these fragments to serve as a tool in research on nucleotide sequence the mechanism of their release had to be better understood. It was also indispensable to be able to study them under rigorously controlled conditions and on a quantitative basis.

The kinetics of the liberation of the pyrimidine nucleoside diphosphates were first studied, in collaboration with Dr. Shapiro, on a series of models, namely, the several deoxyribodinucleotides all having cytidylic acid as one of their components [35]. These investigations served as the basis of a well-controlled, differential hydrolysis procedure which was usually performed in three stages [21, 36]. The diagnostically most valuable results are obtained in Stage I (0·1 M H_2SO_4, 30 min., 100°), when the release of pyrimidine nucleoside diphosphates can be taken to reflect directly the abundance of these units as solitary pyrimidine nucleotides in the polynucleotide chain. In the present survey I shall limit myself to the findings based on this stage of the differential hydrolysis procedure. The results yielded in Stages II and III, which involve longer periods of hydrolysis, are mainly indicative of the secondary cleavage of bunched pyrimidine sequences; they are of great value as further means of differentiation between analytically indistinguishable nucleic acids of different cellular origin. This will be exemplified in the following section.

In its simplest form the cleavage of a polynucleotide chain and the formation of the diphosphates of the pyrimidine nucleosides (Py) may be regarded as a series of β elimination reactions [21].

After the liberation of the purines the first elimination presumably occurs at the broken line A. Since no extraneous sugar fragment is found in ester linkage with the resulting nucleoside diphosphate, a subsequent hydrolysis or elimination must take place at the other flanking sugar (broken line C). It is likely that this cleavage follows a β aldehyde elimination (broken line B), which has left a double bond between the second and third carbon atom of the sugar. Similar considerations apply to the release of bunched pyrimidine sequences. A more than tentative formulation of the reaction mechanism will, however, have to await a better understanding of the fate of the free deoxyribose residues liberated in the initial stage of the removal of purines by acid.

NUCLEOTIDE ARRANGEMENT IN ANALYTICALLY INDISTINGUISHABLE DEOXYRIBONUCLEIC ACIDS OF DIFFERENT CELLULAR ORIGIN

It happens quite often that deoxyribonucleic acids of taxonomically entirely different origin exhibit identity of composition as regards the

TABLE I

DIFFERENTIAL DISTRIBUTION ANALYSIS
OF THREE OTHERWISE INDISTINGUISHABLE DEOXYRIBONUCLEIC ACID PREPARATIONS*

Source:	Ox			Man			*Arbacia lixula*		
DNA fraction:	(0·75 M)			(1·0 M)			(2·6 M)		
	T	C	[TC]	T	C	[TC]	T	C	[TC]
Total pyrimidine, as mole % P	29·9	20·0		29·9	19·8		30·9	19·6	
Solitary pyrimidine, as mole % of total constituent in DNA	15·9	9·2		19·9	6·3		16·0	14·0	
Solitary or bunched pyrimidines, as mole % P	4·75	1·84	1·72	5·95	1·25	1·71	4·94	2·74	1·66
Total T/C, molar ratio	1·50			1·51			1·58		
Solitary T/C, molar ratio	2·58			4·76			1·80		

* The figures are taken from previous papers [21, 36]. The deoxyribonucleic acid fractions are described by the molarity of NaCl employed for the dissociation of the histone nucleate [9]. T designates thymine or thymidylic acid, C cytosine or deoxycytidylic acid, [TC] the two isomeric dinucleoside triphosphates comprising cytidine and thymidine (reported as moles of dinucleoside triphosphate per 100 gm. atoms of nucleic acid phosphorus).

distribution of the nitrogenous constituents. (Compare the example of the deoxyribonucleic acids of the sheep and the salmon cited previously [16]). In such cases, the method of differential distribution analysis discussed in

TABLE II

Differential Distribution Analysis of Animal Deoxyribonucleic Acids*

Source:	Ox			Man			Arbacia lixula			Paracentrotus lividus		
Organ:	Thymus			Spleen			Sperm			Sperm		
	T	C	[TC]	T	C	[TC]	T	C	[TC]	T	C	[TC]
Total pyrimidine, as mole % P	28·1	20·6		28·9	20·4		30·5	19·2		32·1	17·3	
Solitary pyrimidine, as mole % of total constituent in DNA	15·4	9·7		13·2	8·2		17·6	14·1		16·1	15·5	
Solitary or bunched pyrimidines, as mole % P	4·33	2·00	1·44	3·81	1·67	1·35	5·37	2·71	1·43	5·17	2·68	1·52
Total T/C, molar ratio		1·36			1·42			1·59			1·86	
Solitary T/C, molar ratio		2·17			2·28			1·98			1·93	

* All nucleic acids analyzed were total, unfractionated preparations. The figures are taken from a previous paper [21]. For other explanations, compare Table I.

this survey is destined to be of great value. It permits the examination of detailed features of the nucleotide arrangement, far beyond the possibilities of distinction offered by total constituent analysis. I have selected, for inclusion in Table I, three examples of nucleic acid fractions that cannot be distinguished analytically. There can be little doubt about the entirely different sequential plans governing the structure of these polymers if the values for the abundance of solitary pyrimidine units are compared.

NUCLEOTIDE ARRANGEMENT IN DIFFERENT DEOXYRIBONUCLEIC ACIDS OF ANIMAL ORIGIN

Table II compares the distribution findings obtained with total, unfractionated preparations of the deoxyribonucleic acids from calf thymus, human spleen and sperm preparations from two sea urchin species. These data do not exhaust the information gathered by us on different animal nucleic acids [21], but are presented here to indicate the scope of the method.

NUCLEOTIDE ARRANGEMENT IN THE TOTAL DEOXYRIBONUCLEIC ACID OF RYE GERM AND IN A COMPLETE SERIES OF FRACTIONS

The use of a deoxyribonucleic acid from a plant source offers several advantages. These nucleic acids have been shown to contain a fifth nitrogenous constituent, 5-methylcytosine, in appreciable quantity [7, 20]. In the specimens isolated from both wheat and rye germ the concentration of this pyrimidine amounts to 5·9 mole % (Table III). This means that nearly a quarter of the cytosine has been "replaced" by methylcytosine. Since the molar concentration of guanine equals the sum of these two pyrimidines, one may consider them as pleromeric in the sense defined above. Minor constituents of deoxyribonucleic acid (or, for that matter, of ribonucleic acid) are destined to play an important role in future work on the elucidation of nucleic acid structure, as they will serve as additional markers in the array of nucleotides constituting the polymer chain. Furthermore, the presence of a pyrimidine sharing with cytosine the property of being a 6-amino derivative and with thymine that of being a 5-methyl pyrimidine is of the greatest interest for a better understanding of the mechanisms of selection, incorporation, and replication that are at work.

Before the study of the nucleotide arrangement in the deoxyribonucleic acid of rye germ could be undertaken, it was necessary to examine the properties of deoxymethylcytidine 3′,5′-diphosphate whose production is indicative of the frequency of this pyrimidine as a solitary nucleotide [39]. At the same time the two dinucleoside triphosphates comprising 5-methylcytidine and either cytidine or thymidine were also studied.

The investigation of the deoxyribonucleic acid of rye germ [37] offered us, for the first time, the opportunity of comparing the pyrimidine distribution in the total preparation with that found in a complete series of seven fractions isolated through the fractional dissociation of the histone nucleate. These fractions were, in their distribution and composition, remarkably similar to those previously isolated by the fractionation of the deoxyribonucleic acid from wheat germ [38]. The availability of such a complete series of fractions permitted, moreover, a test of the validity of the results given by the differential distribution analysis; a weighted

TABLE III

COMPOSITION OF DEOXYRIBONUCLEIC ACIDS OF RYE GERM AND WHEAT GERM

	Rye germ*	Wheat germ†
	Moles/100-g.-atoms P	
Adenine	27·7	28·1
Guanine	22·6	21·8
Cytosine	16·4	16·8
Methylcytosine	5·9	5·9
Thymine	27·4	27·4
	Molar ratios	
Adenine + thymine to guanine + cytosine + methylcytosine	1·23	1·25
Purines to pyrimidines	1·01	1·0
Adenine to thymine	1·01	1·03
Guanine to cytosine + methyl-cytosine	1·01	0·96
Cytosine to methylcytosine	2·78	2·85

* Taken from a previous publication [37].
† Taken from a previous publication [38].

average of the values recorded for the individual fractions could be compared with those given by the total nucleic acid preparation that had not been subjected to fractionation and showed an excellent agreement [37].

The principal results of this study are, as regards the frequency of solitary pyrimidine nucleotides, shown schematically in Fig. 2. In this histogram, we give a brief description of the total pyrimidine composition of all specimens examined—total deoxyribonucleic acid and seven fractions —and depict the quantities of solitary nucleotide of each of the three pyrimidines as per cent of the total constituent in the preparation. 5-Methylcytosine, it will be seen, has a surprisingly high tendency, when compared with the other 6-aminopyrimidine, cytosine, to occur as a solitary unit, similar in this respect to thymine. I shall return to this point later.

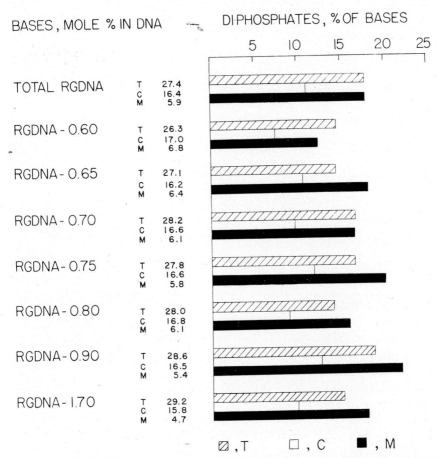

SOLITARY PY. NUCLEOTIDES IN RYE GERM DNA & FRACTIONS

FIG. 2. Pyrimidine distribution analysis of the total deoxyribonucleic acid of rye germ and its fractions. The first column indicates the NaCl molarity at which dissociation of the fraction from its histone salt occurred. The second column summarizes the composition of the specimens in terms of the molar concentrations (per 100 gm.-at. of nucleic acid P) of thymine (T), cytosine (C), and 5-methylcytosine (M). The histogram shows the frequency of the solitary nucleotides, isolated as the nucleoside 3′,5′-diphosphates, relative to the total concentration of the constituent in the nucleic acid. Based on previously published data [37].

NUCLEOTIDE ARRANGEMENT IN A MICROBIAL DEOXYRIBONUCLEIC ACID
OF THE GC TYPE

Our survey has so far all been dealing with deoxyribonucleic acids that belonged to the AT type. It was of interest to see whether the same considerations could be applied to a nucleic acid of the GC type, i.e.,

TABLE IV

DIFFERENTIAL DISTRIBUTION ANALYSIS OF DEOXYRIBONUCLEIC ACID OF BCG*

	T	C	[CC]
Total pyrimidine, as mole % P	16·7	32·3	
Solitary pyrimidine, as mole % of total constituent in DNA	13·6	12·0	
Solitary or bunched pyrimidines, as mole % P	2·27	3·88	1·13
Total T/C, molar ratio		0·52	
Solitary T/C, molar ratio		0·59	

* The figures are taken from a previous paper [40]. [CC] designates dicytidine triphosphate. Compare Table I for other explanations.

one in which guanine and cytosine preponderated. We first discovered this type in tubercle bacilli [24]; but it has since that time been found in many micro-organisms [7, 41]. The distribution analysis of the deoxyribonucleic acid of an avirulent variant (BGC) of bovine tubercle bacilli is shown in Table IV. In the nucleic acids of the AT type, as was shown before, the quantity of thymidine 3′, 5′-diphosphate released during hydrolysis exceeded that of deoxycytidine 3′,5′-diphosphate: this indicated the occurrence of larger quantities of solitary thymine than cytosine; but the ratios of the solitary residues were not those that would have been predicted statistically from the total abundance of these pyrimidines in the polymers. In the nucleic acid of the GC type an inversion in the rates of liberation of the nucleoside diphosphates is observed, as expected; but in this instance, the ratios of solitary and of total pyrimidines are not widely different: 0·59 vs. 0·52.

NUCLEOTIDE ARRANGEMENT IN THE DEOXYRIBONUCLEIC ACID OF E. coli GROWN IN THE ABSENCE AND PRESENCE OF 5-BROMOURACIL

The deoxyribonucleic acid of E. coli is unusual, being composed of nearly equimolar proportions of the four nucleotide constituents [7, 41]. No obvious distinctions appear, even when different variants and mutants are examined, although it is not unlikely that a careful differential distribution analysis would reveal some differences. Such a study has, however, not yet been undertaken.

We have as a first approach to the problem of the effect of a mutagenic agent on the sequence characteristics of a deoxyribonucleic acid, investigated the nucleic acid produced by a thymine auxotroph of E. coli, grown in the presence of thymine, and compared it with that formed by the same organism when supplied also with 5-bromouracil [42]. This halogenated pyrimidine is known to be incorporated in what would seem to be the place of some of the thymine of the nucleic acid [43–45]. The results of our study were, however, quite surprising. When the results of the total analysis of these two nucleic acid specimens are compared (Table V), it

TABLE V

COMPOSITION OF DEOXYRIBONUCLEIC ACID OF *E. coli*
GROWN IN THE ABSENCE AND PRESENCE OF 5-BROMOURACIL*

Growth supplements	Moles constituent per 100 moles total				
	A	G	C	T	B
T	24·8	25·0	25·5	24·8	—
T+B	25·3	24·3	25·1	16·4	9·0

	Molar ratios				
	$\frac{Pu}{Py}$	$\frac{A+T+B}{G+C}$	$\frac{A}{T}$	$\frac{A}{T+B}$	$\frac{6\text{-Am}}{6\text{-K}}$
T	0·99	0·98	1·00	—	1·01
T+B	0·98	1·03	1·54	1·00	1·01

* Based on previously published results [42]. The thymine auxotroph was grown on a synthetic medium (18 hr., 37°) supplemented, per ml., with 2 μg. of thymine or with 2 μg. of thymine and 10 μg. of 5-bromouracil. Abbreviations: A, adenine; G, guanine; C, cytosine; T, thymine; B, 5-bromouracil; Pu, purines; Py, pyrimidines; 6-Am, 6-amino constituents (A, C); 6-K, 6-keto constituents (G, T, B).

will indeed be seen that 5-bromouracil and thymine are pleromeric with respect to the equality of the molar quantities of purines and pyrimidines, of 6-amino and 6-keto nucleotides, and of 6-aminopurine (adenine) and 6-ketopyrimidines (thymine + 5-bromouracil). It could have been concluded that more than one-third of the places originally occupied by thymine in the polynucleotide now were filled by 5-bromouracil. The finer structural details revealed by the differential distribution analysis showed this, however, not to be the case (Table VI). There took place, obviously under the influence of the halopyrimidine, a severe distortion of all features of the nucleotide alignment that were accessible to investigation by our method. I shall return to this problem at the end of this article.

TABLE VI

DIFFERENTIAL DISTRIBUTION ANALYSIS OF *E. coli* DNA
PRODUCED IN THE ABSENCE AND PRESENCE OF 5-BROMOURACIL:
FREQUENCY OF SOLITARY AND COUPLED PYRIMIDINE NUCLEOTIDE UNITS*

Growth supplements	Thymine					Thymine + 5-bromouracil				
	T	B	C	[CC]	[TC]	T	B	C	[CC]	[TC]
Total pyrimidine, as mole % P	24·8	—	25·5			16·4	9·0	25·1		
Solitary pyrimidine, as mole % of total constituent in DNA	15·4	—	7·0			18·4	32·9	14·3		
Solitary or bunched pyrimidines, as mole % P	3·82	—	1·78	0·37	1·13	3·01	2·96	3·60	0·58	1·38
Total solitary pyrimidines, as mole % P			5·60					9·57		
Total T/C, molar ratio			0·97					0·65		
Solitary T/C, molar ratio			2·15					0·84		
Total T/B, molar ratio			—					1·82		
Solitary T/B, molar ratio			—					1·02		
Total T + B/B, molar ratio			—					2·82		
Solitary T + B/B, molar ratio			—					2·02		

* Based on previously published results [42]. Compare Table V for the composition of the DNA preparations and also Tables I and IV for explanations of the designations used.

Summarizing remarks

SEQUENCE CHARACTERISTICS COMMON TO ALL DEOXYRIBONUCLEIC ACIDS

Though the first application of the procedure for the differential analysis of pyrimidine distribution served to demonstrate that deoxyribonucleic acids from different species, even those showing identical base composition, were vastly different with regard to the alignment of their nucleotide constituents (Table I), the more important and interesting uses of this method bear on other aspects of the sequence problem. These relate, in fact, to the existence of sequential patterns that all deoxyribonucleic acids examined heretofore appear to have in common.

The first consequence of our studies may be the statement that in no case can the nucleotide sequence be predicted from the knowledge of the frequency of the individual constituents. The discarded tetranucleotide hypothesis is a primitive example of an attempt to make such a prediction; I have dealt with this a long time ago [1]. This is, incidentally, quite similar to what one would observe in a meaningful text: a certain letter may be particularly frequent; but this does not mean that it will occur, with commensurate frequency, as a doublet. We shall probably find, in general, that the symbols constituting a text are not arranged at random, if this term is understood to refer to an alignment governed only by the relative frequency of the elements, once the requirement of large numbers is fulfilled.

This brings up the problem of the non-randomness of the nucleotide sequence in deoxyribonucleic acids which we have discussed fully in a previous paper [21]. Whether strict randomness is conceivable in a living system capable of orderly replication, at any rate on the level of macromolecular events, is a question which it would be out of place to discuss here. The entire complex of randomness in biology would certainly deserve a more profound examination than I am equipped to perform. In any event, the conclusion that in no case investigated the pattern of nucleotide distribution was that to be expected from a random arrangement of constituents [21, 35, 37, 40] may contribute to the assurance that in studying the nucleotide sequence in a deoxyribonucleic acid we are, indeed, dealing with some sort of meaningful message. If the array of constituents in a biologically functional polynucleotide has been compared to a giant throw of dice, we must conclude that it is a throw of loaded dice.

Another consequence of our studies on deoxyribonucleic acids of animal and plant origin [21, 37] is the conclusion that at least 70% of the pyrimidines occur as oligonucleotide tracts containing three or more pyrimidines in a row; and a corresponding statement must, owing to the equality relationship, apply also to the purines.

POSSIBILITIES OF CLUSTER ANALYSIS

It is quite clear that the various solitary nucleotides and the small bunched oligonucleotides, such as doublets or triplets, will vary in frequency, i.e. in relative quantity, according to the plan governing the nucleotide sequence of the particular deoxyribonucleic acid; but they are most unlikely to exhibit uniqueness of quality and will, therefore, not be sufficient to define a sequence unambiguously. Uniqueness may, however, be expected, at least occasionally, when very large clusters can be included in the survey. We have made a beginning with regard to clusters of pyrimidine nucleotides [46]. When a deoxyribonucleic acid is cleaved by acid under moderate conditions ($0 \cdot 1$ M H_2SO_4, 30 min., $100°$) and the fragments are fractionated on DEAE-cellulose by means of a lithium chloride gradient, the phosphorylated pyrimidine oligonucleotides can be separated in order of increasing chain length. Further separation within the different size groups then is based on two-dimensional chromatography on filter paper. More than 97% of the nucleic acid can be accounted for. Oligonucleotides of more than five pyrimidines in a row are rare, but occasionally perceptible. Almost all possible combinations of pyrimidine nucleotide units are encountered, among them di-, tri-, and tetrathymidylic acids, all carrying an additional terminal phosphate group at $3'$. We are at present engaged in extending the sensitivity of the method by the use of radioactive labels.

These and related methods, employing specific enzymes, will doubtless have to be refined considerably, before more definitive answers to the sequence problem and its biological meaning become possible. It would, for instance, be of the greatest interest to determine the nature of the lethal sequence of a parasitic deoxyribonucleic acid that enables it to impose itself upon, and to paralyze, as it were, the bacterial host.

WHAT IS MEANT BY "REPLACEMENT"?

The platitude that "nobody is irreplaceable"—if it ever holds true— certainly cannot hold for the deoxyribonucleic acids, if they carry the biological functions ascribed to them currently. Nevertheless, one often finds the statement in the literature that an analogue of a purine or pyrimidine, not normally occurring in nature, is, when offered to the cell, incorporated into a deoxyribo- or ribonucleic acid "in the place" of a particular natural constituent of the nucleic acid. Such statements are, of course, derived from the existence of the complementariness principles [1]; i.e. they are based on the fact that certain nucleic acid constituents are pleromers, to use the nomenclature suggested above. Good examples of such pleromerism can be seen in Table III with respect to cytosine and 5-methylcytosine and in Table V with respect to thymine and 5-bromouracil; a more comprehensive selection of such instances will be given at the end of this paper.

What does the assertion that X can be "replaced" in part by Y actually signify? (1) It means that Y is incorporated into the deoxyribonucleic acid chain and that the cell, hence, must possess, or acquire, the enzymic apparatus necessary for the production and utilization of the derivative of Y that is the direct precursor of the polynucleotide chain. (2) If X and Y share the same functional group (e.g. 6-keto or 6-amino) through which alone the selection of the members of the newly forming chain takes place —as foretold by a mechanism postulating the replication of the complementary halves of a double strand [47]—it follows that every X molecule along the chain has an equal chance of being "replaced" by a Y molecule. This is obviously not the case in the two systems studied by us previously [37, 42] and illustrated in Fig. 2 and Table VI. One of these systems is concerned with the selection of a natural analogue, a 6-aminopyrimidine, the other with that of a fraudulent analogue, a 6-ketopyrimidine. In both cases a discrimination, not explainable on the basis of the replication scheme mentioned above, must have been operating. I shall discuss our findings in the next two sections.

SELECTION OF A NATURAL ANALOGUE

When we deal with a natural analogue, such as the 5-methyl derivative of cytosine, it is, of course, meaningless to speak of the replacement of one by the other. Such a statement acquires meaning only in reference to the possible mechanism of the biosynthesis of the polynucleotide chain or to the existence of such principles of pleromerism as those mentioned before. In other respects, in polymer chains that are not constructed haphazardly, each monomeric constituent must have its preordained place; a place that it must have entered, at the time of polymerization, through some form of a specific selection mechanism. A replication mechanism of this nature is, indeed, offered by the scheme [47] postulating a specific pairing of a 6-aminopurine (adenine) with a 6-ketopyrimidine (thymine) and of a 6-ketopurine (guanine) with a 6-aminopyrimidine (cytosine).

This postulate and the fact that 5-methylcytosine is pleromeric with cytosine could have led to the expectation that these two pyrimidines could replace each other at random in the deoxyribonucleic acid chain, selection having regard only to the presence of a 6-amino group in the pyrimidine. The amazingly constant quantity of methylcytosine incorporated into the deoxyribonucleic acids of wheat and rye germ (Table III, and compare also the tabulation given in a previous paper [38]) should, however, render such a conclusion most questionable. In what manner could a guanine residue in the preformed chain exercise a preference for pairing with cytosine, rather than with methylcytosine, in the newly forming counterpart chain? There are surely limits to the amount of foresight that we can attribute to an ostensibly automatic process.

Another observation, made repeatedly [8, 37, 38], has to do with the trend of the distribution of 5-methylcytosine in consecutive fractions obtained by the fractionation of deoxyribonucleic acid from calf thymus, wheat germ, and rye germ. In all instances, the relative abundance of 5-methylcytosine with respect to cytosine varied in such a manner that the percentage contribution of the minor pyrimidine was higher in the earlier fractions. In no case could one have claimed that the two 6-amino pyrimidines replaced each other at random within the polynucleotide chain. I have discussed, in more detail, the significance of the finding of a disproportionate distribution of cytosine and 5-methylcytosine in view of current replication hypotheses at a previous occasion [10].

An even more impressive difference between the ways in which methylcytosine and cytosine are selected for insertion into the poly-nucleotide emerges from the study of the frequency of these pyrimidines as solitary and bunched nucleotides [37]. As will be seen in Fig. 2, a remarkably large proportion of methylcytosine, and a surprisingly small proportion of cytosine, exist as solitary units. These two 6-aminopyrimi-dines can hardly share a common pattern of nucleotide sequence. What is, however, remarkable is that the mole fractions of 5-methylcytosine and thymine appearing as solitary units are nearly equal in most instances. One must conclude that, whereas there is no evidence that the two 6-amino pyrimidines are treated indiscriminately by the selection mechanism, there is some indication that no such distinction is exercised in regard to the two 5-methylpyrimidines. In the terms defined above, cytosine and 5-methyl-cytosine are pleromers, but not homotopes; thymine and 5-methylcytosine appear to be homotopic with respect to the sequence purine–pyrimidine–purine, although they are not pleromeric.

SELECTION OF A FRAUDULENT ANALOGUE

In the instance under discussion, the incorporation of 5-bromouracil into the deoxyribonucleic acid of *E. coli*, the problem of replacement can be posed directly. In the case of a natural satellite, such as 5-methylcytosine, the complement appears to be fixed rigidly by the cell, whereas no obvious cellular mechanism, except the death of the cell, can be seen that would limit the extent of incorporation of the halopyrimidine which the cell presumably cannot but treat as an impostor. If the cellular apparatus is inveigled into treating the fraudulent 6-ketopyrimidine as if it were thymine, does it also insert it as such indiscriminately into the newly forming deoxyribonucleic acid ? This does not appear to be the case. A glance at Table VI will show that the deoxyribonucleic acids made by the cell in the absence and in the presence of bromouracil are vastly different with regard to their sequence characteristics. Not only is there no sign of an equal relative utilization of thymine and bromouracil for common sequences, such as purine–thymine–purine and purine–bromouracil–purine, but the intrusion of the halopyrimidine seems to have brought about so drastic a reorganization of the nucleotide pattern as to imply the existence of two distinct populations of polymers. We may be able to fool the cell, but it is no longer the same cell.

In the cells that were cultivated in the presence of the halopyrimidine, the nucleic acid contains nearly twice as many solitary pyrimidine residues as does the normal preparation; the frequency of the sequences purine–cytosine–purine has doubled; and, relative to the total concentration of thymine, even the runs of purine–thymine–purine have increased. In addition—and this is quite remarkable—almost one-third of the incorporated bromouracil is found flanked by purines in the form of solitary units. The abundance of the coupled unit purine–cytosine–purine has, however, been relatively little changed.

At the same time, as Table V shows, 5-bromouracil and thymine definitely are treated as pleromers.

THE CONCEPTS OF PLEROMERISM AND HOMOTOPY AND THE NEIGHBOUR
PROBLEM

The definitions of the suggested terms "pleromer" and "homotope" have been given above. The compilation in Table VII, by no means complete, gives a few examples of such pleromeric relationships in deoxyribonucleic acids. There can be little doubt that in all these instances the established pairing relationships would have been destroyed, had the minor pleromer been omitted from the computations. Only one satellite normally occurring in nature, viz. 5-methylcytosine, could be included in the Table. Another minor component—if it can be classified as a normal constituent—namely, N-methyladenine, plays a baffling role. It has been reported to occur, among other instances, in the deoxyribonucleic acid of a thymine auxotroph of *E. coli* in not inconsiderable quantity [49]. Under special conditions of growth, its concentration increases, somewhat in measure with a decrease in the amount of thymine. It is, however, at the moment difficult to see through what mechanism a 6-ketopyrimidine and a 6-methylaminopurine could function as pleromers.

Pleromic relationships in ribonucleic acids are much more difficult to establish, as the only complementariness useful for scrutiny is the equality of the 6-amino and 6-ketonucleotides [19]. Of the three examples listed in Table VIII only the one dealing with the incorporation of 5-fluorouracil (52) carries conviction. It is not impossible that, when more careful analyses become available, 8-azaguanine and guanine will also emerge as pleromers.

The usefulness of the concept of homotopy is, for the time being, more

TABLE VII

EXAMPLES OF PLEROMERIC RELATIONSHIPS IN DEOXYRIBONUCLEIC ACIDS

| Source of DNA | Pleromers | | Molar ratios | | |
	Analogue or natural satellite (mole %)	Normal pyrimidine (mole %)	Complementariness ratio*	6 Am/ 6K†	Reference
Wheat germ	5-Methyl- 5·9 cytosine	Cytosine 16·8	0·96	1·03	38
Rye germ	5-Methyl- 5·9 cytosine	Cytosine 16·4	1·01	1·00	37
E. coli	5-Chloro- 14·2 uracil	Thymine 7·9	1·06‡	1·00‡	48
E. coli	5-Bromo- 9·0 uracil	Thymine 16·4	1·00	1·01	42
E. coli	5-Iodo- 4·1 uracil	Thymine 19·6	1·01	0·99	48
Phage T2r+	5-Bromo- 16·1 uracil	Thymine 15·9	1·01	0·97	48

* In the case of 6-aminopyrimidines (cytosine, 5-methylcytosine), this is the molar ratio of guanine to the sum of 6-aminopyrimidines; in the case of the halopyrimidines, the complementariness ratio is the molar ratio of adenine to the sum of 6-keto pyrimidines.

† Molar ratio of 6-amino nucleotides to 6-keto nucleotides.

‡ N-Methyladenine (1·4 mole %) omitted from the calculations.

evident with respect to the amino acid sequence in proteins than to the nucleotide arrangement in nucleic acids. More and more instances of such homotopic relationships are being revealed as knowledge on specific sequences in proteins increases. As concerns the deoxyribonucleic acids, we are largely limited to the consideration of simple sequences, such as purine–pyrimidine–purine, or of small bunches of pyrimidine nucleotides. The development of the study of larger clusters, mentioned before, will doubtless contribute much to our knowledge. I have emphasized above a possible instance of homotopy, namely, the remarkable similarity in distribution, as solitary nucleotides, of the two 5-methyl pyrimidines (thymine and 5-methylcytosine) in rye germ deoxyribonucleic acid [37]. Examples of the absence of homotopic relationships, where they would have been expected, are more numerous: cytosine and 5-methylcytosine, e.g. in rye

TABLE VIII

EXAMPLES OF PLEROMERIC RELATIONSHIPS IN RIBONUCLEIC ACIDS

| Source of RNA | Pleromers | | 6-Am/6-K* | Reference |
	Analogue or natural satellite (mole %)	Normal pyrimidine nucleotide (mole %)		
Rat liver, soluble RNA	Pseudouridylic acid 3·3	Uridylic acid 17·4	0·95	50
E. coli, soluble RNA	Pseudouridylic acid 2·1	Uridylic acid 15·0	0·98†	51
E. coli, total RNA	5-Fluoro-uridylic acid 9·8	Uridylic acid 11·4	0·94	52

* Ratio of the molar sum of adenylic and cytidylic acids to that of guanylic, uridylic and pseudo- or 5-fluorouridylic acids.

† Ribothymidylic acid (1·1 mole %) included among the 6-keto nucleotides.

germ nucleic acid [37]; thymine and 5-bromouracil in the nucleic acid of *E. coli* [42]. It goes without saying that, at the present state of our knowledge, such statements as the presence or absence of homotopy must be taken as valid only in the most general statistical terms. Specific homotopic replacements may, of course, have taken place even where no all-embracing positional replacement can be affirmed.

One could conclude provisionally that in the deoxyribonucleic acids pleromers are not necessarily homotopes, and homotopes not necessarily pleromers. Before the law of pleromerism all bases are equal as long as they pair off according to functional groups. But the rules of segregation applied to them, once they have gone through the door, still are obscure. These rules are, I am afraid, much less simple and predictable than would please the advocates of biological automation.

This brings me to the last topic of the present survey, namely, the neighbour problem. It was, I believe, first stated in the following terms [10]. "The frequency of methylcytosine being linked to guanine in a dinucleotide as compared with that of cytosine being so attached is twenty times as high in calf thymus nucleic acid, and thirteen times as high in the wheat germ preparation, than would have been expected for non-selective incorporation. The unexpectedly high proportion of 5-methyldeoxycytidylic acid that is linked to deoxyguanylic acid [53, 54] makes one, in fact, wonder whether it is not the adjoining nucleotide rather than the one

opposite that directs the incorporation." This remarkable phenomenon—
the high tendency of methylcytosine to be next to guanine—was again
touched upon in our study on the sequence characteristics of the deoxyribonucleic acid of rye germ [37]. Several analogous observations also
were discussed there of which one may be mentioned. When, in this
nucleic acid, the coupled dipyrimidine units are surveyed, it is found that
methylcytosine has a greater tendency to be linked to either thymine or
cytosine than the latter has to associate with itself or with thymine; and
there is a definite bias in favour of methylcytosine–cytosine units. In our
recent investigation of the bromouracil-containing nucleic acid of *E. coli*
[42] a more general formulation of the neighbour problem was attempted:
"One gains the impression that, after the selection of equal numbers of
6-aminopurines and 6-ketopyrimidines, on one hand, and of 6-keto
purines and 6-aminopyrimidines on the other, a second mechanism—an
exclusion principle, as it were—comes into play, so that certain neighbours
are tolerated and others not, or rarely."

Somewhat similar observations have also been made in the case of the
ribonucleic acids in which the analysis of neighbouring tendencies is
easier because of the facility of obtaining any given nucleoside as either
the 3' or the 5' phosphate. An examination of this type has, for instance,
been made with ribonucleic acid preparations from different cellular
portions of rat liver [55]. A particularly instructive example of the neighbour principle is offered by the "soluble" ribonucleic acids of the cytoplasm concerned with the specific transfer of amino acids [56], in which the
terminal sequence adenine–cytosine–cytosine is required; a sequence that
can apparently be enforced by a specific enzymic mechanism.

The manner in which a growing deoxypolynucleotide chain could
guarantee the quality of its continuation is not yet a topic encouraging
speculation.* Our present ideas about the enzymes taking part in the biosynthesis of specific polymers will probably have to undergo a stringent
revision before the directed synthesis of complicated sequences will
begin to be understood. For this, more than a biological form of Scotch
tape is required. Certain sequential restrictions could, incidentally, be
explained if, under circumstances, runs of more than one nucleotide were
the immediate precursors of the polymer chain. We have, for instance,
discussed the evidence, in rye germ nucleic acid, of the two dinucleotides
cytosine–guanine and methylcytosine–guanine being able to substitute
each other at random [37].

In considering the problem of the nucleotide sequence in deoxyribonucleic acids we have barely turned the corner. There is a long road before
us; and we shall not see its end.

* "Whereof one cannot speak, thereof one must be silent." Wittgenstein,
Tractatus Logico-Philosophicus.

Acknowledgments

The experimental work forming the basis of this essay has had the generous support of several agencies, especially, the National Institutes of Health, United States Public Health Service; the National Science Foundation; The American Cancer Society; and the Rockefeller Foundation. I wish to thank my colleagues whose names appear in the Bibliography; an especial debt of gratitude is due to Dr. H. S. Shapiro without whose work much of what is presented here could not have been written.

References

1. Chargaff, E., *Experientia* **6,** 201 (1950).
2. Chargaff, E., *in* "The Origin of Life on the Earth" (I.U.B. Symposium Series, Vol. 1). Pergamon Press, London, 297 (1959).
3. Chargaff, E., *in* "Transactions, 4th International Congress of Biochemistry", Vol. XIV. Pergamon Press, London, 21 (1959).
4. Edsall, J. T., *in* "The Proteins", Vol. I, ed. H. Neurath and K. Bailey. Academic Press, New York, 549 (1953).
5. Sadron, C. L., *in* "The Nucleic Acids", Vol. III, ed. E. Chargaff and J. N. Davidson. Academic Press, New York, 1 (1960).
6. Montague, M. D., and Morton, R. K., *Nature, Lond.* **187,** 916 (1960).
7. Chargaff, E., *in* "The Nucleic Acids", Vol. I, ed. E. Chargaff and J. N. Davidson. Academic Press, New York, 307 (1955).
8. Chargaff, E., Crampton, C. F., and Lipshitz, R., *Nature, Lond.* **172,** 289 (1953).
9. Crampton, C. F., Lipshitz, R., and Chargaff, E., *J. biol. Chem.* **211,** 125 (1954).
10. Chargaff, E., *in* "Fibrous Proteins and their Biological Significance" (Symp. Soc. Exp. Biol.) **9,** 32 (1955).
11. Watson, J. D., and Crick, F. H. C., *Nature, Lond.* **171,** 737 (1953).
12. Cavalieri, L. F., Rosenberg, B. H., and Deutsch, J. F., *Biochem. Biophys. Res. Comm.* **1,** 124 (1959).
13. Bernardi, G., Champagne, M., and Sadron, C., *Nature. Lond.* **188,** 228 (1960).
14. Crampton, C. F., Lipshitz, R., and Chargaff, E., *J. biol. Chem.* **206,** 499 (1954).
15. Chargaff, E., Schulman, H. M., and Shapiro, H. S., *Nature, Lond.* **180,** 851 (1957).
16. Chargaff, E., "The Harvey Lectures", Series 52. Academic Press, New York, 57 (1958).
17. Ryle, A. P., Sanger, F., Smith, L. F., and Kitai, R., *Biochem. J.* **60,** 541 (1955).
18. Brown, H., Sanger, F., and Kitai, R., *Biochem. J.* **60,** 556 (1955).
19. Elson, D., and Chargaff, E., *Biochim. biophys. Acta* **17,** 367 (1955).
20. Wyatt, G. R., *Biochem. J.* **48,** 584 (1951).
21. Shapiro, H. S., and Chargaff, E., *Biochim. biophys. Acta* **26,** 608 (1957).
22. Chargaff, E., *Cold Spr. Harb. Symp. quant. Biol.* **12,** 28 (1947).
23. Chargaff, E., Vischer, E., Doniger, R., Green, C., and Misani, F., *J. biol. Chem.* **177,** 405 (1949).
24. Vischer, E., Zamenhof, S., and Chargaff, E., *J. biol. Chem.* **177,** 429 (1949).
25. Hodes, M. E., and Chargaff, E., *Biochim. biophys. Acta* **22,** 361 (1956).
26. Tamm, C., Hodes, M. E., and Chargaff, E., *J. biol. Chem.* **195,** 49 (1952).
27. Tamm, C., and Chargaff, E., *J. biol. Chem.* **203,** 689 (1953).
28. Tamm, C., Shapiro, H. S., Lipshitz, R., and Chargaff, E., *J. biol. Chem.* **203,** 673 (1953).

29. Burton, K., and Petersen, G. B., *Biochem. J.* **75,** 17 (1960).
30. Levene, P. A., and Jacobs, W. A., *J. biol. Chem.* **12,** 411 (1912).
31. Thannhauser, S. J., and Ottenstein, B., *Z. physiol. Chem.* **114,** 39 (1921).
32. Levene, P. A., *J. biol. Chem.* **48,** 119 (1921).
33. Thannhauser, S. J., and Blanco, G., *Z. physiol. Chem.* **161,** 116 (1926).
34. Dekker, C. A., Michelson, A. M., and Todd, A. R., *J. chem. Soc.* 947 (1953).
35. Shapiro, H. S., and Chargaff, E., *Biochim. biophys. Acta* **26,** 596 (1957).
36. Shapiro, H. S., and Chargaff, E., *Biochim. biophys. Acta* **23,** 451 (1957).
37. Shapiro, H. S., and Chargaff, E., *Biochim. biophys. Acta* **39,** 68 (1960).
38. Lipshitz, R., and Chargaff, E., *Biochim. biophys. Acta* **19,** 256 (1956).
39. Shapiro, H. S., and Chargaff, E., *Biochim. biophys. Acta* **39,** 62 (1960).
40. Tsumita, T., and Chargaff, E., *Biochim. biophys. Acta* **29,** 568 (1958).
41. Belozersky, A. N., and Spirin, A. S., *in* "The Nucleic Acids", Vol. III, ed. E. Chargaff and J. N. Davidson. Academic Press, New York, 147 (1960).
42. Shapiro, H. S., and Chargaff, E., *Nature, Lond.* **188,** 62 (1960).
43. Weygand, F., Wacker, A., and Dellweg, H., *Z. Naturf.* **7b,** 19 (1952).
44. Dunn, D. B., and Smith, J. D., *Nature, Lond.* **174,** 305 (1954).
45. Zamenhof, S, and Griboff, G., *Nature, Lond.* **174,** 306 (1954).
46. Spencer, J. H., and Chargaff, E., *Fed. Proc.* **20,** 353 (1961).
47. Watson, J. D., and Crick, F. H. C., *Nature, Lond.* **171,** 964 (1953).
48. Dunn, D. B., and Smith, J. D., *Biochem. J.* **67,** 494 (1957).
49. Dunn, D. B., and Smith, J. D., *Biochem. J.* **68,** 627 (1958).
50. Lipshitz, R., and Chargaff, E., *Biochim. biophys. Acta* **42,** 544 (1960).
51. Dunn, D. B., Smith, J. D., and Spahr, P. F., *J. mol. Biol.* **2,** 113 (1960).
52. Horowitz, J., and Chargaff, E., *Nature, Lond.* **184,** 1213 (1959).
53. Smith, J. D., and Markham, R., *Nature, Lond.* **170,** 120 (1952).
54. Sinsheimer, R. L., *J. biol. Chem.* **208,** 445 (1954).
55. Shigeura, H. T., and Chargaff, E., *J. biol. Chem.* **233,** 197 (1958).
56. Hoagland, M. B., *in* "The Nucleic Acids", Vol. III, ed. E. Chargaff and J. N. Davidson. Academic Press, New York, 349 (1960).

Discussion

DAVIS: I don't quite understand what you mean in saying that methylcytosine has to replace thymine. Are there not solitary pyrimidine places where the methyl-cytosine may have replaced cytosine?

CHARGAFF: I have to refer you to recent papers with Dr. Shapiro in which we discussed at great length the problem of the solitary methylcytidylic units versus thymidylic and cytidylic units. What I had tried to point out is that you can look at the formation of such a chain—whether it is double or single is immaterial in this case—as being a two-stage process. First, through a sieve as it were, an equal number of 6-amino and 6-keto compounds are selected. These guarantee the pairing principles which I have mentioned before, but what goes next to each other seems to be controlled by what I have called, for want of a better term, an exclusion principle. For instance, you can say that in the case of bromouridylic acid in *E. coli* much more occurs as solitary units between two purines than would have been predicted. You only have to compare the total molar sums of solitary thymidylic acid and of solitary thymidylic plus bromouridylic acids. In other words, there is a principle operating which says that bromouracil likes to be between two purines. This intruder has been segregated in the chain entirely differently from the way in which the thymine is arranged; and a similar thing happens with cytosine *versus* methylcytosine. In the latter case, one cannot speak of "replacement", because you don't replace one natural compound by another, but must infer that they occupy very different places in the chain.

DISCHE: These changed sequences of pyrimidines and purines which are brought about by bromouracil appear to be very difficult to reconcile with the function of the nucleotide sequences as a coding system. If you get a complete redistribution of the solitary pyrimidines then you get also a complete change in the sequence of the purines. It is difficult to see how this organism can have any similarity to its parents if you make such a complete change in the sequence of practically all molecules of the nucleic acids. I think this is really a most remarkable phenomenon. The second question I should like to ask is whether the pairing is found also in the one strand DNA?

CHARGAFF: To answer your first question: on the one hand you have a hypothesis and on the other you have some meagre findings. I don't know whether I should be called upon to reconcile the experimental findings with a hypothesis. It should be the other way around. The fact is that in normal *E. coli* DNA 15% of the thymine is solitary. This is the only 6-ketopyrimidine present in DNA. *E. coli* treated with bromouracil gives 18% of the thymine as solitary plus 33% of the bromouracil which has been incorporated as solitary unit. In other words, whereas in the first case 15% of the ketopyrimidines are flanked by purines, almost 27% are so arranged in the second case. You are perfectly right that if there is any information coded into the DNA, looking at the figures you would believe that we are dealing with two entirely different organisms. I leave it to you to draw your own conclusion. I don't want to speculate too much at this early stage. It could, of course, be that not all the DNA is functional in a strict sense. Those fractions that really carry information may be left relatively unattacked. In answer to your second question, there is no obvious pairing discernible in Sinsheimer's analysis. In any event, none of the regularities which one encounters in the other DNAs is found in this.

Problems in Polynucleotide Biosynthesis

J. N. Davidson

*Department of Biochemistry, University of
Glasgow, Scotland*

One of the most exciting recent developments in biochemistry has been the now classical work on the biosynthesis of deoxyribonucleic acid (DNA)* by Kornberg and his colleagues (for summary see ref. [1]) who showed that extracts of *Escherichia coli* contain kinases which bring about the phosphorylation of deoxribonucleotides to the triphosphate stage and a polymerase which acts on the triphosphates in the presence of a suitable DNA primer with the production of deoxyribopolynucleotide macromolecules built to the design of the primer molecule.

Such enzymes are also present in mammalian tissues. They have been the subject of extensive investigations by Potter and his colleagues in Wisconsin [2, 3, 4] and Canellakis in Yale [5, 6, 7] using regenerating rat liver, and by our own group in Glasgow [8, 9, 10, 11, 12, 13, 14, 15] using extracts of Ehrlich ascites carcinoma cells. Similar systems are present in calf thymus [16] and mouse leukaemic cells [17]. The following account is based largely on the work of a group of investigators including Dr. R. M. S. Smellie, Dr. H. M. Keir, Dr. E. D. Gray, Dr. S. M. Weissman, Dr. J. Richards, Dr. J. Paul and Mr. D. Bell.

The process of DNA biosynthesis can be divided into three separate stages:

(i) The biosynthesis of the purine and pyrimidine nucleotides and their conversion to the deoxyribonucleoside monophosphates.

(ii) The phosphorylation of the deoxyribonucleoside monophosphates to the corresponding triphosphates by appropriate kinases.

* The following abbreviations are used in this paper: DNA for deoxyribonucleic acid; dAMP, dGMP, dCMP, dUMP, UMP, OMP, IMP, and TMP for the 5'-monophosphates of deoxyadenosine, deoxyguanosine, deoxycytidine, deoxyuridine, uridine, orotidine, inosine and thymidine respectively; dATP, dADP, dGTP, dGDP, dCTP, dCDP, TTP and TDP for the 5'-tri- and diphosphates respectively of deoxyadenosine, deoxyguanosine, deoxycytidine and thymidine; TdR for thymidine; ATP for adenosine-5'-triphosphate; DPN for diphosphopyridine nucleotide; tris for 2-amino-2-hydroxymethyl propane-1:3-diol; TdR kinase, TMP kinase and TDP kinase denote respectively the enzyme systems responsible for the formation of TMP, TDP and TTP.

(iii) The polymerization of the triphosphates in the presence of DNA primer to yield new deoxyribopolynucleotide under the influence of the polymerase enzyme.

The enzymes involved in these reactions are freely soluble in water or buffer solutions and are present in extracts obtained by centrifuging disrupted cells at high speeds to remove particulate material. The overall reaction involved in the combination of the second and third steps mentioned above can readily be demonstrated by incubating such extracts with labelled thymidine (TdR) and following its incorporation into DNA (Fig. 1). Thymidine has several advantages for this purpose: it is a specific precursor of DNA and it can readily be obtained commercially, labelled with tritium at high levels of activity. For these reasons it has been extensively employed in autoradiographic studies on DNA biosynthesis,

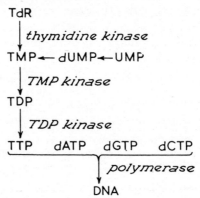

FIG. 1. Pathway of incorporation of thymidine into DNA.

especially as tritium is a label peculiarly suitable for autoradiography (for bibliography see ref. [18]). But thymidine has the further advantage, as will be mentioned later, that the enzymes involved in its phosphorylation to its triphosphate (TTP) increase and decrease according to the state of proliferation of the tissue whereas those involved in the phosphorylation of the deoxyribonucleoside monophosphates of adenine, guanine and cytosine show a much smaller, if any, variation [13, 14].

Against these advantages it might be argued that thymidine is not a normal metabolite on the anabolic pathway to TTP *in vivo* since the formation of thymine derivatives proceeds at the nucleotide level by way of UMP and dUMP to TMP (Fig. 1), but this is not a serious disadvantage since the kinase involved in the phosphorylation of thymidine to TMP appears to run parallel with the kinases phosphorylating TMP to TTP [13].

The incorporation of [³H]-TdR into DNA by the enzyme systems in cell-free extracts of several tissues is illustrated in Table I. As might be

TABLE I

The Incorporation of [³H]-TdR into DNA by Soluble Enzymes Prepared from Sonically Disrupted Rabbit Tissues [8]

The reaction mixture contained 0·1 M phosphate buffer pH 8·1, 50 μmoles glucose/ml., 2·5 μmoles ATP/ml., 2·5 μmoles DPN/ml., 4μ moles $MgCl_2$/ml., 500 μg.DNA/ml., 20 μmoles NaCl/ml., and 2 μC [³H]-TdR/ml. Incubation time: 2 hr.

Tissue	DNA specific activity (c.p.m./μmole DNA-P)
Rabbit bone marrow	24 750
Rabbit thymus	9 275
Rabbit appendix	1 485
Rabbit liver	131
Rabbit kidney	71

expected, the lowest values are found for the non-proliferating tissues such as liver and kidney and the highest values in tissues such as bone marrow in which cell division is very active. Extracts of such rapidly prolifering tissues may be used to illustrate the net synthesis of DNA. Table II shows

TABLE II

Synthesis of Polynucleotide by Polymerase Present in Extracts of Ehrlich Ascites Tumour Cells [10]

The reaction mixture contained 100 μmoles tris buffer pH 7·9, 0·25 μmole DPN, 5 μmoles $MgCl_2$, 25 μg. ascites DNA and 0·7 ml. ascites cell extract in a total vol. of 1 ml. Incubation time: 4 hr. Figures in parenthesis represent the number of determinations.

Additions	Total DNA/tube (μg.)
Nil	26·2 (4)
0·3 μmole each of dATP, dGTP, dCTP and TTP	47·7 (4)

net synthesis by the polymerase present in a cell-free extract of Ehrlich ascites carcinoma cells incubated with the four deoxyribonucleoside tri-phosphates in the presence of primer DNA, magnesium ions and DPN.

The activities of the kinases responsible for the formation of TTP are shown in Fig. 2. Again the highest activity is found in extracts of those tissues showing the most active cell proliferation. The activity in liver tissue is very low indeed but when cell proliferation is induced by partial hepatectomy a rise in the ability of extracts of the resulting regenerating liver tissue to form TTP from TdR is apparent within 24 hr. and is very

E

pronounced 48 hr. after operation [3, 4, 6, 7, 11, 13, 19]. The polymerase activity is also increased. This behaviour of the thymidylate kinase system is in striking contrast to that of the kinases phosphorylating dAMP, dGMP and dCMP which are very little elevated in regenerating, as compared with normal, liver [3, 14].

A detailed study of the three kinases in regenerating rat liver at various times after partial hepatectomy shows that the appearance of the enzymes tends to be sequential, TdR and TMP kinases appearing before TDP kinase [13].

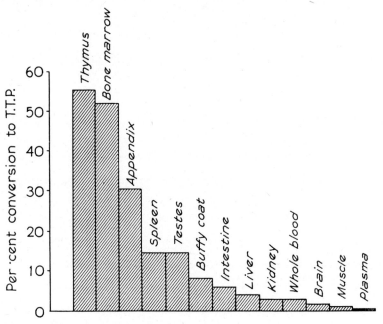

FIG. 2. Per cent conversion of thymidine to TTP by kinases present in extracts of various rabbit tissues.

By 24 hr. the TdR and TMP kinases have begun to increase sharply, reaching maximum activity after about 30 hr. The activity of TDP kinase develops more slowly, reaching its peak at about 48 hr., which is also the time of maximum incorporation of [³H-]TdR into DNA in the overall reaction. Subsequently all kinases decline in activity.

A similar sequential pattern of kinase appearance is also found in cultures of the L strain of mouse subcutaneous fibroblasts [11, 13]. Such cells in the resting phase after exhaustion of the medium show either no kinase activity or only TdR kinase activity. On inoculation into fresh medium a period of rapid growth occurs after a lag phase. The TdR kinase appears early, rises sharply and remains elevated. The TMP kinase activity rises later but before the TDP kinase, and both enzymes reach their peak of activity during the early part of the growth phase and decline before growth (increase in cell number) has stopped. This pattern can be greatly modified by adding thymidine to the cultures without affecting the growth rates. While there is little effect on the enzymes during the early period of growth, the TdR kinase activity remains elevated for a much longer period in the test cultures and TMP and TDP kinases rise to a second peak during the period when these activities in the control cultures decline [11, 13]. These elevations on the kinase activities can be produced only during the growth phase and are apparently due to true enzyme induction.

Although extracts of normal liver tissue show very little activity in synthesizing DNA they nevertheless contain an active polymerase which can be separated by ammonium sulphate fractionation [14]. The low

TABLE III

EFFECT OF LIVER EXTRACT ON PARTLY PURIFIED POLYMERASE AND KINASES FROM ASCITES TUMOUR EXTRACTS [14]

	Polymerase	Kinases		
	mμ moles TTP^{32} incorporated into DNA in 2 hr. per mg. protein	$\mu\mu$ moles ester formed in 1·5 hr. per mg. protein		
		TMP	TDP	TTP
Ascites enzymes	4·7	430	830	2130
Ascites enzymes + liver extract	0·4	14	12	0

activity of whole extracts of liver suggests that they might contain factors which interfere with polymerase or kinase action and this has indeed been found to be the case [12, 14]. Addition of extract of normal rat liver to partly purified polymerase and kinases for the thymidine system prepared from extracts of Ehrlich ascites cells causes a very pronounced drop in activity (Table III). Similarly the addition of extract of normal liver to extract of regenerating liver greatly reduces the polymerase and kinase activity in the latter. The activity of these enzymes in bone marrow is likewise reduced by extracts of normal liver.

The presence of factors interfering with polymerase and kinase activity is not confined to liver tissue. Factors inhibiting polymerase are pronounced in liver, kidney and serum but not in brain or muscle. The phosphorylation of thymidine is strongly inhibited by liver extracts but not by extracts of other tissues so far tested while the formation of TDP and TTP is inhibited by liver and kidney extracts, by serum and to a much less pronounced extent by muscle extracts. The polymerase used in most of these tests has been purified from Ehrlich ascites tumour cells but polymerases from spleen thymus and bone marrow are likewise affected.

The interfering factors are thermolabile, acid-precipitable and non-dialysable but so far have not been identified with any known enzyme or

TABLE IV

INHIBITION OF ENZYMES BY FRACTIONS PREPARED FROM EXTRACTS OF NORMAL
RAT LIVER

	Inhibition of		
Fraction	TdR kinase	TMP kinase	Polymerase
A	±	+	+
B	±	+	—
C	—	+	+
D	—	—	+

enzymes. They appear to be different from the enzymes which hydrolyse the deoxyribonucleoside triphosphates with the release of inorganic phosphate. The distribution of the interfering substances in various tissues suggests that different factors are involved in the inhibition of the various enzymes and this has been confirmed by fractionation of liver

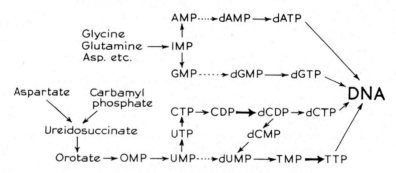

FIG. 3. Pathways involved in the biosynthesis of DNA.

extract with purification and separation from each other of the factors inhibiting TdR kinase, TMP kinase and the polymerase [15] (Table IV).

Kinase inhibitions so far discussed have referred to the system producing TTP. The pattern of results obtained with the kinases for dAMP, dGMP and dCMP is quite different in that these enzymes in ascites cell extracts are not inhibited by extracts of normal liver. The kinase system for producing TTP would accordingly appear to be unique both in its tendency to vary with the state of proliferation of the tissue and in its susceptibility to the action of the interfering factors present in extracts of normal resting liver. It must therefore exercise a profound effect in the regulation of DNA biosynthesis. Such a conclusion would be in agreement with the well-known views of Potter [20, 21].

The overall picture of DNA formation is illustrated in Fig. 3. In addition to feedback mechanisms controlling nucleotide biosynthesis [20, 21] at least two main mechanisms seem to control polynucleotide formation. One is the conversion of cytidylate to deoxycytidylate which appears from the recent work of Reichard, Canellakis and Canellakis [22] to occur at the diphosphate level and to be controlled by the triphosphate level in the cell; the second is the system involved in the formation of TTP from TMP. It may well be that a third method of control lies in the presence in certain tissues of inhibitors for the polymerase.

References

1. Kornberg, A., *Science* **131,** 1503 (1960).
2. Bollum, F. J., and Potter V. R. *J. biol. Chem.* **233,** 478 (1958).
3. Bollum, F. J., and Potter, V. R., *Cancer Res.* **19,** 561 (1959).
4. Bollum, F. J., Anderegg, J. W., McElya, A. B., and Potter, V. R., *Cancer Res.* **20,** 138 (1960).
5. Canellakis, E. S., and Mantsavinos, R., *Biochim. biophys. Acta* **27,** 643 (1958)
6. Mantsavinos, R., and Canellakis, E. S., *J. biol. Chem.* **234,** 628 (1959).
7. Canellakis, E. S., Jaffe, J. J., Mantsavinos, R., and Krakow, J. S., *J. biol. Chem.* **234,** 2096 (1959).
8. Smellie, R. M. S., Keir, H. M., and Davidson, J. N., *Biochim. biophys. Acta* **35,** 389 (1959).
9. Keir, H. M., and Smellie, R. M. S., *Biochim. biophys. Acta* **35,** 405 (1959).
10. Smellie, R. M. S., Gray, E. D., Keir, H. M., Richards, J., Bell, D., and Davidson, J. N., *Biochim. biophys. Acta* **37,** 243 (1960).
11. Weissman, S. M., Paul, J., Thomson, R. Y., Smellie, R. M. S., and Davidson, J. N., *Biochem. J.* **76,** 1P (1960).
12. Weissman, S. M., Gray, E. D., Thomson, R. Y., Smellie, R. M. S., and Davidson, J. N., *Biochem. J.* **76,** 26P (1960).
13. Weissman, S. M., Smellie, R. M. S., and Paul, J. (1960), *Biochim. biophys. Acta* **45,** 101.
14. Gray, E. D., Weissman, S. M., Richards, J., Bell, D., Keir, H. M., Smellie, R. M. S., and Davidson, J. N. (1960), *Biochim. biophys. Acta* **45,** 111.
15. Weissman, S. M., *et al.* (unpublished results).
16. Bollum, F. J., *Fed. Proc.* **18,** 194 (1959).
17. Mantsavinos, R., and Canellakis, E. S., *Cancer Res.* **19,** 1239 (1959).
18. Lima-de-Faria, A., *Hereditas, Lund.* **45,** 632 (1959).
19. Hiatt, H. H., and Bojarski, T. B., *Biochem. biophys. Res. Comm.* **2,** 35 (1960).
20. Potter, V. R. *Univ. Mich. med. Bull.* **23,** 401 (1957).
21. Potter, V. R., and Auerbach, V. H., *Lab. Investigation* **8,** 495 (1959).
22. Reichard, P., Canellakis, Z. N., and Canellakis, E. S., *Biochim. biophys. Acta* **41,** 558 (1960).

Discussion

DISCHE: You indicated in a slide that the deoxycytidine kinases did not increase in regenerating liver but that the thymidine kinase strongly increased; is that because the original activity of the deoxycytidine kinase in the liver was so much higher than that of the thymidine kinase?

DAVIDSON: Yes, the activity of deoxycytidine kinase in the liver is much higher than that of thymidine kinase and the same holds for the kinases for deoxyAMP, and deoxyGMP; and this may well be the reason why they do not increase because they are abundant already.

REICHARD: I should like to ask you two questions with regard to the inhibition of the syntheses; one is: have you tried to fortify the system by adding an ATP-regenerating system which might overcome this inhibition? The second question is: does the factor which inhibits the polymerase have any deoxyribonuclease activity?

DAVIDSON: We have investigated both of these points. We haven't added an ATP-regenerating system, we have infused ATP into the system without effect. We have looked into the question of deoxyribonuclease activity and as far as we can see this has nothing to do with the action of the inhibitory factor.

SIEKEVITZ: I should like to ask Prof. Davidson a couple of questions. Another possibility of regulation of DNA synthesis derives from the possibility that DNA itself may be a cofactor for the enzyme. Could it be that the availability of the right kind of DNA which acts as a primer could act as a regulator of DNA synthesis? In the resting cell DNA could not act as a primer for the enzyme but at a certain point something happens, it can act as a primer, and when finished it "rejuvenates" itself until it is no longer active.

DAVIDSON: Offhand I am not very convinced about it, but I should point out that conditions in the resting cell are very different from those in a cell-free system such as ours.

REICHARD: If I understood Dr. Siekevitz right he implies that a specific DNA must be present in the system in order to start off DNA synthesis. Kornberg's data would argue strongly against this, since one can use any DNA as a primer for a polymerase from *E. coli*.

SIEKEVITZ: Is that single strand or double strand DNA?

REICHARD: That's a different question again, which is not cleared up. Even in our crude preparations, extracts of chick embryos, we get very little DNA synthesis when we add highly polymerized double-stranded calf thymus DNA. As soon as we heat this preparation for 10 min., this treatment is supposed to split the double strands, the DNA will act as a primer.

SIEKEVITZ: But that might be just the point. There comes a time in the life of the cell when single strand DNA is formed to act as a primer, and this splitting of the RNA might be the point where regulation could occur.

REICHARD: I think that is quite true and that it might be an important regulating mechanism in living cells.

DAVIDSON: I think I should perhaps mention that in the experiments which I described we use heated DNA as our primer but, of course, this is a cell-free system.

Enzymic Formation of Deoxyribonucleic Acid from Ribonucleotides

PETER REICHARD

*Department of Chemistry I, Karolinska Institutet,
Stockholm, Sweden*

The work of Kornberg and his associates [1] has established that DNA* is formed enzymically through the polymerization of deoxyribonucleoside triphosphates. It is thus evident that cells which carry out a rapid synthesis of DNA require a constant supply of these compounds, and the biological source of the deoxyribonucleotides becomes of major importance.

Earlier *in vivo* experiments [2, 3] made it very likely that deoxyribosyl compounds in many different types of cells are formed through a direct reduction of the corresponding ribosyl compounds. More recently it was possible to demonstrate such conversions with enzymes from chick embryos and *Escherichia coli*, and it was then found that this reduction took place at the diphosphate level, e.g. deoxycytidine diphosphate was formed from cytidine diphosphate [4, 5].

Here I will describe experiments in which the enzymes catalyzing the reduction of ribonucleotides are coupled with the enzymes synthesizing DNA from deoxyribonucleotides. Thus in these experiments we studied the over-all reaction sequence leading from ribonucleotides to the synthesis of DNA. This work was carried out during a recent visit to the Department of Pharmacology, Yale University, New Haven, U.S.A., in collaboration with Drs. Z. N. and E. S. Canellakis.

One major purpose of our investigation was to study possible regulatory mechanisms during *in vitro* DNA synthesis. The reduction of a ribotide to the corresponding deoxyribotide represents the first step in a reaction sequence which ultimately results in the synthesis of DNA. All the preceding enzyme reactions leading to the formation of the ribotide can be

---

* Abbreviations used: DNA, deoxyribonucleic acid; CMP, CDP and CTP, mono-, di- and triphosphates of cytidine, respectively; GMP, GTP, mono- and triphosphates of guanosine, respectively; ATP, adenosine triphosphate; TTP, thymidine triphosphate; deoxycompounds are denoted by the prefix d-.

visualized to have at least a threefold purpose: (1) The synthesis of RNA; (2) the synthesis of coenzymes; and (3) the synthesis of DNA:

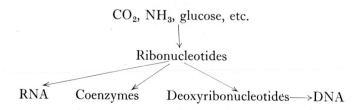

CO_2, NH_3, glucose, etc.

Ribonucleotides

RNA　　　Coenzymes　　　Deoxyribonucleotides⟶DNA

In view of these considerations it seemed an attractive hypothesis to consider the reductive step as a possible "pace maker" for DNA-synthesis, and it was hoped that the construction of an *in vitro* system carrying out the synthesis of DNA from ribonucleotides might serve as a model system, in which the influence of different factors on this hypothetical pace maker might be studied. Ample evidence exists that such a first step in a reaction sequence may indeed act as a rate-limiting step [6] and that it can be influenced and regulated by the products of later reactions.

In all experiments to be described here the source of enzyme was a high-speed supernatant fraction from a homogenate of 5-day-old chick embryos. Both cytidine and guanosine ribonucleotides were used as substrates for DNA formation.

First it was necessary to establish that our enzyme preparation could synthesize DNA from labelled deoxynucleotides. It was found that incorporation of radioactivity from labelled dCMP or dGMP into DNA required the presence of ATP, Mg^{++} and "primer" DNA. This incorporation was further stimulated by the addition of a complementary set of the other deoxynucleoside triphosphates. These results demonstrate that the chick embryo extract contained enzymes which catalyze the formation of DNA from deoxyribonucleotides by a mechanism similar to that described earlier for other systems [1, 7, 8].

Next the formation of radioactive DNA from labelled ribonucleotides (CMP and GMP) was studied. It was found that this process again required the addition of ATP, Mg^{++} and "primer" DNA. When either ^{32}P-labelled or tritium(=base)-labelled CMP was used as substrate, it was found that identical amounts of isotope were incorporated into DNA (Fig. 1). This experiment demonstrates that the intact nucleotide was used for DNA synthesis and that the incorporation of isotope did not occur as a result of, e.g., transglycosylation.

It was then necessary to investigate in which manner the ribonucleotide had been used for DNA synthesis. With techniques used earlier by Adler *et al.* [9] it was possible to demonstrate that in our experiments the isotopic ribonucleotide was first reduced to the deoxyribonucleotide, and that the labelled deoxyribonucleotide was subsequently used for DNA synthesis. In the experiment described in Fig. 2 DNA was synthesized

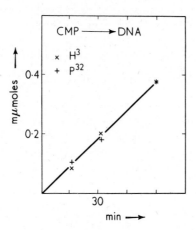

FIG. 1. Time curve of DNA formation from tritium or ^{32}P-labelled CMP, as measured by the incorporation of isotope into DNA [7, 8]. Incubation conditions for one time point: 0·1 μmole of labelled CMP, 1·0 μmole of ATP, 5·0 μmoles of MgCl$_2$, 0·1 mg. of heated DNA (10 min. at 100°) and 4·5 mg. of "enzyme", final volume 0·41 ml., pH 7·4, 37°.

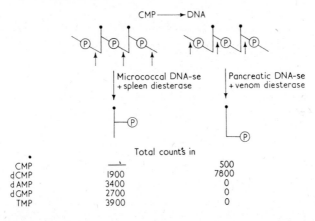

FIG. 2. Enzymic degradation [9] of DNA formed from P^{32}-CMP. 60 min. incubation with conditions as in Fig. 1.

from ^{32}P-CMP and, after isolation, degraded enzymically in two different ways:

(*a*) With pancreatic DNA-se + snake venom diesterase. These enzymes split DNA as indicated by the arrow in Fig. 2 and produce 5′-deoxy-ribonucleotides. Since 5′-labelled CMP was the precursor in the synthesis

E*

of DNA, the isotope stays attached to the nucleotide used as substrate for the DNA polymerase.

(b) With micrococcal DNA-se + spleen diesterase. This results in the formation of 3′-nucleotides. ^{32}P is no longer attached to the nucleotide used as substrate, but is transferred to the neighbour nucleotide.

The results of Fig. 2 obtained by degradation according to (a) show that CMP was used for DNA synthesis after transformation to dCMP, since about 95% of the isotope resides with this deoxyribonucleotide. After degradation according to (b) the isotope is distributed among all four deoxyribonucleotides. This in turn demonstrates that labelled dCMP (formed from CMP) in DNA was linked to all four deoxynucleotides in internucleotide linkage.

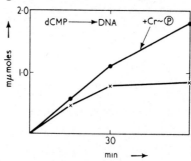

FIG. 3. Stimulation of DNA formation from dCMP by an ATP-regenerating system. Conditions as in Fig. 1 (0·011 μmole of dCMP substituted for CMP). Where indicated 4·5 μmoles of creatine phosphate + 0·1 mg. of creatine kinase were added.

The results obtained so far strongly indicate that the chick embryo enzyme preparation carried out the synthesis of DNA from ribonucleotides according to the following general reaction sequence:

Ribonucleotide⟶Deoxyribonucleotide⟶DNA

It was now possible to study some of the factors which might influence this overall pathway of DNA synthesis.

The first question studied was how the process was influenced by the ATP-level in the system. It might be expected—and has been shown already for other similar systems—that a high level of triphosphates, as is obtained by the addition of an ATP-regenerating system, is favourable for the synthesis of DNA from a deoxyribonucleotide. Figure 3 demonstrates that the addition of creatine phosphate + kinase stimulated isotope incorporation from labelled dCMP into DNA, and that the chick embryo system thus conformed to expectation.

However, DNA formation from a ribonucleotide, such as CMP, was decreased when an ATP regenerating system was added (Fig. 4). The inhibition was located in the reductive step, as shown by the results of Fig. 5. Our interpretation of these results is the following: the addition of ATP + Mg^{++} to this crude enzyme system resulted in the phosphorylation of CMP to CDP and CTP. As found by paper chromatography an

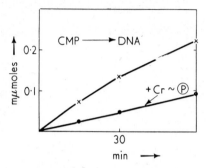

Fɪɢ. 4. Inhibition of DNA formation from CMP by an ATP-regenerating system. Conditions as in Fig. 1. Where indicated 4·5 μmoles of creatine phosphate + 0·1 mg. of creatine kinase were added.

equilibrium between mono-, di- and triphosphates was rapidly established and CDP was the predominating nucleotide. However, when the ATP-regenerating system was added, this resulted in a very efficient phosphorylation of CMP to CTP, and little CDP was left in the system. Since CDP is

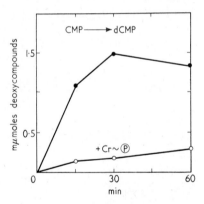

Fɪɢ. 5. Inhibition of CMP-reduction by an ATP-regenerating system. Conditions as in Figs. 1 and 4. The formation of dCMP + deoxycytidine was measured as described earlier [4].

the substrate for the reduction, the addition of the ATP-regenerating system greatly decreased ribotide reduction. According to this interpretation our experiments indicate that *in vitro* the synthesis of DNA from ribonucleotides is dependent on the maintenance of a critical level of diphosphates and is inhibited by an excess of ATP, which increases the level of triphosphates but decreases the diphosphate level.

As mentioned earlier, the synthesis of DNA from one labelled deoxynucleotide was stimulated by the addition of the three other non-labelled

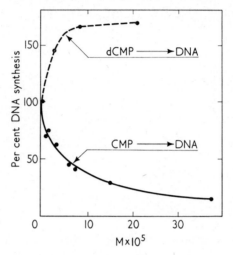

Fig. 6. Influence of an equimolar mixture of TTP, dATP and dGTP on DNA formation from dCMP and CMP, respectively.

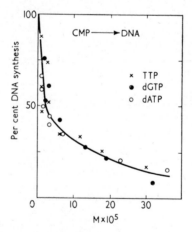

Fig. 7. Comparison of different deoxynucleoside triphosphates as inhibitors of DNA formation from CMP.

deoxynucleoside triphosphate. This is demonstrated for [¹⁴C]-dCMP by the upper curve of Fig. 6. With [¹⁴C]-CMP, however, isotope incorporation into DNA was strongly inhibited by the addition of an equimolar mixture of the triphosphates of thymidine, deoxyadenosine and deoxyguanosine

(Fig. 6 lower curve). Furthermore, it was found (Fig. 7) that each single deoxynucleoside triphosphate inhibited DNA formation from CMP to about the same extent.

It seemed obvious that here again the reductive step was the point of inhibition, and we therefore studied the influence of the different deoxynucleoside triphosphates on the formation of dCMP from CMP. A strong inhibition by dATP and dGTP was observed, TTP inhibited much less, while dCTP showed almost no effect (Fig. 8). Addition of the purine deoxyribonucleotides thus resulted in about a 50% inhibition at an initial concentration of 10^{-5} M. The initial concentrations of ATP and CMP in these experiments were $2 \cdot 5 \times 10^{-3}$ M and $0 \cdot 4 \times 10^{-3}$ M, respectively.

Similar experiments were also carried out with guanine nucleotides. It was found that DNA synthesis from dGMP was stimulated more than

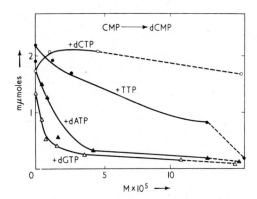

FIG. 8. Effects of deoxynucleoside triphosphates on the reduction of CMP.

twofold by an equimolar mixture of dCTP, dATP and TTP. The effects of such a mixture on the incorporation of isotope from GMP into DNA were quite small and inconsistent. When each triphosphate was added alone, different types of effects were observed (Fig. 9). Thus DNA formation from GMP was strongly inhibited by the addition of dATP, but was stimulated by the two pyrimidine deoxynucleoside triphosphates. Similar divergent effects were observed when the formation of dGMP from GMP was investigated (Fig. 10). In this case the effect of dGTP could also be investigated and it was found that this deoxyribonucleotide acted as a strong inhibitor. Thus the results for the GMP→dGMP transformation showed that purine deoxyribonucleotides were inhibitors while pyrimidine deoxyribonucleotides, stimulated the reaction.

We believe that our results show that in an *in vitro* system with soluble enzymes the reduction of both a purine and a pyrimidine ribonucleotide was regulated to a large extent by the levels of deoxynucleotides present

in the system. I should like to stress the point that the reduction of ribonucleotides was controlled not only by the product-deoxynucleotide of the

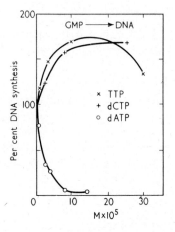

FIG. 9. Effects of deoxynucleoside triphosphates on DNA formation from
GMP. Conditions as in Fig. 1 with labelled GMP in place of CMP; individual
deoxynucleoside triphosphates added as indicated on the abscissa.

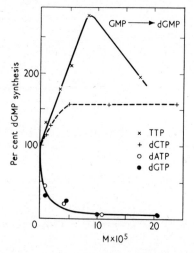

FIG. 10. Effects of deoxynucleoside triphosphates on the reduction of GMP.
The conditions of incubation and of the assay were as described in an earlier
paper [5].

respective reactions, but also by the other deoxynucleotides; e.g. dATP
and dGTP greatly inhibited the reduction of CMP, and the pyrimidine
deoxyribonucleotides stimulated the reduction of GMP.

Our results were obtained with soluble enzymes and it remains to be shown whether they have any bearing on the problem of DNA synthesis in living cells. It is not yet possible to decide this point with any degree of certainty, but it seems to be relevant that recent experiments by Klenow [10] and by Morris and Fischer [11] have shown that effects similar to those I have discussed here can be obtained with living cells. It is thus not inconceivable that such effects are parts of an important homeostatic mechanism for DNA synthesis.

References

1. Kornberg, A., *in* "The Chemical Basis of Heredity", ed. W. D. McElroy and B. Glass, Johns Hopkins Press, Baltimore, 579 (1957).
2. Hammarsten, E., Reichard, P., and Saluste, E., *J. biol. Chem.* **183,** 105 (1950).
3. Rose, I. A., and Schweigert, B. S., *J. biol. Chem.* **202,** 635 (1953).
4. Reichard, P., and Rutberg, L., *Biochim. biophys. Acta* **37,** 554 (1959).
5. Reichard, P., *Biochim. biophys. Acta* **41,** 368 (1960).
6. Pardee, A. B., *in* "The Enzymes I", ed. P. D. Boyer, H. Lardy, and K. Myrbäck. Academic Press Inc., New York, 681 (1959).
7. Bollum, F. J., *J. Amer. chem. Soc.* **80,** 1766 (1958).
8. Mantsavinos, R., and Canellakis, E. S., *J. biol. Chem.* **234,** 628 (1959).
9. Adler, J., Lehman, I. R., Bessman, M. J., Simms, E. S., and Kornberg, A., *Proc. nat. Acad. Sci., Wash.* **44,** 641 (1958).
10. Klenow, H., *Biochim. biophys. Acta* **35,** 412 (1959).
11. Morris, N. R., and Fischer, G. A., *Biochim. biophys. Acta* **42,** 183 (1960).

Discussion

CHARGAFF: I was wondering whether Dr. Reichard has any explanation of the peculiar fact that usually analogues are incorporated only into one of the two types of nucleic acid. For instance, fluorouracil when given to *E. coli* will appear only as ribofluorouridylic acid in RNA and not a trace seems to go as the deoxy compound into DNA; similarly in the plant nucleic acids which I have mentioned in my talk high amounts of 5-methylcytosine are found in the DNA only. I was wondering whether you had any explanation for this.

REICHARD: In the case of uracil—and I think this also applies to fluorouracil, because from all the work which has been published now it appears that fluorouracil behaves with enzymes as does uracil—the explanation put forward by Kornberg is that there are no kinases for deoxy-UMP; this would also be true for fluoro-deoxy-UMP. This is a reasonable explanation, but on the other hand I am a little worried about the fact that our own findings indicate that the reduction might take place at the diphosphate level. I don't know whether it is really UDP which is reduced to deoxy-UDP although I believe so. What one might look for would be a special phosphatase like the one which has been found in T2 infected *E. coli* for deoxy-CTP, but in this case it would be specific for deoxy-UTP. That could be an explanation.

DAVIDSON: Is there evidence that the reduction step takes place at the diphosphate level in other cases than deoxy-CDP?

REICHARD: In the case of G—yes, and in the case of U—no, and for A we have no evidence.

HESS: What is the reducing system involved or have you any experience about the type of system you would expect ? I ask because a reducing system can also act as a controlling mechanism upon the synthesis of DXPP from XDP. Certainly, the reducing equivalents in growing cells are available in high concentrations, i.e. speaking for the TPNH level, which in a given control range could well be a critical metabolite.

REICHARD: I think you might be quite right but I do not know very much about the events during the reduction. We know that it is a complicated series of reactions and not a single reaction. We also know that we can demonstrate a stimulation of the dialysed or ion exchange-treated enzyme preparation by TPNH. Now you could draw the tentative conclusion that TPNH is the source of hydrogen during the reduction, but on the other hand it might be an indirect effect. I don't know yet but we are just starting to purify the enzymes.

Studies on the Mechanism of Synthesis of Soluble Ribonucleic Acid*

E. S. CANELLAKIS† AND EDWARD HERBERT

*Department of Pharmacology, Yale University
Medical School, New Haven, Conn., U.S.A.*
and
*Department of Biology, Massachusetts
Institute of Technology, Cambridge, Mass. U.S.A.*

Our studies have been concerned with the mechanism of synthesis of the soluble RNA (S-RNA) present in the soluble cytoplasmic fraction of rat liver. In this fraction of rat liver, enzymes concerned with the incorporation of ribonucleotides into terminal positions of S-RNA have also been found. Within the allotted space I shall attempt to present a summary of our studies on the synthesis of soluble-RNA, rather than present in detail any one particular aspect of the problem.

1. Fractionation of ribonucleotide incorporating enzyme and S-RNA

By a series of fractionation techniques outlined in Table I and Figs. 1 and 2, we have been able to achieve an approximately 100–200 fold purification of three protein and S-RNA components from rat liver. These three fractions have been termed S-RNA-proteins α-, β- and -γ based on the order of their elution off the hydroxylapatite columns. Each of these fractions will incorporate ribonucleotides into the corresponding S-RNA in terminal positions. We have been further able to separate the protein from the S-RNA by the use of diethylaminoethylcellulose (DEAE) (Fig. 3). Thus separated, neither the RNA nor the protein by itself will incorporate ribonucleotides into an acid insoluble form; full activity is restored upon recombination of the protein and the S-RNA.

* Detailed experimental evidence for the material published in this summary may be found in the following articles which have been published or are in press. Canellakis, E. S., and Herbert, E., *Proc. nat. Acad. Sci., Wash.* **46,** 170 (1960); Herbert, E., and Canellakis, E. S., *Biochim. biophys. Acta* **42,** 363 (1960); Canellakis, E. S., and Herbert, E. (S-RNA II, IV, V), *Biochim. biophys. Acta* **45,** 133 (1960), **47,** 78 (1961), **47,** 85 (1961).

† Senior Research Scholar of the U.S.P.H.S. wishes to thank this Service for financial aid associated with this trip to Stockholm, Sweden.

TABLE I

SUMMARY OF PURIFICATION PROCEDURE

	Specific activity*	Yield	RNA	mg. Protein mg. RNA
		% of soluble cytoplasm	mg	
Soluble cytoplasm	5–10	"100"	135	100
Ammonium sulphate (0·55–0·86)	30–50	80	70	60
pH 5 precipitate	100–150	60	35	15
Hydroxylapatite Ribonucleoprotein α	80–100	4	3	I
,, β	750–1000	15–20	15–20	I
,, γ	400–600	10–15	10–15	I
DEAE-cellulose "protein"	750	50	—	100
"RNA"	—	—	8–10	0·05

* The specific activity unit is expressed as $\mu\mu$moles of [^{14}C]-AMP incorporated into S-RNA in the presence of I mg. protein in 6 min. at 25°.

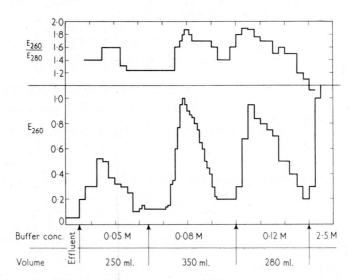

FIG. 1. Stepwise procedure for elution of ribonucleoproteins from an hydroxy-apatite column. The width of the steps in the chromatogram represents the volume of eluate collected in each fraction. These volumes are as follows in the order of potassium phosphate buffer pH 7·2 concentrations listed under the chromatogram (0·05 M, 0·08 M, and 0·12 M); 20 ml., 10 ml., and 25 ml. Column dimensions 2·5 cm. × 20 cm.

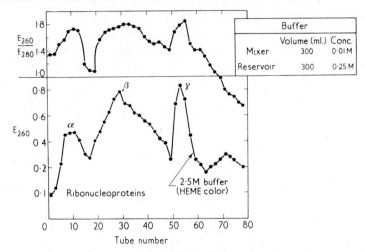

FIG. 2. Linear gradient procedure for elution of ribonucleoproteins from an hydroxylapatite column with potassium phosphate buffer pH 7·2. The volume of eluate collected per tube is 10 ml. The 2·5 M buffer is added directly to the column and collected in 10 ml. portions. Column dimensions 2·5 cm. × 20 cm.

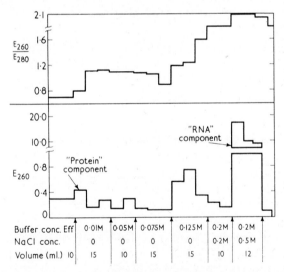

FIG. 3. Stepwise elution and separation of protein and RNA component on a DEAE column, with potassium phosphate buffer pH 7·2 and sodium chloride. Column dimensions 1·5 cm. × 2 cm.

We have termed these S-RNA-protein fractions "ribonucleoproteins" for the following reasons: (a) the protein and the S-RNA fractionate together during an extensive purification process, (b) the protein and the

S-RNA separate into three well-defined columns and (*c*) each component contains its own RNA and ribonucleotide incorporating enzyme. We believe that the exact type of physical relationship that exists between these fractions will be best elucidated by detailed enzymatic studies which

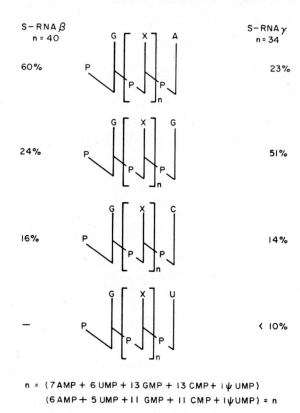

$$n = (7\,AMP + 6\,UMP + 13\,GMP + 13\,CMP + 1\psi\,UMP)$$
$$(6\,AMP + 5\,UMP + 11\,GMP + 11\,CMP + 1\psi\,UMP) = n$$

FIG. 4. Schematic presentation of the variety of S-RNA molecules present in S-RNA-β and S-RNA-γ. The column of figures on the left and right correspond to the ribonucleotide content and per cent composition of S-RNA-β and S-RNA-γ respectively.

are at present under way. Because of the experimental simplicity involved in isolating the β- and γ- fractions, our work has been largely limited to a study of the properties of these two fractions.

2. Analytical data on S-RNA-β and -γ

Analytical studies on S-RNA-β as well as S-RNA-γ have shown that they can be grossly distinguished as four molecular species differentiated by their end-groups (Fig. 4). All four molecular species of both S-RNA-β and -γ start with guanylic acid, that is, upon alkaline hydrolysis guanosine diphosphate is the only diphosphate which can be found. S-RNA-β is rich in the molecular species which terminates in adenylic acid (yielding adenosine upon alkaline hydrolysis) and has no detectable S-RNA species terminating in uridylic acid. S-RNA-γ is rich in the molecular species which terminates in guanylic acid and has some of the molecular species which terminates in uridylic acid.

The ribonucleotide analyses of these two families of S-RNA indicate that approximately one pseudouridylic acid molecule corresponds to one chain (Table II). In addition, the adenylic acid content of S-RNA-β

TABLE II

COMPOSITION OF S-RNA-β AND S-RNA-γ

	Ribonucleosides*				
Component	Adenosine	Uridine	Guanosine	Cytidine	Guanosine diphosphate*
S-RNA-β	0·60	—	0·24	0·10	1·02
S-RNA	0·23	0·10	0·51	0·14	0·95

	2'(3')-Ribonucleotides*						
	AMP	UMP	ψ-UMP	GMP	CMP	Total of nucleot. per chain*	Wt. of chain
S-RNA-β	7·2	6·0	1·01	13·0	13·2	42	15 000
S-RNA-γ	6·0	5·0	1·21	11·1	11·0	36	13 800

* Molar composition calculated by assuming that one terminal ribonucleoside residue corresponds to one polynucleotide chain. Chromatographic analysis made on the alkaline hydrolysates of S-RNA-β and of S-RNA-γ.

† Including one of the nucleoside end and one guanosine diphosphate.

and of S-RNA-γ approximates the sum of uridylic acid plus pseudouridylic acid whereas the guanylic acid content approximates that of cytidylic acid. From the end-group analysis (assuming one end-group per chain), a molecular weight of approximately 15 000 can be derived.

3. The effect of pyrophosphate

Incubation of the enzyme with S-RNA-β plus -γ, [14C]-CTP, inorganic pyrophosphate and Mg^{++}, results in an enhanced incorporation of [14C]-CMP into the S-RNA (Table III). This effect can also be observed if the enzyme and the S-RNA are preincubated with inorganic pyrophosphate, the S-RNA then extracted and reincubated with a fresh enzyme preparation and [14C]-CTP in the absence of pyrophosphate. It

TABLE III

THE EFFECT OF PYROPHOSPHATE
ON THE INCORPORATION OF [^{14}C]-CMP INTO S-RNA

Treatment	[^{14}C]-CMP incorporated (c.p.m.)
1. None	150
2. Pyrophosphate included in incubation mixture	600
3. S-RNA pretreated with pyrophosphate*	610

2·0 E$_{260}$ units of S-RNA-β and -γ were used throughout this experiment. The first tube contained [^{14}C]-CTP (30 mμmoles, 2 × 10^6/c.p.m./μmole), S-RNA, Mg^{++} 2·0 μatoms, and ribonucleotide incorporating enzyme in 0·08 M potassium phosphate buffer. Final volume 1·0 ml. The second tube contained in addition to above, 1·0 μmole pyrophosphate. The S-RNA used in the third tube had been pretreated with the ribonucleotide-incorporating enzyme, Mg^{++} 2·0 μatoms, 1·0 μmoles pyrophosphate in 0·08 M potassium phosphate buffer. Final volume 1·0 ml. This was then isolated free of the ribonucleotide incorporating enzyme, and re-incubated in an incubation mixture identical to that in the first tube.

* Inorganic pyrophosphate does not enhance the incorporation of [^{14}C]-CTP into S-RNA if during the preincubation either the S-RNA or the ribonucleotide-incorporating enzyme is omitted.

TABLE IV

LIBERATION OF RIBONUCLEOSIDE 5′-TRIPHOSPHATES INTO THE
ACID-SOLUBLE FRACTION BY THE PYROPHOSPHOROLYSIS OF S-RNA

	Radioactivity recovered in the ribonucleoside 5′-triphosphates (c.p.m.)			
	ATP	CTP	UTP	GTP
Experiment 1	7000	2600	1350	850
Experiment 2	1160	310	330	180
Experiment 2A	6600	950	2070	1320

In Experiment 1, S-RNA-β and -γ was pyrophosphorylyzed in the presence of [^{32}P]-inorganic pyrophosphate, the ribonucleotide-incorporating enzyme, 2·0 μatoms Mg^{++} per ml. and 20 mμmoles each of non-radioactive ATP, CTP, UTP and GTP in 0·08 M potassium phosphate, pH 7·2. Final volume 1·0 ml. In Experiments 2 and 2A, [^{32}P]-S-RNA (prepared by isolating S-RNA from rat liver which had been labelled with ^{32}P *in vivo*) was incubated with 1·0 μmole of non-radioactive inorganic pyrophosphate, 2·0 μatoms Mg^{++}, 20 mμmoles each of non-radioactive ATP, CTP, UTP and GTP, in the absence (Experiment 2) and in the presence (Experiment 2A) of added non-radioactive ribonucleotide-incorporating enzyme. The small but definite liberation of ribonucleoside 5′-tri-phosphate in Experiment 2 may be due to contamination of the S-RNA preparation with the ribonucleotide-incorporating enzyme.

may therefore be concluded that the inorganic pyrophosphate exerts its effect on the S-RNA; in order that this effect be elicited the concomitant presence of the enzyme is required but not that of the CTP.

The effect of inorganic pyrophosphate has been elucidated as being one of pyrophosphorolysis of the S-RNA (Table IV) because incubation of the enzyme with S-RNA and [^{32}P]-pyrophosphate results in the liberation of ^{32}P-labelled ribonucleoside triphosphates into the medium.

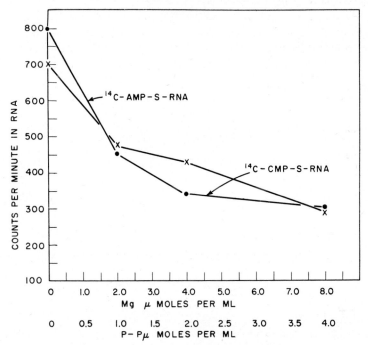

FIG. 5. Pyrophosphorolysis of the terminal ribonucleotides of S-RNA. Two portions of S-RNA-β and -γ containing 30 E$_{260}$ units each were labelled separately with [C^{14}]-AMP and with [C^{14}]-CMP respectively. They were then extracted free of the ribonucleotide-incorporating enzyme, and Mg^{++} and pyrophosphate in the indicated amounts under standard conditions. At the end of the incubation period the residual radioactivity on each type of labelled S-RNA was determined.

If the converse experiment is performed, that is if ^{32}P-labelled S-RNA (obtained after *in vivo* labelling with ^{32}P), is incubated with non-radioactive pyrophosphate and enzyme, again ^{32}P-labelled ribonucleoside triphosphates are liberated into the medium.

Pyrophosphorolysis seems to be directed primarily towards the end of the S-RNA molecule (Fig. 5). This can be shown by using S-RNA which has been labelled *in vitro* with either [^{14}C]-ATP or with [^{14}C]-CTP which are known to be incorporated in the end of the S-RNA molecule. When such a radioactive S-RNA preparation is added to an incubation medium containing the ribonucleotide-incorporating enzymes, and varying concentrations of Mg^{++} and pyrophosphate, a progressive loss of radioactivity occurs, indicating the removal of the terminal ribonucleotides in the S-RNA molecule.

Since pyrophosphate results in the degradation of the end of the S-RNA and in an increased incorporation of cytidylic acid, it is reasonable to expect that new sites in the S-RNA may be exposed. If these new sites accept cytidylic acid, then incubation of the pyrophosphorylyzed S-RNA with [^{32}P]-CTP (^{32}P-P-P) followed by alkaline hydrolysis of the CM^{32}P-labelled S-RNA should result in the identification of the site of attachment of the cytidylic acid. We have performed this experiment under conditions of low and maximal pyrophosphorolysis of S-RNA, and compared the results with those obtained with non-pyrophosphorylyzed S-RNA. Pyrophosphorolysis results in the unveiling of adenylic acid as the new site of attachment of [^{32}P]-CMP. The distribution pattern of the ^{32}P obtained with maximally pyrophosphorylyzed S-RNA (Table 5) shows the ^{32}P to be equivalently distributed between 2′ (3′)-cytidylic acid and 2′ (3′)-adenylic acid. These results make the following interpretation plausible:

$$P\text{-}P + AMP\text{—}CMP\text{—}CMP\text{—}AMP\text{—}S\text{-}RNA \rightarrow$$
$$AMP\text{—}S\text{-}RNA + ATP + 2CTP$$

$$^{32}P\text{-}CTP + AMP\text{—}S\text{-}RNA \rightarrow$$
$$^{32}P\text{-}CMP\text{—}^{32}P\text{-}CMP\text{—}AMP\text{—}S\text{-}RNA + P\text{-}P$$

In other words, pyrophosphorolysis of S-RNA has exposed a terminal adenylic acid which now accepts two cytidylic acid residues. This S-RNA upon alkaline hydrolysis would yield equivalent amounts of [^{32}P]-cytidylic acid and adenylic acid. This would therefore indicate adenylic acid to be the fourth ribonucleotide in the terminal sequence. Although this interpretation is in keeping with the observed facts it can in no way be considered to be the only possible interpretation. We therefore wish to suggest this as a temporary explanation, reserving final judgment until a more homogeneous preparation of S-RNA is available.

This interpretation of these results raises the question as to the source of the guanosine triphosphate and of the uridine triphosphate found in the acid-soluble fraction after pyrophosphorolysis of the S-RNA. We believe that since guanylic acid and uridylic acid exist as terminal ribonucleotides in our S-RNA preparations (Fig. 4), these may well be pyrophosphorylyzed in a manner similar to that in which the terminal adenylic acid and cytidylic acid are pyrophosphorylyzed. This is supported by the fact that pyrophosphorylyzed S-RNA as compared to normal S-RNA, also shows an enhanced incorporation of uridylic acid similar to that of cytidylic acid.

4. The effect of snake venom phosphodiesterase

If S-RNA-β plus -γ is treated with snake venom phosphodiesterase under conditions of limited degradation, a somewhat random degradation occurs as evidenced by the fact that [^{32}P]-CTP attaches to a variety of terminal groups (Table V), as contrasted to its attachment to cytidylic

TABLE V

THE SITE OF ATTACHMENT OF [^{32}P]-CMP ON NATIVE AND PYROPHOSPHORYLYZED S-RNA

	Radioactivity in the 2′ (3′)-ribonucleoside mono-phosphates isolated after alkaline hydrolysis of the ^{32}P-S-RNA			
	Results expressed as per cent of total c.p.m. incorporated			
	AMP	CMP	UMP	GMP
Native S-RNA (0·0 μmoles P-P, 2·0 μatoms Mg)	<5	90	5–10	<5
P-P-treated S-RNA (1·0 μmoles P-P, 2·0 μmoles Mg)	15	85	<5	<5
P-P-treated S-RNA (4·0 μmoles P-P, 8·0 μmoles Mg)	48	50	<5	<5
Phosphodiesterase treated S-RNA	20	55	11	14

S-RNA-β and -γ was incubated with the ribonucleotide-incorporating enzyme under standard conditions and with the amounts of pyrophosphate and Mg^{++} indicated within parentheses above. The fourth sample of S-RNA was pre-treated with phosphodiesterase. The various S-RNA preparations were then extracted and incubated with [^{32}P]-CTP (^{32}P-P-P) and the ribonucleotide-incorporating enzyme under standard conditions. At the end of the incubation each S-RNA was isolated, hydrolyzed with alkali and the radioactivity in the various ribonucleotide fractions determined.

acid alone when native S-RNA is the substrate or to cytidylic acid and adenylic acid when pyrophosphorylyzed S-RNA is the substrate.

The experiment summarized in Table VI was designed to establish whether, after degradation of the S-RNA by snake venom phosphodies-terase to such a degree that its ability to accept amino acids is lost, it is possible to restore this ability by re-incorporating ribonucleotides into the partly degraded S-RNA.

The combined S-RNA-β and -γ was partly degraded with snake venom phosphodiesterase. The partly degraded S-RNA was incubated with the ribonucleotide-incorporating enzymes, in the presence of the non-radioactive ribonucleoside triphosphates listed in Table VI. At the end of 10 min. the amino acid-activating enzyme was added to each tube together with radioactive threonine and the capacity of the S-RNA to accept a radioactive threonine was measured.

TABLE VI

RECONSTITUTION OF THE CAPACITY OF S-RNA-β AND -γ TO ACCEPT THREONINE

	Pretreatment	Incorporation of ^{14}C-threonine into S-RNA	
	Ribonucleotide-incorporating enzyme plus:	c.p.m.[1] mg. RNA	mμ moles/ mg. S-RNA
Normal S-RNA	o	606	0·17
	ATP, CTP, UTP, GTP	707	0·22
Diesterase treated S-RNA	o	203	0·058
	ATP	70	0·020
	ATP, CTP	385	0·11
	ATP, CTP, UTP	450	0·13
	ATP, CTP, UTP, GTP	690	0·197

The phosphodiesterase treated S-RNA was prepared by treatment of the S-RNA with snake venom phosphodiesterase, and was then isolated free of the phosphodiesterase. The pretreatment of the S-RNA was carried out as follows: 0·15 ml. of S-RNA-β and -γ ($E_{260} = 40$) were incubated with the equivalent amount of ribonucleotide-incorporating enzyme (0·15 ml.), 1 μmole of $MgCl_2$, 0·25 μmole of the indicated ribonucleoside 5'-triphosphate in 0·08 M potassium phosphate buffer, pH 7·2; the total volume was 0·5 ml. After incubation for 15 min. at 37°, 0·5 ml. of a mixture containing 0·2 ml. of the amino acid activating-enzyme fractions, 0·05 μmole of [^{14}C]-threonine (3·5 × 10^6 c.p.m./μmole), 4 μmoles of ATP and 2 μmoles $MgCl_2$, all in the 0·08 M potassium phosphate buffer, were added to each tube and the incubation was continued for 10 min. more at 37°. The S-RNA was then isolated, freed of contaminant radioactivity and counted.

Degradation of the S-RNA with phosphodiesterase results in a decrease in its capacity to accept threonine. If the degraded S-RNA was pretreated with the ribonucleotide-incorporating enzyme and ATP, a further decrease in its capacity to accept threonine was noted. In contrast to this, when pretreatment was carried out in the presence of ATP and CTP, the capacity of the degraded S-RNA to accept threonine was greatly enhanced. Pretreatment with ATP, CTP and UTP further enhanced the ability of the S-RNA to accept threonine, and finally, pretreatment of the S-RNA with all four ribonucleoside 5′-triphosphates resulted in almost complete reconstitution of the capacity of this previously degraded S-RNA to accept threonine (93% of the capacity of the control).

We know that at least three of the four ribonucleotides can be incorporated into S-RNA (Table VII), and have presented evidence that all four

TABLE VII

EFFECT OF PHOSPHODIESTERASE ON THE INCORPORATION OF ^{14}C-ATP, CTP, AND UTP INTO S-RNA-β AND -γ

	Ribonucleotide additions		Radioactive ribonucleotide incorporated
	Radioactive	Non-radioactive	mμmoles per mg. S-RNA
(1) Normal S-RNA	^{14}C-ATP	None	2·0
	^{14}C-ATP	CTP, UTP, GTP	2·68
Diesterase S-RNA	^{14}C-ATP	None	0·99
	^{14}C-ATP	CTP, UTP, GTP	13·68
(2) Normal S-RNA	^{14}C-CTP	None	2·2
	^{14}C-CTP	ATP, UTP, GTP	2·2
Diesterase S-RNA	^{14}C-CTP	None	38·7
	^{14}C-CTP	ATP, UTP, GTP	46·0
(3) Normal S-RNA	^{14}C-UTP	None	0·26
	^{14}C-UTP	CTP, GTP, ATP	0·11
Diesterase S-RNA	^{14}C-UTP	None	1·8
	^{14}C-UTP	CTP, GTP, ATP	0·17

ribonucleotides are required to restore the amino acid-incorporating capacity of the partly degraded S-RNA; we may therefore conclude that whatever the type of reconstitution of the S-RNA that is occurring it is not limited to the reconstitution of the terminal sequence—CMP—CMP—AMP but is more extensive.

These experiments represent a first crude attempt to synthesize a defined ribonucleotide sequence in a ribonucleic acid-complex, based on the underlying *a priori* assumption that the ribonucleotide sequence of the S-RNA determines the specificity of the amino acid attachment. The results are unduly complicated by the fact that we probably do not have a single species of S-RNA, but are at present using as a substrate a mixture of ribonucleic acid molecules, as evidenced both by the ability of the S-RNA to accept a variety of amino acids and by the results of the end-group analysis.

Discussion

TISELIUS: May I ask did you get complete separation into S-RNA-α, -β, -γ?

CANELLAKIS: Yes, we do get complete separation.

TISELIUS: Are the salt concentrations eluting the various components very far apart?

CANELLAKIS: I think they are of the order of 0·05 M to 0·2 M.

TISELIUS: So you don't get much overlap between them?

CANELLAKIS: They come out as distinct peaks.

ALLFREY: I would like to ask if you have tried reconstituting this esterase-treated RNA, not with the normal nucleoside triphosphates but with azaguanosine phosphates or fluorouracil phosphates and see whether you still get functional RNA?

CANELLAKIS: No, we have not tried that.

ALLFREY: It is interesting because the question is: does the specificity arise in that end of the molecule or in the rest of it?

CANELLAKIS: I agree that it is interesting. I think eventually we would like to try this experiment.

DAVIS: Do you have any indication of the extent to which the diesterase has degraded the molecule, whether it has acted selectively at the ends or whether it has also attacked the middle?

CANELLAKIS: On prolonged incubation we can get some attack in the middle. We think that it is probably due to some endonuclease action in our preparation but for a half hour or so we seem only to be getting terminal degradation.

HERBERT: I should like to add that if you incubate for prolonged periods you release 40 or 50% of the ribonucleotides as acid-soluble material. You can then no longer reconstitute the amino acid-accepting capacity of our system.

VON DER DECKEN: Do you obtain the pyrophosphate exchange when you use S-RNA-amino acid complex instead of S-RNA?

CANELLAKIS: I don't believe that our data permit us to answer that question.

MICROSOMES AND PROTEIN SYNTHESIS

The Endoplasmic Reticulum: Some Current Interpretations of Its Forms and Functions

Keith R. Porter

The Rockefeller Institute, New York, U.S.A.

Among the several discoveries in cell morphology which must be credited to electron microscopy, one of the most significant is that which has described the cytoplasmic ground substance as extraordinarily rich in membrane limited elements. The presence of these in such amounts and in such complicated forms was not really suspected from light microscopy. Their presence in the ground substance was first recognized in the electron microscope image of cultured cells about 15 years ago, though it must be admitted that the early images were not very convincing [1]. Subsequently, and with increasing vigour, they have been studied in a wide variety of animal cells and more recently in plant cells until, at the present time, they are looked for and recognized as a standard element of cell fine structure. The unit of structure—if such can be defined—is vesicular or tubular in thin section profiles; i.e. a membrane-enclosed cavity or vesicle, itself usually devoid of any internal structure. When followed through serial sections into the depth dimension, these profiles can be seen to represent two-dimensional images of structures which are really part of a complex three-dimensional system of tubules and vesicles extending into most regions of the cytoplasm. This statement holds true for the majority if not all cell types.

It is also now recognized and accepted as a law of fine structure that the nuclear envelope is part of this general system. This conclusion is supported by the structural similarity evident between the cytoplasmic elements of the system and the nuclear envelope as well as by the impressive continuity between the envelope and the cytoplasmic units [2, 3]. The envelope is essentially a large flattened or lamellar vesicle wrapped around the nucleus. It is reasonable, therefore, to regard the nuclear envelope and the cytoplasmic formations as part of a single unit system of the cell, in the same sense that we regard the mitochondria or plastids as representing unit systems. The nuclear envelope is the most constantly occurring part of the system, being found in all forms from yeast cells on up the scale of plant and animal species. It is conceptually useful and possibly valid to think of the cytoplasmic part of the system as an outgrowth of the envelope.

This is the system that has come to be known as the endoplasmic reticulum, or for short, the ER [4]. In one structural expression or pattern it adopts, there are many lamellar sacs or cisternae in parallel array and this form corresponds to the cytoplasmic component, referred to for 60 years as the ergastoplasm [5]. But this is only one of many complex organizations that are encountered and which are characteristic of different cell types. In some other cells the system is represented in large part by a tri-dimensional latticework of tubules. In cells of the early animal embryo or the plant meristem, before differentiation is completed, the ER is usually simple compared with the patterns and complexities achieved in the completely differentiated unit. This suggests that it is designed to play an important role in the particular activity of the differentiated cell, whether this is secretion, contraction or impulse conduction.

These and other observations make it evident, then, that we are dealing with a complex, finely-divided vacuolar system which ramifies and extends to all parts of the cytosome. This effectively creates within the cytoplasm an internal phase which is separated from the continuous matrix phase of the cytoplasm by a membrane. These facts of morphology, as depicted by electron microscopy and supported by phase contrast observations on living cells, have been the basis for diverse speculations regarding the function of the system. It has, e.g., been suggested that the system satisfies a need in larger cells for channelled diffusion and segregation of metabolites. Its peculiar morphological relation to the myofibrils in striated muscle has prompted the proposal that its limiting membrane is electrically polarized and possibly capable of transmitting intracellular impulses. The large surfaces provided by the system have been recognized as suitable for the support and patterned disposition of enzymes within the cytoplasm.

This information and speculation regarding the ER is now fairly well known and probably needs no further comment. It can be found in a number of recent reviews with ample illustration of the more important points [5, 6, 7]. The system described has been an object of interest and study in our laboratory for a number of years. Large blocks of what we now know about the system have been discovered and described by G. E. Palade and P. Siekevitz, and I am particularly grateful to them for valuable discussions and permission to republish a few of their micrographs.

It is the purpose of this review to present a morphological background against which the subsequent biochemical papers on this programme may be presented. I shall focus your attention principally on functions of the ER—functions that are suggested or defined by (a) morphological variations observed in cells with similar and different functions (comparative cytology), and (b) modulations related to naturally occurring or experimentally induced changes in physiological function. If, as now seems possible, these observations can be tied to biochemical observations on fractions of cells identified as coming from this or that part of the ER, we have a good start on the over-all analysis of the role of the ER in the intact unit. Needless to say, we are still very ignorant about the reticulum. However, some correlations of function and structure are being achieved and with the possibilities provided by modern techniques (as yet unexplored) the progress toward greater understanding should be rapid. I am encouraged to believe that even the suggestive evidence provided by observations on morphological associations of structural elements involved in different cell functions will be of interest to biochemists who are more experienced in cell fractionation procedures and their potentials.

Forms and modulations of ER

The cytoplasmic part of this membranous system, as distinct from that part comprising the nuclear envelope, appears in a wide variety of forms. These are readily recognized as characteristic of particular cell types whether found in one or different species of animal. It is apparent, moreover, that cells performing certain similar functions, whether otherwise related, show similarities in the predominant form of the reticulum in their cytoplasms.

In some cells the system is represented in large part by only one of these differentiations or configurations. In other instances two or more forms may be prominently represented in a single cell and obviously linked into a single system by morphological continuity. There are also cells in which a predominant form of the ER shows local specializations or differentiations, designed, presumably, to perform a particular function. The system under consideration is therefore one of great variability, possessing infinite possibilities to accommodate or control subtle functional activities of the cell.

These various patterns or designs displayed by the system are of course not fixed or rigid, but modulate within limits as the cell performs its functions or responds to environmental stimuli. The pattern most regularly encountered in microscopic examination of any cell type is regarded or generally accepted as representing the preferred form of the system.

The granular or rough form

The picture of the endoplasmic reticulum that is most familiar to biochemists consists of arrays of parallel lines encrusted with small dense particles (Figs. 1 and 4). In actual fact, of course, the lines represent membranes which limit relatively large lamellar vesicles and it is charac-

F

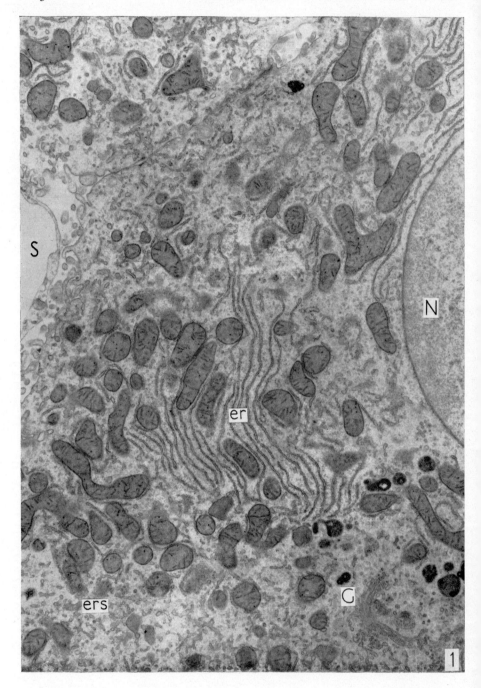

teristic for these to lie parallel in groups or stacks of several units. Sometimes these vesicles or cisternae may possess dimensions of several microns in the plane of the lamellae and have a thickness not greater than 50 mμ. Such large cisternae are further characterized by having large populations of small particles (150 to 200 Å) attached to their outer surfaces. This is the surface contiguous with the matrix phase of the cytoplasm and, indeed, the particle may properly be regarded as a component of the cytoplasmic matrix. In pancreas cells, such cisternae with particles occupy about three-fourths of the volume of the cytoplasm. In liver cells they are less prominent and occur in small arrays scattered throughout the cell (Fig. 1). In both these cells and in others as well, such arrays are observed to coincide with the more intensely basophilic parts of the cytoplasm (ergastoplasm) in which, histochemical tests have shown, there are high concentrations of RNA [8, 9]. This form of the ER has a widespread occurrence among cells and is now regarded as present in one or another minor variation in all cells known to be engaged in the synthesis of a protein for secretion (or export) from the cell. These facts of morphology, together with much older observations on the behaviour of the ergastoplasm during phases of secretion and recovery, would convince one, even without other evidence, that this form of the ER is somehow functional in protein synthesis [10, 11]. The investigation of this topic has not, however, stopped with microscopic cytological and histochemical studies, and much more convincing evidence of this functional association is now available.

The microsome

This body, the subject of this session of the current symposium, was identified and characterized first as a submicroscopic unit or particle of the cell that could be consistently separated out (from a variety of animal cells) by following a certain schedule of centrifugal fractionation [12, 13]. The microsome fraction was further characterized by Claude as being rich in phospholipids and RNA, and as being related in some manner to the

---

FIG. 1. This depicts the fine structure of a normal liver cell of the laboratory rat. The nucleus (*N*) is at the right; the marginal part of a blood sinusoid (*s*) is at the left. Mitochondria are numerous and readily identified by their characteristic morphology. The endoplasmic reticulum is represented by two distinct forms. One, shown in the centre of the field (*er*), consists of large, thin, lamellar vesicles or cisternae with small (150 Å) dense particles attached to their surfaces. In thin sections these appear as rough, line-limited profiles, associated in groups which coincide with the basophilic component of the light microscope image. The other form is particle-free or smooth and is constructed of fine tubular elements *ca.* 50 mμ in diameter (*ers*). These comprise in liver cells what appears as a loose tri-dimensional lattice. The Golgi component is represented at *G*.

chromophilic material of the liver cell cytoplasm (1943). A definitive
demonstration of the intracellular origin of the microsome was not, however, provided until about 12 years later when Palade and Siekevitz [14]
published micrographs of sections through the pellet representing the

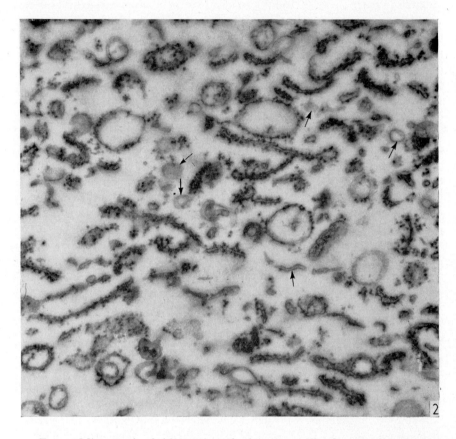

FIG. 2. Micrograph of thin section of microsome pellet from rat liver homogenization and fractionation. The long slender profiles are readily identified as
fragments of intracellular, particle-studded (rough) cisternae of the endoplasmic
reticulum (see Fig. 4 for comparison of rough ER in intact cell). There are also in
the field (at arrows) a few profiles of vesicles without particles (smooth or agranular).
These are thought to be derived from the smooth form of the reticulum observed
in liver cells. Mag. × 70 000. (Micrograph courtesy of G. E. Palade.)

microsome fraction. These pictures showed profiles of particle-studded
units which by their morphology could be unmistakably identified as
fragments or pieces of the endoplasmic reticulum of the intact rat liver
cell (Fig. 2). Thus the microsome became part of a well characterized

system of the cytoplasm and all the data and information that had previously been gathered on liver microsomes became applicable to the intact system. The rough form of the ER could be said to incorporate amino acids into proteins, as shown for the microsome by the pioneering experiments of Hultin [15] and Borsook et al. [16]. Then also it became valid to ascribe to the ER glucose-6-phosphatase activity and 40 to 50% of the RNA in the whole tissue (liver in this case). These and other properties described by more refined procedures will doubtless be considered in subsequent papers. The sole purpose here is to relate the microsome to the ER.

As noted above, the term "rough" is applied to this form of the reticulum because of the presence in its surface of numerous particles. Thus the microsome is made up of at least three parts: the particles, the membrane, and the contained space. Interest in the specific functions and properties of these had led to several studies on them as separate entitics. With the aid of deoxycholate (DOC), the particles have been separated from the membranes, and by electron microscopy have been shown to be relatively free from contamination [14]. Examination of such preparations have further shown these particles to contain 80 to 90% of the RNA of the intact or complete microsome and only 20% of the protein nitrogen. The particles are therefore appropriately referred to as RNP particles or ribosomes. The other two parts of the microsome, the membrane and content have been freed of particles with versene, likewise examined for purity in the E.M., and investigated for other properties. As might be expected, they possessed the other properties of the intact microsome before the ribosomes were removed, i.e. most of the protein, nearly all of the phospholipid, and the DPNH-cytochrome c reductase activity.

Here again, with these fractions of the microsomes, isotope incorporation studies have been fruitful and, as is well known, have described the ribosome as possessing the capacity to combine free labelled amino acids into proteins. Thus, in the case of protein synthesis, the particle rather than the membrane is the important structure and would seem to be responsible for determining the character of the protein synthesized. This conclusion finds strong support in the recent studies of Siekevitz and Palade [17, 18] on the relation of RNP particles to the synthesis of pancreatic enzymes.

With a specific function assigned to the ribosome, it is of some interest to inquire into the role of the membrane and cavity of the intact system. As previously noted, it obviously provides a large surface for the disposition of the particles. There is, moreover, pictorial evidence that this distribution follows certain repeating designs presumably related to patterns in the membrane [19]. Whether there is some functional purpose in this is not clear. That the membranes are not essential to the synthetic

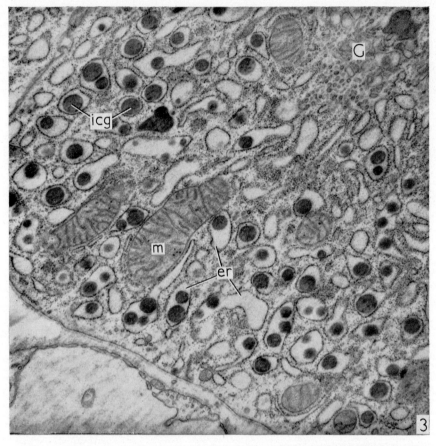

FIG. 3. Micrograph of part of an acinar cell of the guinea-pig pancreas. The basal surface of the cell crosses the figure at the lower left; the apical pole, with a few elements of the Golgi (*G*) showing, is at the upper right. The specimen was fixed during the recovery phase following secretion of zymogen granules.

The objects of greatest interest here are the large, dense, spherical granules within the cisternae of the ER. Now known as intracisternal granules, these units have been shown to possess the enzymic activities of purified zymogen granules. It is thought that in acinar cells of guinea-pig pancreas the zymogen portions, sequestered in the cavities of the ER, condense out as granules before being transported to the Golgi component in the apical pole for packaging as secretory granules. The intracisternal granules are indicated at *icg*; the mitochondria at *m*. Small (150 Å) dense granules are abundant in the cytoplasm of these cells and particularly on the surfaces of the ER. The specimen was fixed in OsO_4 and stained with lead. (Micrograph courtesy of G. E. Palade.)

activity of the ribosome is suggested by the fact that in growing cells, e.g., the particles seem to perform their synthetic role without membrane support. The distinction to be made is that protein production in this latter instance is for *internal* consumption rather than for *export*. Only in other instances where particles are associated with the membranes of the ER, is the product prepared for secretion and the external environment of the cell.

For observations on the role of the ER in this phenomenon one must turn to studies on intact cells engaged in protein synthesis. In an early paper, Weiss [20] noted that the cisternae of rat pancreas cells appeared swollen and filled with a material which he interpreted as zymogen during the synthetic phase of the cell's activity. The real nature of the intra-cisternal material was not, however, demonstrated. Later, Palade [6], in some observations on guinea-pig pancreas, observed that during the period of gland recovery after secretion, relatively large granules, having the density of zymogen granules, appeared within the cisterna of the ER (Fig. 3). These granules were subsequently isolated and analyzed [21, 22] and found to have the properties of zymogen granules as normally secreted by the cell. In this instance, then, and probably in every other case of ergastoplasm function, the product of synthesis is, so to say, separated or segregated from the site of synthesis (the ribosome) by the membrane limiting the ER cisterna. One can say that the product is externalized with respect to the continuous phase of the cytoplasmic matrix, where, if it were left, it would presumably diffuse away among the structural proteins of the cytoplasm.

Once sequestered within the cavities of the ER it appears to move, in a dissolved or diffusible form, to the Golgi region in the apical pole of the cell, where it is apparently prepared for secretion. Some evidence of at least temporary continuity between elements of the ER and the Golgi component, which would provide channels for transport, have recently been described [23]. Thus, in addition to its role in sequestering the product of synthesis, the ER appears to function in transporting metabolic products from one point to another in the cell. It may be recalled that this was mentioned earlier as a logical function of the system.

The smooth form of the ER

In all the attention given the more striking, rough form of the ER and the ribosomes, other configurations of this intracellular system are seem-ingly overlooked. Yet there are probably as many types of cells with prominent differentiations of the smooth ER as there are with the rough form. In some instances, as mentioned earlier, the two are mixed in one and the same cell and where this is the case, microsome fractions can be shown to contain both types (Fig. 2). Thus in one of the earliest studies of liver microsomes, note was taken of a substantial content of smooth-surfaced vesicles derived, it was thought, from the smooth-surfaced portions of the endoplasmic reticulum [14].

This smooth form, like the particle-encrusted portions of the ER possesses a characteristic morphology. The unit of structure is tubular (50 to 100 Å in diameter), and these are arranged in varying degrees of compaction to form complex tri-dimensional lattices. Such configurations occur in a wide variety of cell types. In some instances their development appears to be related to maintenance of form, e.g., in the sustentacular cells of the frog olfactory epithelium [24]. In cells of the pigment epithelium of the frog retina a development of the smooth ER occupies a large part of the cytoplasm and shows no affinity for the few ribosomes present [25]. It is the predominant form in the sarcoplasm of striated muscle cells and shows a pattern differentiation related to the sarcomeres of the myofibrils [26]. What if any role it performs in common in these widely different cells is a large question.

In at least one class of cells, that engaged in the synthesis of lipid materials for export, the smooth surfaced form of the ER occurs consistently. It has, e.g., been described as the dominant form in the more mature cells of the sebaceous glands (Meibomian gland of the rat) [27]. The secretory (lipid) droplets form initially in these cells in close relation with the tubular elements of the ER and appear later to be segregated for secretion within the vacuoles of the Golgi complex. A similar development of the agranular ER has been reported in cells producing steroid hormones, for example the interstitial cells of the opossum testis [28]. Here the ER is entirely devoid of dense particles and the cells are intensely acidophilic. These observations have special interest and significance because Lynn and Brown [29] in a biochemical study on similar material found evidence that enzymes involved in the production of testosterone from progesterone are associated with microsomes and that, though inactivated by lipases, they are unaffected by ribonuclease at concentrations that normally inhibit protein synthesis in liver and pancreatic homogenates. The inference is that the enzymes active in steroid synthesis are associated with the RNA-free microsomal membranes. This is further supported by observations on fetal zone cells of the human adrenal in which there is a richly developed smooth ER [29a].

These three instances suggest a correlation between the agranular ER and contain phases of lipid metabolism, especially where a product is synthesized for export from the cell. The exact site of synthesis with respect to the ER has not in these cases been clearly defined. Thus one cannot say that it is sequestered within the cavities of the ER and transported thence to the Golgi, though involvement of the Golgi component would suggest that the sequence encountered in protein synthesis may be followed here as well.

In this regard the morphological phenomena observed in intestinal epithelial cells of the rat during fat absorption can be interpreted to have some significance. The story comes from recent investigations of Palay and Karlin [30]. These authors, in following the uptake of fat by epithelial cells of the intestinal villus of the rat, observed that small fat droplets (~ 50 mμ in diameter), which appeared to traverse the cortex of the cells in pinocytotic vesicles, reappeared in the cavities of the ER. They were then transported within the channels of the system to the lateral margins of the cell and thence, presumably through intermittently established openings, into the inter-cellular spaces. All compartments of the ER including the nuclear envelope were seen to contain droplets of fat within 30 min. after intragastric instillation of corn oil [31]. Besides providing evidence of transport within the ER, these observations are descriptive of continuity within the system. The authors express the opinion that the fat particles which appear in the cisternae of the ER are transported directly there by pinocytotic vesicles. It follows from this opinion that the passage of fat through the epithelial cell is to all intents and purposes an extra-cellular phenomena.

This interpretation of events in fat absorption is introduced into this discussion because it bears on the question of the relation of the ER to the plasma membrane and the cell surface, and also because there is an alternate interpretation which seems to more nearly fit the observations and related information. According to the Palay–Karlin interpretation, materials taken up in small bits or sips (quanta) at the cell surface are discharged helter-skelter into the lumina of the ER. This means that a space designed to sequester the products of synthesis may also receive all manner of metabolites and non-metabolites from the environment. These concepts have grown out of observations on pinocytic activity at the cell surface [6] and some evidence of occasional and probably intermittent continuity between membranes of the ER and the cell surface [32]. They remain, however, as concepts and much of the evidence available on uptake of particulate material visible with the E.M. fails to support them [33, 34]. As a rule, a barrier of two membranes (plasma and ER) and a layer of cytoplasmic matrix always lies between the extracellular space and the cavities of the ER on the uptake side. Even the Palay–Karlin observations may be interpreted to fit this principle. They admit in their report that definite evidence of continuity between pinocytotic vesicles and the ER is not available and that furthermore it is difficult, through the apparent pinocytotic activity, to account for the rapid fat absorption. There is good evidence, moreover, that long-chain fatty acids provided in dietary triglycerides are rearranged in the fats in the chylomicrons on the other side of the epithelium [35]. These points support an alternate interpreta-tion that only the products of triglyceride hydrolysis pass the plasma membrane and enter the cytoplasmic matrix; that these are reassembled at the membrane limiting the ER and resynthesized into fats which are

F*

sequestered as droplets within the cisternae. This scheme would provide for the production of triglycerides at all levels in the ER—a possibility suggested as well by the appearance of large quantities of fat globules in the ER in deep parts of the cell within a short time after fat digestion begins. The sequence of synthesis, sequestration and transport is obviously analogous to that encountered in zymogen granule formation as depicted in the guinea-pig pancreas.

Glycogen metabolism

The instances already cited in which the smooth or agranular ER is a prominent component of cell fine structure do not exhaust the known occurrences. Other reports include observations of agglomerations of agranular vesicles and tubules in liver cells of the rat [36, 6]; and a remarkable tri-dimensional lattice of small tubular elements as part of the glycogen-rich paraboloid found in the inner segment of the turtle cone cell [37, 38]. Continuity between the smooth elements and adjacent rough cisternae describe them as parts of a single system, the endoplasmic reticulum. In each of these instances, unlike those previously noted, the smooth ER is specifically associated with glycogen deposits.

One of the earliest descriptions of this smooth form of the ER in liver cells appeared in a paper by Fawcett [36]. In the liver cells of rats, fasted

---

FIG. 4. The image shown here represents parts of two adjacent liver cells (rat) plus a neighbouring sinusoid (s). In the cell at the bottom of the picture, one can identify the nucleus (N) with its typical envelope; mitochondria (m); long profiles of cisternae comprising the granular or rough form of the ER or ergastoplasm (er); and a few profiles of elements belonging to the agranular or smooth ER (ers). The rough ER (within the rectangle) is particularly suitable for identifying the source of the microsomes in Fig. 3.

The part of a cell at the upper left, beside the bizarre mitochondrion, contains two elements of particular interest here. The first is very dense (following staining with $Pb(OH)_2$) and represents the glycogen (gl). The unit structure, which appears as a cluster of granular subunits, usually does not exceed a maximum size of about 150 mμ. From this, the size ranges downwards to individual subunits. This is the liver cell component that fluctuates with physiological conditions leading to glycogen storage or depletion. It varies directly with intensity of PAS staining and is removed by diastase. A number of investigators have referred to it as glycogen.

These dense bodies are interspersed with less dense, line-limited elements, which are interpreted as vesicles and tubules of the smooth ER (ers). They seem to form an irregular lattice. While the diameters of these elements are not uniform, it is obvious that they fall within a fairly narrow range of variation.

This is the picture of association between ER and glycogen found during the storage phase. The specimen was taken 2 hr. after re-feeding following a 24-hr. fast. When taken later at 4 or 6 hr., the cells show much more glycogen and the ER profiles intermingling with the glycogen are relatively fewer. The specimen was fixed in OsO_4, embedded in Epon 812, and, after sectioning, stained with $Pb(OH)_2$.

and re-fed, he noted compact masses of "small vesicles and short tubules", especially at the periphery of the cell. A subsequent investigation discovered that this smooth form of the ER undergoes a great hypertrophy in

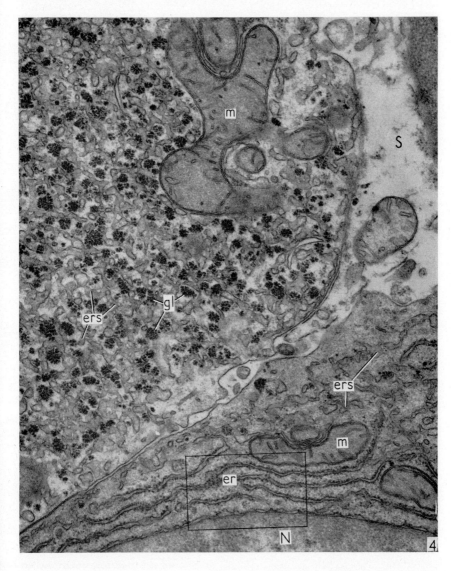

liver cells of rats given the toxic azo dye, 3′-methyl-4-dimethyl aminoazo-benzene [39]. This is a substance which, when fed to these animals, blocks glycogen storage in affected liver cells, and eventually induces liver tumours. In this study it was noted that these prominent developments of

the smooth ER appeared initially in association with glycogen deposits and
that concomitantly with their development the glycogen was depleted and
did not reappear while the dye was included in the diet. It was these

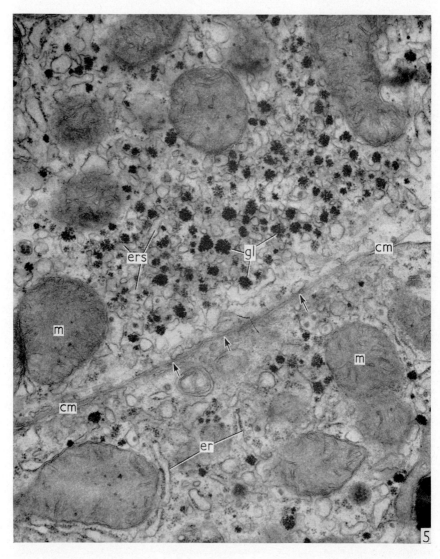

observations that stimulated an investigation into the possible relationship
between the smooth ER and glycogen metabolism which is still continuing.
The following summary is drawn from experiments made in collaboration
with Drs. Giuseppe Millonig and Thomas Ashford. Detailed accounts of
the results will be published elsewhere.

The initial observations were derived from a systematic examination of liver tissue from animals fasted for 24 hrs. and for 5 days and from similar animals after periods of re-feeding varying from 1 to 6 hr. Electron micrographs of the liver cells of these animals reveal a constant and specific association between the smooth ER and glycogen. The development of the system is particularly striking during the period of glycogen synthesis at, e.g., 2 hr. after re-feeding following a fast of 24 hr. (Fig. 4). Pictures of this kind supported the early speculation that the membranes and vesicles might contain factors significant in glycogenesis [39]. When the stores of glycogen have reached a maximum (e.g. 6 hr. after re-feeding), the profiles of vesicles intermingling with the glycogen are relatively far less numerous. Whether this represents an absolute reduction in the extent of the system (a reversal of the absolute increase that occurs with re-feeding) or is simply a result of dilution by the glycogen stores has not been determined. Following a period of fast (e.g. 24 hr.), the vesicular component of the residual glycogen complexes is again relatively prominent (Fig. 5), though not so impressive in absolute terms as shortly after re-feeding. The system in the fasted cells is morphologically distinctive; many of the vesicles show a low density content and are more closely compacted with the glycogen units. There are, in other words, distinguishing differences to be noted between the smooth ER and the fasted and re-fed cells (compare Figs. 4 and 5). The image of the glycogen and associated ER in the cell of the fasted animal is repeated in animals that have been given glucagon or epinephrine. Furthermore, the effects of fasting and of glucagon and epinephrine are repeated as well in the fine structure of rat livers perfused under isolation for periods of 4 to 6 hr. [40].

There are, unfortunately, several ways to interpret these observations. The structural association of the smooth ER and the glycogen is a specific

---

Fig. 5. This shows parts of two adjacent rat liver cells. In this case, in contrast to that shown in Fig. 4, the specimen was taken at the end of a 24-hr. fast period.

The cells are depleted of their glycogen (*gl*) except for residual units in small marginal zones of the cytoplasm, as shown here. Following glucagon injections even these residual units are mobilized and many cells appear devoid of any glycogen. The space between the residual glycogen units is filled by somewhat expanded or bloated vesicles of the smooth ER. These seem to fill the available space and crowd close to the glycogen, possibly for functional purposes. Essentially the glycogen is vesicle-locked. The vesicular profiles vary more in size and shape than those in Fig. 4 and seem to have a content of lower density (possibly because something has dissolved out). A number of these vesicles can be seen in close proximity to and possibly blending with the cell surface or membrane (arrows).

The cell margins are contiguous and run from (*cm*) to (*cm*). It is obviously difficult to follow the plasma membranes along this stretch, perhaps because it is discontinuous. Mitochondria (*m*) are obvious; rough ER (*er*) is randomly scattered. The specimen was fixed in OsO_4, embedded in Epon, and stained after sectioning.

one and naturally suggests a functional relationship. Particularly is this so
when, as in the azo dye experiments, a hypertrophy or abnormality in one
is accompanied by a diminution in the other. But whether the association
is important in glycogenesis and storage or in glycogenolysis (or both) is
not clearly evident. By way of resolving the problem one can cite certain
instances where glycogen is stored without apparent involvement of the
smooth ER. In diabetes mellitus, for example, the nuclei of liver cells show
large glycogen stores. The same have been reported in liver nuclei of young
frog tadpoles [41] and in the nuclei of cells of a chicken sarcoma [42],
where membranous elements of the ER are not normally found. Also in
chondrocytes, the cytoplasmic deposits of glycogen apparently put down
for future use of the cell, show no prominent membrane components. If
one excludes the possibility that the fixation or staining (or even the
timing of the fixation) have not been appropriate in these instances to
preserve this form of the ER, one is left with the conclusion, also supported
by recent report of Revel *et al.* [43], that the ER is not an obligate associate
of glycogen synthesis.

This encourages one to focus on the depletion side of the metabolism
cycle, in which the liver cell has a more unique function to perform. As is
well known, it has to export glucose on demand and keep it unavailable to
the general carbohydrate metabolism of the liver cell itself. It is important,
therefore, to have it sequestered near the site of storage or availability and
thence transported to the cell surface. If functional in this manner, the
smooth ER in the liver cell would be performing a role closely analogous
to that of the system in other types of cells described earlier in this report.

It is not difficult to find in the pictorial data, evidence to support this
concept. The morphology of the ER relative to the glycogen is identical
during the depletion phases in fasting animals and after glucagon. At such
times the association of vesicle and glycogen is more intimate. The vesicles
show a very low density suggesting that these contents are soluble. And
it is usual to find the glycogen complexes close to the cell margins with
many of the smooth surfaced vesicles up against the adjacent plasma
membrane, possibly preparatory to discharging their contents, assumed to
be glucose. Also in this regard, the association of glucose-6-phosphatase
with microsomal membranes (presumably agranular) is not to be overlooked. Since, however, these observations constitute the only information
we have, it is clear that the final chapters in this investigation of the smooth
ER and glycogen have yet to be written.

Endoplasmic reticulum in plant cells

Thus far in this review the observations we have considered have been
derived from animal cells. Certain generalizations have been presented

relative to the structure and function of this newly defined system—again based on animal material. Obviously if these are to be accepted as principles of cytology, they should be equally applicable to plant cells. Therefore a good deal of interest has been displayed in electron microscopy of plant cells. The early attempts were less than satisfactory because of the technical problems encountered. These early observations were, however, of sufficient value to show that the plant cell had in common with the animal a membrane limited system, homologous to the ER of animal cells [44, 24]. Since that time, technical developments have provided improved images which leave no doubt that plant cells of several kinds have in their fine structure organelles and systems identical in many respects to those found in the animal units [44a, 45,]. Thus the nuclear envelope shows the characteristic two membranes and pores, and continuity at certain points with the cytoplasmic part of the system. Cisternal units of the ER, though randomly oriented in the meristematic cells of the root (Fig. 7), do achieve patterns of organization in cells in more advanced stages of differentiation (Fig. 6). The RNP particles in plant cells do not show the extreme affinities for cisternal surfaces that one notes in animal cells, but particles are attached to some parts of the system and not to others so that one can recognize rough and smooth divisions (Fig. 6).

The functions of the ER in the plant cell are of course not more clearly shown by a few pictures than they were in the animal equivalent. However the material lends itself very readily to controlled experimental study and one can reasonably hope that a substantial amount of new information may come from this source. Then also certain features of interest are peculiar to plant cells, and one can hope to exploit these for clues to function not displayed to the same advantage in animal cells. At the outset we can reasonably assume that the little we have learned from animal material can be transferred to the plant.

One structural association especially has held our interest and it is to this that attention will be specifically directed (see Porter and Machado, [46]).

The majority of the structures representing the ER in meristematic plant cells are large, lamellar units. When these reach out to the cell surface they show at their margins distinctive changes in morphology. These are reflected in the thin section by changes in the dimensions of the profiles. Thus, instead of being long and narrow, they appear short and often circular, which indicates that at this level the system is constructed of tubular rather than lamellar units (Fig. 7). These are joined together at this level into a reticular structure which can be more readily visualized when included in the plane of the section (Fig. 8). Again, for the morphologist this suggests a functional involvement of the ER in events taking place at the cell surface. These events include of course some exchange of

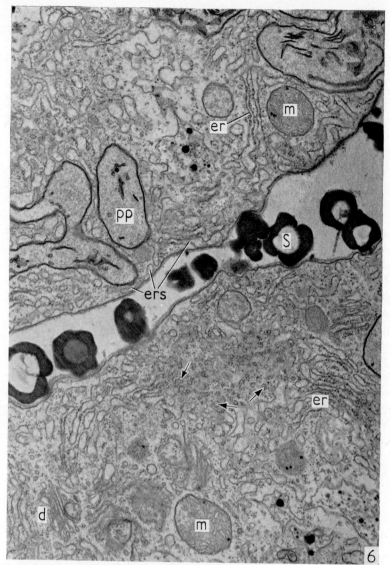

Fig. 6. Micrograph of parts of adjacent cells in tapetal layer found in anthers of *Saintpaulia ionatha*. The cytoplasms of the fully differentiated plant cells are richly supplied with elements of the ER. In a way peculiar to these cells, the ER shows some of the features which characterize it in animal cells. Some of the cisternae are lamellar and arranged in groups or clusters. These show the most pronounced association with RNP particles. As in animal cells, these particles show some tendency to form miniature patterns in their distribution on membrane surfaces (arrows). Other vesicles and tubules are essentially free from particles— and most especially those close to the cell surface. Mitochondria (*m*) are similar to those in animal cells. Otherwise the figure shows proplastids (*pp*), a few dictyosomes (*d*), and some extracellular granules (*s*).

The specimen was fixed in OsO_4, embedded in Epon 812, and sectioned with a diamond knife. Contrast was improved with lead hydroxide. (Micrograph courtesy Dr. Myron Ledbetter.)

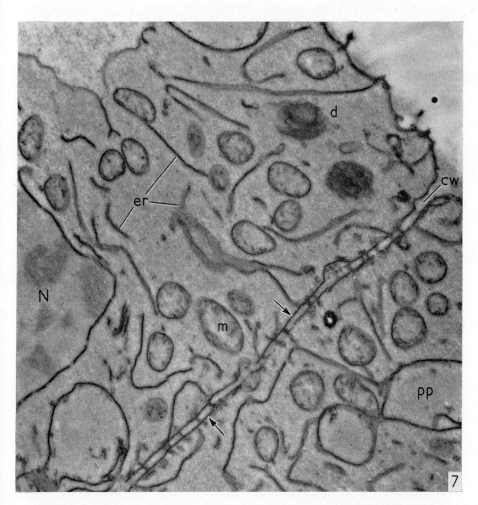

FIG. 7. This shows the corners of two contiguous meristematic cells of the onion root tip. The primary wall (*cw*) separating the cells passes across the lower right corner; the nucleus of one cell is at *N*. The wavy lines in the cytoplasm are actually paired lines or membranes with an intervening space (see Figs. 11 and 12 for higher magnification of same). They represent sections through large lamellar units of the ER. Where these approach closely to the cell surface they branch and reticulate to give in section only small circular profiles (see long surfaces indicated by arrows). Figure 8 shows the appearance of this when section coincides with plane of wall. Other components include mitochondria (*m*), proplastids (*pp*), and dictyosomes (*d*).

The specimen, from an onion root tip, was fixed in $KMnO_4$, embedded in methacrylate, and sectioned with a diamond knife.

metabolites and the production and deposition of materials important in wall formation. In Fig. 7, e.g., the separation of the cells is a product of a recent division, and primary wall formation is probably in progress. The real purpose of the association is, of course, not indicated. But it is of some value to compare the picture at this cell surface with other instances where wall formation is also in progress and especially where wall formation is more clearly the major activity at the moment of fixation.

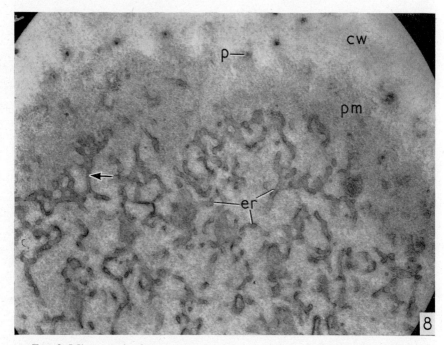

FIG. 8. Micrograph of section cut in plane of surface of onion root tip cell. The section includes a part of the cytoplasm (bottom half) and passes out of cell obliquely through the plasma membrane (*pm*) and then into region of wall (*cw*). The small densities with a ring around them represent cross sections of plasma-desmata (*p*). The component of particular interest here is the endoplasmic reticulum and its distribution just within the plasma membrane. It obviously consists of many tubular units interconnected to form a reticular structure which is contiguous with the inner surface of the plasma membrane (see arrow).

One example of this latter situation is encountered in the formation of the cell plate [47]. As is well known, this structure is characteristic of dividing plant cells and first appears in light microscopy as a row of small pectin vesicles arranged along the equator of the telophase spindle [48]. In the electron microscope image the vesicular phase of plate development is preceded by another structure which has the following developmental history.

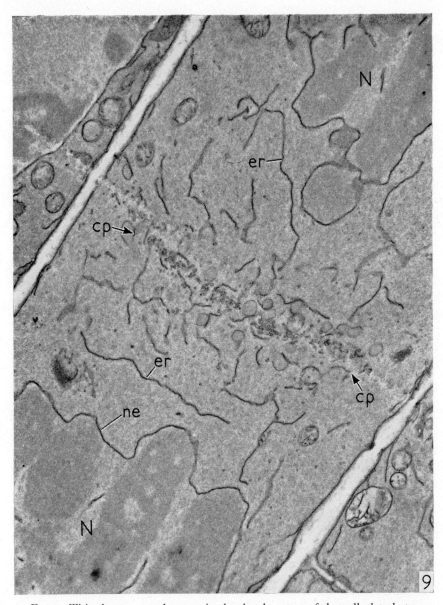

FIG. 9. This shows an early stage in the development of the cell plate between two daughter cells of onion root meristem. The telophase nuclei are at *N* and a new nuclear envelope has just reformed (*ne*). Long slender profiles of the ER, present in the interzone, appear noticeably shorter toward the plate region (*cp*), and at this level they reticulate and intermingle from the two sides to form a dense, irregular lattice of tubules. Within this structure, which has its origins in the marginal extensions of the ER, the early pectin vesicles of the plate first appear (see Fig. 10) for later stage). These grow in number and size and eventually fuse to separate the two daughter cells. (From Porter and Machado, 1960.)

During anaphase of mitosis, lamellar and tubular elements of the ER, now divided between the two ends of the cell, invade the spindle from the poles and sides and approach, from opposite directions, the equator of the

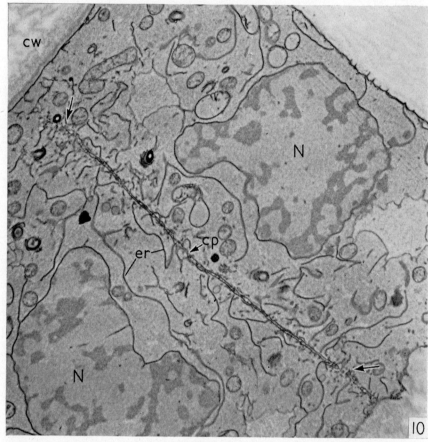

FIG. 10. Micrograph showing dividing cell in cortex of onion root tip. Telophase nuclei are indicated at N, cell plate at cp, and surrounding walls at cw. Numerous slender profiles of the endoplasmic reticulum (er) are scattered throughout the cytoplasm. At the level of the plate, and especially at its margins (arrows), the ER profiles are much shorter and describe the existence here of a compact, irregular lattice of tubular elements. Within this there appear first the small pectin vesicles which by their growth and fusion achieve the separation of the daughter cells. At the centre of the plate (cp) this has already happened, but at the margins, the cells are still not divided.

spindle. As they reach this level, they reticulate very much as they do at the cell surface (Fig. 9). There results from this a tri-dimensional inter-mingling of tubular elements from the two daughter protoplasts and it is within this lattice that the so-called pectin vesicles appear (Figs. 10 and 11). These increase in number and size from the centre of the plate outwards, and finally fuse to complete the separation of the two cells [45]. It is not possible at this time to account for the origin of the vesicles, but it would seem that small, restricted loci in the spindle matrix are lysed or otherwise changed and enclosed by a membrane—possibly by virtue of this

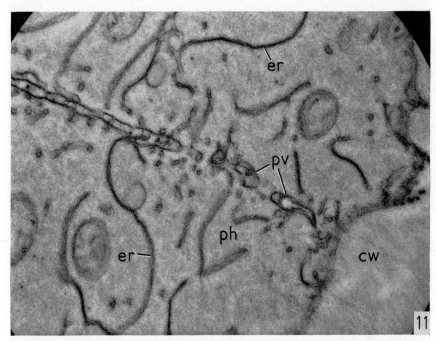

FIG. 11. This shows, at higher magnifications, the right-hand margin of the cell plate in Fig. 10. The region of the phragmoplast is indicated at *ph*. Within the lattice of tubules, which marks the phragmoplast and the advancing margin of the plate, the pectin vesicles (*pv*) first appear. To the left, in this image and toward the centre of the plate, these have already fused. The outer surface and wall of the cell are at *cw*.

change. The important thing for present purposes is to note the very intimate association of this ER or ER derivative with the events of plate and new wall formation. Whether the small marginal units of the ER contribute enzyme or substrate to the biochemical events leading to pectin and/or early cellulose formation cannot be decided from evidence available. One may suggest, however, that the results of any participation which the ER may take in plate and primary wall formation should reflect any patterns or irregularities in the distribution of elements in the ER.

The intimacy shown here between the ER and the cell surface is again

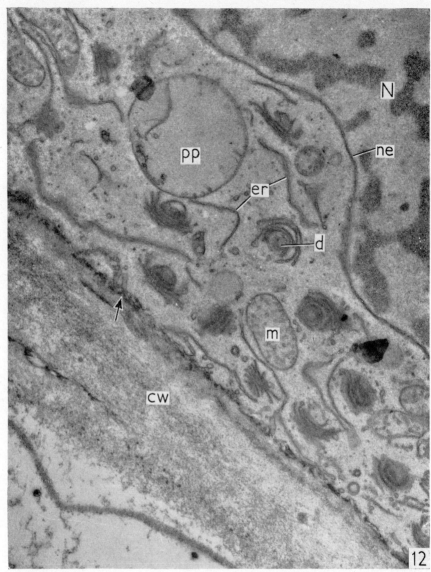

FIG. 12. This is identified as the external margin of an epidermal cell of the onion root tip. The nucleus is at *N*, a nuclear envelope at *ne*. Organelles of the cytoplasm include mitochondria (*m*), dictyosomes (*d*), proplastids (*pp*), and endoplasmic reticulum (*er*). The surface of the protoplast and its relation to the extracellular wall (*cw*) are the points of major interest. It appears that the wall has been put down in layers, reflecting, possibly, phases of wall formation. The surface of the protoplast in this instance shows no continuous plasma membrane but only short fragments. In places (arrow), the ends of ER elements project beyond the surface defined by these membrane fragments as though blending with the extracellular material. We interpret this image as descriptive of a process of wall formation in which a cortical layer of the cell, with fragments of the contained organelles, is externalized by the development of a new plasma membrane behind it.

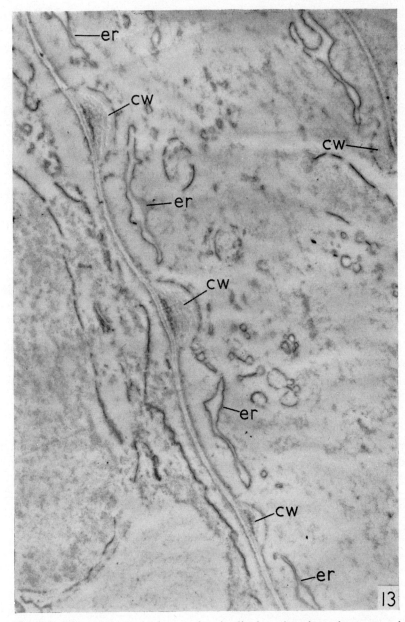

FIG. 13. This micrograph shows a longitudinal section through a protoxylem cell of the onion root tip. This cell, in the final stages of its differentiation, shows secondary ring thickenings in the wall characteristic of early xylem units. Cross sections of these thickenings are marked *cw*. The point of interest here is that the ER is patterned with respect to these thickenings; the evident profiles are marked *er*.

evident during secondary wall formation (Fig. 12). As before, the ER is represented by small profiles at the cell surface, a reflection of the smaller units comprising the system at this level. At a phase in active wall formation, presumably depicted in Fig. 12, a layer of the cell cortex is externalized and the peripheral elements of the ER with it. In this process of ecdysis, as pointed out in the figure-legend, a new plasma membrane appears to form back of the margin. Again the morphological involvement of the ER is taken to suggest functional involvement and one would gather from the micrographs that parts of the ER are used up in the process [46].

If now these peripheral elements are functionally significant, let us say in cellulose polymerization, any patterns in their distribution at the surface should find some reflection perhaps in the thickness of the wall. One can therefore with profit and interest explore cells where one finds ring or spiral thickenings, as in primitive tracheids. These represent the final stage in the differentiation of these cells and they contain only a small residue of cytoplasm. This and its properties make fixation difficult. Nonetheless when, after sectioning, these cells are examined, it is found that residual elements of the ER are distributed in a pattern relative to the secondary thickenings (Fig. 13). Earlier stages in the formation of these rings have not been observed as yet, so the character of the ER which anticipates their location cannot be depicted or commented upon.

The question of organization in the ER and its role, if any, in the determination of cell form and polarity and the disposition of secondary products of differentiation, is of course a large one and not to be solved with a few electron micrographs. It does seem, however, that the form the ER adopts is determined in part at least by the molecular architecture of the system itself and more remotely by genic information. In determining through its morphology the spatial intracellular disposition of biochemical reactions, it becomes an instrument for the nuclear control of these phenomena.

References

1. Porter, K. R., Claude, A., and Fullam, E., *J. exp. Med.* **81,** 161 (1945).
2. Hartmann, J. F., *J. comp. Neurol.* **99,** 201 (1953).
3. Watson, M. L., *J. biophys. biochem. Cytol.* **1,** 257 (1955).
4. Porter, K. R., *J. exp. Med.* **97,** 727 (1953).
5. Hagunau, F., *Int. Rev. Cytol.* **7,** 426 (1958).
6. Palade, G. E., *J. biophys. biochem. Cytol.* **2** suppl., 85 (1956).
7. Porter, K. R., *in* "The Cell", eds. J. Brachet and A. E. Mirsky, Vol. II. Academic Press. 621 (1961).
8. Brachet, J., *Arch. Biol.* **53,** 207 (1941).
9. Caspersson, T., "Cell Growth and Cell Function." New York, Norton (1950).
10. Garnier, Ch., Contribution à l'étude de la structure et du functionnement des cellules glandulaires séreuses. Du role de l'ergastoplasm dans la sécrétion. Thesis, Nancy, No. 50 (1899).

11. Mathews, A., *J. Morphol.* **15** suppl., 171 (1899).
12. Claude, A., *Cold Spr. Harb. Symp. quant. Biol.* **9**, 263 (1941).
13. Claude, A., "Biological Symposium." The Jacques Cattell Press, Lancaster, Pa. **10**, 111–130 (1943).
14. Palade, G. E., and Siekevitz, P., *J. biophys. biochem. Cytol.* **2**, 171 (1956).
15. Hultin, T., *Exp. Cell Res.* **1**, 376 (1950).
16. Borsook, H., Deasy, C. L., Haagen-Smit, A. J., Keighly, G., and Lowy, P. H., *J. biol. Chem.* **187**, 839 (1950).
16a. Littlefield, J. W., Keller, E.B, Gross, J., and Zamecnik, P.C. (1955). *J. Biol. Chem.* **8**, 347.
17. Siekevitz, P., and Palade, G. E., *J. biophys. biochem. Cytol.* **7**, 619 (1960).
18. Siekevitz, P., and Palade, G. E., *J. biophys. biochem. Cytol.* **7**, 631 (1960).
19. Palade, G. E., *J. biophys. biochem. Cytol.* **1**, 59 (1955).
20. Weiss, J. M., *J. expl. Med.* **98**, 607 (1953).
21. Siekevitz, P., and Palade, G. E., *J. biophys. biochem. Cytol.* **4**, 203 (1958).
22. Siekevitz, P., and Palade, G. E., *J. biophys. biochem. Cytol.* **4**, 309 (1958).
23. Palade, G. E., "Symposium on Electron Microscopy." Brit. Anat. Assoc., Arnold Press, London (1960).
24. Porter, K. R., The Harvey Lectures, Series 51, 175 (1957). Academic Press, New York.
25. Porter, K. R., and Yamada, E., *J. biophys. biochem. Cytol.* **8**, 181 (1960).
26. Porter, K. R., and Palade, G. E., *J. biophys. biochem. Cytol.* **3**, 269 (1957).
27. Palay, S. L., *in* "Frontiers in Cytology," ed. S. L. Palay. Yale University Press, New Haven, Conn. 350 (1958).
28. Christensen, A. K., and Fawcett, D. W., *Anat. Rec.* **136**, 333 (1960).
29. Lynn, W. S., Jr., and Brown, R. H., *J. biol. Chem.* **232**, 1015.
29a. Ross, M. H., Pappas, G. D., Lanman, J. T., and Lind, J. (1958) *J. biophys. biochem. Cytol.* **4**, 659.
30. Palay, S. L., and Karlin, S. J., *J. biophys. biochem. Cytol.* **5**, 373 (1959).
31. Palay, S. L., *J. biophys. biochem. Cytol.* **7**, 391 (1960).
32. Epstein, M. A. (1957) *J. biophys. biochem. Cytol.* **3**, 851.
33. Hampton, J. C., *Acta. Anat.* **32**, 262 (1958).
34. Karrer, H. E., *J. biophys. biochem. Cytol.* **7**, 357 (1960).
35. Peterson, M. L., The Transport of Fat in Man: A Study of Chylomicrons. Thesis submitted for the Ph.D. degree at The Rockefeller Institute (1960).
36. Fawcett, D. W., *J. nat. Cancer Inst.* **15** suppl., 1475 (1955).
37. Yamada, E., *J. Electronmicroscopy* **9**, 1 (1960).
38. Yamada, E., and Porter, K. R., *J. biophys. biochem. Cytol.*, in press (1961).
39. Porter, K. R., and Bruni, C., *Cancer Res.* **19**, 997 (1959).
40. Asford and Porter (1961).
41. Himes, M., and Pollister, A. W., *Anat. Rec.* **132**, 453 (1958).
42. Bingelli, M. F., *J. biophys. biochem. Cytol.* **5**, 143 (1959).
43. Revel, J. P., Napolitano, L., and Fawcett, D. W., *J. biophys. biochem. Cytol.* **8**, 575 (1960).
44. Buvat, R., and Carosso N., *C. R. Acad. Sci.*, Paris **224**, 1532 (1957).
44a. Whaley, W. G., Mollenhauer, H. H., Kephart, J. E., *J. biophys. biochem. Cytol.* **5**, 501 (1959).
45. Porter, K. R., and Machado, R., *J. biophys. biochem. Cytol.* **7**, 167 (1960).
46. Porter, K. R., and Machado, R., European Regional Conference on Electron Microscopy, Delft, (in press) (1960).
47. Porter, K. R., and Caulfield, J. B., "Proc. 4th Internat. Conference on Electron Microscopy." Springer-Verlag, Berlin, 503 (1958).

48. Becker, W. A., *Bot. Rev.* **4,** 446 (1938).
49. Godman, G. C., and Porter, K. R., *J. biophys. biochem. Cytol.* **8,** 719 (1960).
50. Porter, K. R., and Bruni, C., *Anat. Rec.* **136,** 260 (1960).

Discussion

MAZIA: Do you know what Dr. Palade meant when he entitled his talk "The endosplasmic reticulum; its good fortune during the last 5 years"?

PORTER: I think he intended to show how well or fortunately the system had lent itself to investigation.

DAVIS: Would the available information exclude the possibility that a major function, perhaps more important than the synthetic function, would be that of transport? In lipid deposition, for example, I presume that at a time when the animal is fed, glucose must get from the exterior to the sites of formation and deposition, while in starvation it moves in the other direction. Is it not possible that the endoplasmic tubes furnish means of communication, the enzymes then being in the proper regions for the process but not necessarily part of the tubes?

PORTER: I think it very unlikely that glucose or glucose-6-phosphate finds its way into the cavities of the ER on the uptake side of metabolism. There is, in any case, no evidence of any continuity between pinocytotic vesicles and the ER. Transport of lipid and of fully formed proteins is indicated and presumably the limiting membrane functions in the sequestration of these if not in their synthesis.

ALLFREY: I am no morphologist but I am brash enough to think that one can answer this question on the penetration of substances into cells by the type of experiment that we have been doing with frog ovocytes. If you take a frog ovocyte and put it into a medium containing radioactive sodium and leucine and then do an autoradiograph, you find that the substance penetrates the nucleus without an apparent prior accumulation in the cytoplasm. We have checked this at a very early time, and it suggests that there is a direct connection between the medium and the membrane system around the nucleus, I would take the argument for transport very seriously.

PORTER: There are others who feel as you do about this, but where the examination of uptake has been studied with particulate materials which could be visualized afterwards in electron micrographs, no evidence could be found for the migration of particles from the outside into the cavities of the ER. It is conceivable that in this particular material, which Dr. Allfrey knows better than I, there are infoldings of the plasma membrane which reach to considerable depths into the cytoplasms of these cells, and function in transport. It is also possible, I suppose, that the metabolites he mentions move by unchannelled diffusion. If there is continuity between the internal phase of the endoplasmic reticulum and the cell's exterior, even intermittent continuity, and some uptake, it would mean that all manner of materials of the environment would be carried to the cell's interior and even to the surface of the nucleus. This would give the cell a substantial problem in sorting out the useful and rejecting the unuseful. Furthermore it seems to me as rather unlikely that a system obviously used for segregation and sequestration of products of synthesis would be designed to accept miscellaneous components of the environment.

JAGENDORF: I think there is one type of cellular synthesis which is not associated with these membranes. Dr. Beer now at Johns Hopkins has looked at stem collenchyma cells which continue to grow even after being secondarily thickened and his impression is that the new cellulose is deposited very much removed from the cell membrane.

PORTER: This is a possibility, of course, and I suppose there is no reason why cellulose precursors should not diffuse away from the cell surface before polymerization.

HESTRIN: When you see a vesicle in the vicinity of a cellulose fibre, the possibility must of course be considered that the fibre arose from the vesicle. This is not however the only possible explanation. In the case of a bacterium *Acetobacter xylinum*, cellulose occurs, at a distance from the cells and does not appear to be in necessary physical connection with the cells. It seems necessary to assume for this case that cellulose was excreted in the form of a diffusible particle and that fibre formation occurred in the medium by a process akin to crystallization, one might be allowed on a basis of analogy to speculate that within plant cells cellulose can also exist in a diffusible form.

PORTER: Well, in the first instance I should have emphasized, if I failed to, that this is strictly a morphological association which requires or asks for further investigation. I think you may agree, however, that the association of the ER with the cell surface is a selective one and is probably not without some significance. What it really means is, of course, not evident at this time. Now, in regard to the other point, I recognize that cellulose polymerization or crystallization can take place at points removed from the cell surface, but it was my impression that the polymerization is influenced by a factor that is heat-labile and probably enzymic and produced by the cell. One might expect it to act at the cell surface where liberated. Am I wrong in this?

HESTRIN: No other assumption can reasonably be made.

Pinocytosis

H. Holter

Carlsberg Laboratory, Copenhagen, Denmark

Dr. Porter's report has shown very clearly how intimately the endo-plasmic reticulum and its morphology are related to the problems of protein synthesis. The relevance of pinocytosis in this session is much more doubt-ful; but since my paper has been included here I shall try to make it as relevant as I can.

Perhaps I may be allowed, for the benefit of those who are not quite familiar with the process of pinocytosis, to recapitulate very briefly its main morphological features.

The term "pinocytosis", coined by Warren Lewis in 1931 [14], was originally intended to designate a process of active drinking by cells. In pinocytosis, fluid is taken up discontinuously, in droplets that are engulfed or sucked in by the cell, and the primary products of this activity are fluid-filled vacuoles or vesicles, by which a certain amount of the surrounding medium is transferred to the interior of the cell. Pinocytosis therefore amounts to an uptake of substances, but let me say at once that the term "uptake" should be understood primarily in a spatial sense, as long as the contents of the pinocytosis vesicles remain separated from the cyto-plasm by a vacuolar membrane; whether or not the process also amounts to an uptake in the physiological sense, depends therefore on the later fate of the vacuoles.

Morphologically, pinocytosis displays quite a variety in mechanism and a very wide range of dimensions. In tissue culture cells, the classical object, pinocytosis is brought about by the activity of membranous ruffle pseudo-podia which, by undulating movements, form folds that enclose a certain amount of fluid. The second variety of pinocytosis, very beautifully dis-played by amoebae, is that of invagination (Fig. 1). In this process the cell surface forms cavities, in extreme cases long narrow tubes, from which the pinocytosis vacuoles are pinched off. Pinocytosis by invagination is fairly variable with regard to the shape of the cavities formed, and extremely variable with regard to dimensions. In amoebae the average diameter of the primary pinocytosis vacuoles is about 1–2 μ, while in many other objects it is only discernible by means of the electron microscope, the diameter of the vesicles being from 100 Å upwards (Fig. 2).

Regardless of these differences in mechanism and dimensions, the morphologically essential feature is the same; a certain area of the surface membrane of the cell encloses a droplet of the surrounding medium, separates from the surface and migrates into the cell.

Another important feature of pinocytosis is that it does not occur in all media and all the time but is *induced* by the presence of certain substances in the medium. So far, the induction of pinocytosis has been studied most extensively in amoebae [13, 9, 5, 6] with regard to proteins, amino acids and certain salts. Typical non-inducers are, for instance, the

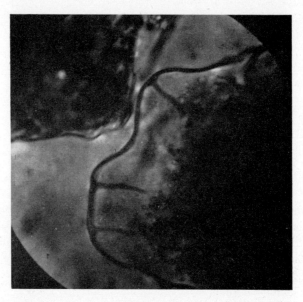

FIG. 1. Pinocytosis channels in *Amoeba proteus*, induced by 1·5% solution of bovine plasma albumin. (After Chapman-Andresen and Prescott [9].)

carbohydrates. Induction depends on the size of the molecule, pH and other factors connected with electric charge. In amoebae there seems to be a certain not very dramatic molecular specificity; but for mammalian cells at least one case of highly specific induction of pinocytosis has been reported, namely the action of insulin on HeLa cells [23] and adipose tissue [2].

The findings regarding pinocytosis induction support a hypothesis pronounced by Bennett [3] according to which one of the essential features of pinocytosis consists in the adsorption of molecules or ions to the cell surface membrane, followed by an invagination of the surface at the loaded area, a sliding of the membrane into the invagination. The first experimental support of this hypothesis came from papers by Brandt [4] and

Schumaker [27]. Brandt induced pinocytosis in amoebae by means of a fluorescent protein, and could directly demonstrate that a fluorescent film is adsorbed to the surface of the amoeba and that the same film coats the inside of the pinocytosis channels and pinocytosis vacuoles. Since then, other examples for the surface adsorption of pinocytosis-inducers have been found [21, 15]. With regard to the nature of the adsorbing sites the hypothesis has been advanced by Marshall, Schumaker, and Brandt [15] and by Chapman-Andresen [6] that they are furnished by the mucous coat that is known to occur at the surface not only of amoebae but of many, perhaps all, pinocytic cells. I believe that Dr. Marshall will tell you more about this problem.

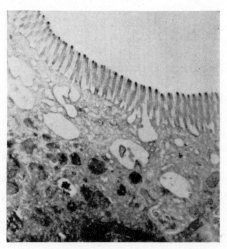

FIG. 2. Electron micrograph of jejenum of 3-day-old mouse (original magnification × 6500) showing pinocytic vesicles of varying size originating from the brush border. (After Clark and Wochner [9a].)

According to this well-supported hypothesis, therefore, we may assume that the adsorption of a suitable inducer brings about a surface reaction by which the adsorbed substance, *together* with some of the solvent, is transported into the cell. This is in good agreement with the morphological observations. The question is now: What is the physiological significance of such a process? Is the physiologically predominant feature of pinocytosis the specific uptake of the absorbed substance, often high-molecular, or is it the accompanying uptake of the fluid?

This question cannot be answered in a general way on the basis of our present knowledge. Important features of the process are certainly different after the induction, for instance, by salts and by proteins, and my personal guess is that different cells in different situations will be found to utilize the possibilities of pinocytosis for different physiological means.

However this may be, it is certain that pinocytosis can be a means of introducing certain substances, including proteins and amino acids, into vesicles that migrate into the cell interior. The next question is then: Are such substances available for the metabolism of the cell? This question is not only a figure of speech; we must not forget that many of the substances which have been found to enter by pinocytosis, are high-molecular compounds to which the cell membrane is assumed to be impermeable— the same membrane, in fact, which by the mechanism of invagination becomes the boundary of the pinocytosis vesicles. The properties of this membrane, therefore, and its possible changes inside the cell become the main problem in our understanding of the physiological significance of pinocytosis.

During the migration of the vesicles from the periphery toward the interior there occurs a rather intense dehydration which is often plainly discernible in time-lapse movies as a shrinkage of the vacuoles. However, just as often this process of shrinkage is counteracted or even overcompensated by another frequent occurrence, namely, the fusion of the original small vesicles to larger vacuoles, so that the actual view in the microscope usually presents an array of vacuoles of very different sizes. In spite of this, the actual occurrence of dehydration causing a concentration of the vacuolar contents was made rather probable by Marshall and myself [13] by means of centrifugation experiments in which we found that after pinocytosis the density of the pinocytosis vacuoles, identifiable as such by the content of a fluorescent marker, was steadily increasing.

Recently Roth [26] has published very interesting observations regarding the changes occurring in pinocytosis vacuoles after ingestion. He has shown that the vacuolar membrane displays a rather intense form of "internal micropinocytosis" by which, as he assumes, the contents of the primary vacuoles are distributed in the cytoplasm. Roth [26] also points to an important fact, which perhaps had not been sufficiently considered by previous authors: pinocytosis, and especially if repeated in a second step internally, results in an enormous increase of active internal surface available for diffusion. Chapman-Andresen and Nilsson [8] in our laboratory have found that this process of secondary micropinocytosis begins during channel formation (Fig. 3).

The only morphological change of the vacuolar membrane in amoebae that can be observed in the electron microscope is that the mucous coat that covers the plasmalemma and after invagination forms a lining on the inside of the pinocytosis vacuoles, disappears after some time. Müller and Rappay [16] have reported that the periodic acid-Schiff reaction which is given both by the plasmalemma and the vacuolar lining, disappears later on in the vacuole. In our laboratory [7] we studied the permeability of pinocytic vacuoles to radioactive glucose and have obtained evidence which we interpreted to indicate that the permeability of the vacuolar membrane is changed after interiorization, with the effect that at least some of the substances confined in the vacuoles can penetrate into the cytoplasm. How this penetration occurs, and whether or not it involves some sort of a breakdown, could not be decided by our experiments.

Thus, while there are some indications that a change in the membrane of the pinocytosis vacuole occurs during its migration to the interior of the

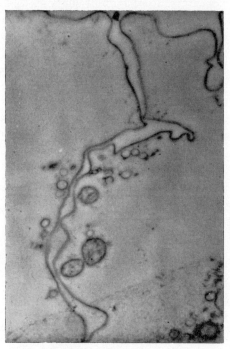

FIG. 3. Electron micrograph of pinocytosis channel in *Amoeba proteus*, showing micropinocytic vesicles and mitochondria close to the channel. (After Chapman-Andresen and Nilsson [8].)

cell we can from the evidence so far discussed derive no hint as to how this change might be brought about. I believe, however, that this question may be answered in time, when we know more about another problem of pinocytosis which I should now like to discuss. It concerns the relationship between pinocytosis vesicles and certain of the cytoplasmic structures inside the cell.

There are at present two main schools of thought regarding this question. One connects the pinocytosis vesicles with the *lysosomes*, the other with the *endoplasmic reticulum*, and I shall try very briefly to outline the two views.

The first important observation that ought to be mentioned in this connection was made by Rose [25] who in a strain of HeLa cells by means of a time-lapse film demonstrated that certain granules, which he called "micro-kinetospheres", actively make contact with newly ingested pinocytosis vacuoles, and fuse with them. He assumes that by this process certain enzymes are injected into the vesicles, and that this is a necessary condition for the later shrinkage and change in refraction index of the vesicles which he observes. Rose himself suggests that the microkinetospheres might be identical with the *lysosomes*.

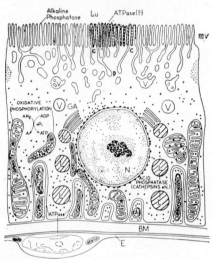

FIG. 4. Diagrammatic representation of a cell in the proximal convolution of the rat kidney. (After Novikoff [18].) Micropinocytosis vacuoles (p) are shown forming at the ends of the canalicular structures (c) extending into the cell between adjacent microvilli (mv) of the brush border. These are shown fusing into larger vacuoles (v), which are transformed into lysosomes (L). Other abbreviations are: A, oxidized substrate; ADP, adenosine diphosphate; AH_2, reduced substrate; ATP, adenosine triphosphate; ATPase, adenosine triphosphatase; BM, basement membrane; E, endothelial cell of blood capillary; GA, Golgi apparatus; N, nucleus; and Pi, orthophosphate.

Lysosomes were detected and named by deDuve and his coworkers [10] who have shown them to be the carriers of a whole array of hydrolytic enzymes and who assume that they are the main instruments of intracellular digestion. Rose's interpretation, that pre-existing lysosomes by fusion convey digestive enzymes to the pinocytic vesicles is certainly a very tempting one. It conflicts, however, to a certain degree with another point of view according to which the pinocytic vesicles are transformed into lysosomes. This point of view is held by Straus [29] who studied the uptake of peroxidase, a protein marked by its enzymic activity, and described its "segregation" into granules which he called phagosomes. Recently, [17, 18] Novikoff has devoted himself to the question of a possible connection between pinocytosis and lysosomes. His hypothesis is summarized in the diagram shown in Fig. 4, which he has kindly permitted me to use. According to this interpretation the lysosomes are *derived* from pinocytosis vacuoles and are regarded as the end products of their transformation inside the cell. The exact nature of this assumed transformation is not clear, and especially not the way in which the outfit of hydrolytic enzymes which defines the lysosomes, should be acquired. One interesting suggestion is based on the fact that at least one of the characteristic enzymes of lysosomes, namely acid phosphatase, has been found by Novikoff [18] to occur in those regions of the cell membrane of *Amoeba proteus*, to which food particles attach before engulfment. This might indicate that an essential feature of the formation of lysosomes is the transport of surface enzymes into the cell interior by means of pinocytosis, and this would of course tie in very nicely with Bennett's views on membrane flow from the surface into the cell.

Closely connected with the problem of a relation between pinocytosis vacuoles and lysosomes is probably the similar claim of a connection between pinocytosis vacuoles and mitochondria. This claim was put forward by Gey and his coworkers [11] and has recently been revived by Robineaux and Pinet [24] on the basis of their interference-microkine-photographic investigations of protein uptake by macrophages. It seems to me that the question is in reality one of being able morphologically to differentiate between lysosomes and mitochondria, which may be difficult without the aid of the electron microscope and cytochemical technique.

The other school of thought links the fate of the pinocytic vesicles to the endoplasmic reticulum. This goes back to the work of Palade [19] who claimed the continuity of the cell surface with the membrane system of the reticulum. I should like to present to you this view by means of another schematic diagram, taken with the author's kind permission, from Siekevitz's [28] Ciba lecture (Fig. 5).

The essential part of the diagram for us at the moment is that depicting the migration of pinocytic vesicles toward, and fusion with, the intracellular spaces of the endoplasmic reticulum. This process is an important feature of Bennett's [3] and Palade's [19] views regarding the connection between surface membrane and the endoplasmic reticulum, but its reality was not strictly proven and it is therefore also marked off as hypothetical in Siekevitz's diagram. Very recently, however, Palay [20] has described an example of the process. He studied fat absorption by the cells of the intestinal wall of rats, and found that fat droplets that enter these cells by means of pinocytic vesicles could be observed again as inclusions in the perinuclear space. If this observation can be shown to be valid (and we have learned from Dr. Porter's review that other interpretations are possible) then it would certainly seem to indicate the existence of a spatial continuity between pinocytic vesicles and the endoplasmic reticulum.

In Siekevitz's diagram two alternatives are given for the fate of the pinocytic vesicles. One is their fusion with the channels of the endoplasmic reticulum, discussed above, the other is their disappearance into the general cytoplasmic matrix. As we have seen, a third possibility would be their transformation into granular cell organelles, perhaps of the lysosome type. At present we cannot decide if only one of these possibilities is actually realized or if several processes operate at the same time, perhaps with shifting preponderance, according to the metabolic needs of the

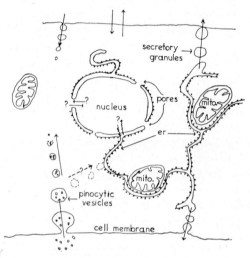

FIG. 5. Stylized representation of a cell, showing a channel of the endoplasmic reticulum (er) and its relation to the perinuclear space and pinocytic and secretory processes. (After Siekevitz [28].)

cell. All possibilities are highly interesting, but today the situation is not ripe for too-detailed speculation.

There is, however, another aspect of the matter that I should like to mention. It is well known that at least in amoeboid cells the process of pinocytosis has its counterpart in the vacuolar discharge of material. This is realized for instance in the filling up of the contractile vacuole [22] by fluid-filled vesicles that fuse with the main vacuole, and also, with certain morphological modifications, in the process of defaecation (Fig. 6). One might say that pinocytosis works both ways, and it has also been necessary to assume processes of inverted pinocytosis in several cases where pinocytosis was considered to mediate not only the introduction of substances *into* cells but also the transport of substances *through* cells. As depicted in

Siekevitz's diagram (Fig. 5) and as discussed in Dr. Porter's review, a similar process is generally assumed to occur in the discharge of secretion products formed in the endoplasmic reticulum. It would seem that the endoplasmic reticulum, if it really can be shown to form the link between the ingestion and secretion pathways of the cell, might provide a mechanism that could explain the selectivity of pinocytosis.

With regard to this problem of selectivity we are still very much in the dark. It is true that the process of surface adsorption prior to pinocytosis affords a specific enrichment of the adsorbed solute in the pinocytosis vacuoles. But this can cover only part of the problem. So far no one has been able to give a satisfactory answer to the question: What happens to

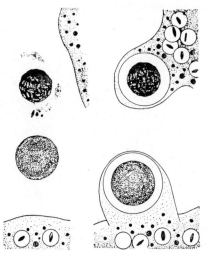

FIG. 6. Defaecation in amoebae. Two instances of defaecation. Above: food remnants; below: cluster of crystals. In both instances the vacuole is seen at the right, brought close to the surface in the tip of a short pseudopod. At the left, the objects have been expelled by rupture of the membrane and lie free in the medium. (After Andresen and Holter [1].)

substances which are dissolved in the fluid ingested together with the surface membrane and which are of no use, or even toxic, to the cell? There must be some opportunity for a highly specific process of discrimination somewhere, but it has not seemed very satisfactory to explain any high degree of discrimination on the basis of mere changes in the permeability of the vacuolar membrane. For this it seems necessary to assume the action of some sort of active transport mechanism in the interior of the cell, situated either at the membranes of the pinocytosis vesicles, or perhaps in the membrane system of the endoplasmic reticulum. Again the experimental evidence at the present time does not justify more than very tentative speculation on this important point.

The trouble is that most of the experimental work on pinocytosis so far has been done with amoebae, and in these organisms very little is known about an endoplasmic reticulum, if indeed there exists a recognizable equivalent of this organelle in the amoeba's constantly streaming cytoplasm. What we need is an experimental study of pinocytosis in some mammalian cells of well-known submicroscopic anatomy.

I should like to wind up by a short, but perhaps not wholly superfluous, discussion of terminological problems.

There is no doubt that pinocytosis is a word that at present enjoys a certain popular appeal, in marked contrast to the situation only a few years ago. Once in a while one cannot help being afraid that the label "pinocytosis" is applied without much regard to definition in many instances in which an actual evidence simply consists in the observation of vesicles of unknown origin. On the other hand many new names are being created—too many to mention here—and the revival of the Greek language has been quite considerable in an attempt to describe more or less specialized instances of phenomena that seem to be quite adequately covered by the two oldest and most widespread terms, namely phagocytosis and pinocytosis.

However, the real issue is whether or not even these two terms should be maintained as separate concepts. Personally I have repeatedly expressed the view [12] that there is no sharp delimitation between phagocytosis and pinocytosis, since the main difference seems not to be the mechanism of the process, but only the nature of the ingested material. The results of most investigations in the last years certainly seem to support the tendency of minimizing the difference between the various forms of surface invagination.

I have tried to present to you the present state of the pinocytosis problem, as it stands. It is a rapidly developing field, full of contradictions and unsolved questions. But nevertheless I feel that some progress has been made in the last years, and that some of the perspectives that have been opened up are of great interest for all branches of cell biology and therefore, in an indirect way perhaps, also relevant to the topics of this symposium.

References

1. Andresen, N., and Holter, H., *C. R. Lab. Carlsberg Sér. chim.* **25,** 107-146 (1944).
2. Barrnett, R. J., and Ball, E. G., *J. biophys. biochem. Cytol.* **8,** 83-101 (1960).
3. Bennett, S., *J. biophys. biochem. Cytol.* **2,** Part 2 *Suppl.* 99-103 (1956).
4. Brandt, P. W., *Exp. Cell Res.* **15,** 300-313 (1958).
5. Chapman-Andresen, C., *C. R. Lab. Carlsberg.* **31,** 77-92 (1958).
6. Chapman-Andresen, C., "Proceedings of Symposium of Society for Cell Biology", Paris (1960).

7. Chapman-Andresen, C., and Holter, H., *Exp. Cell. Res.* Suppl. **3,** 52-63 (1955).
8. Chapman-Andresen, C., and Nilsson, J. R., *Exp. Cell Res.* **19,** 631-633 (1960).
9. Chapman-Andresen, C., and Prescott, D. M., *C. R. Lab. Carlsberg, Sér. chim.* **30,** 57-78 (1956).
9a. Clark, S. L., Jr., and Wochner, D., *Anat. Rec.* **130,** 286 (1958).
10. deDuve, Chr., *in* "Subcellular Particles", ed. T. Hayashi. Ronald Press, New York, 128-159 (1959).
11. Gey, G. O., Shapras, P., and Barysko, E., *Ann. N.Y. Acad. Sci.* **58,** 1089 (1954).
12. Holter, H., *in* "Internation. Review of Cytology", Vol. 8, ed. G. H. Bourne and J. F. Danielli. Academic Press, New York, 481-504 (1959).
13. Holter, H., and Marshall, J. M., Jr., *C. R. Lab. Carlsberg Sér chim.* **29,** 7-26 (1954).
14. Lewis, W. H., *Johns Hopk. Hosp. Bull.* **49,** 17-28 (1931).
15. Marshall, J. M., Jr., Schumaker, V. N., and Brandt, P. W., *Ann. N.Y. Acad. Sci.* **78,** 515-523 (1958).
16. Müller, M., and Rappay, G., *Mag. Tud. Akad. Biol. Csoport.Kozl.* **3,** 81-86 (1959).
17. Novikoff, A. B., *in* "Developing Cell Systems and Their Control", ed. D. Rudnick. Ronald Press, New York (1960).
18. Novikoff, A. B., *in* "Biology of Pyelonephritis", ed. E. Quinn and E. Kass. Little, Brown and Co., Boston (1960).
19. Palade, G. E., *J. biophys. biochem. Cytol.* **2,** Suppl. 85 (1956).
20. Palay, S. L., *J. biophys. biochem. Cytol.* **7,** 391-392 (1960).
21. Pappas, G. D., *10th Int. Congr. Cell Biol.* 94-95 (1960).
22. Pappas, G. D., and Brandt, P. W., *J. biophys. biochem. Cytol.* **4,** 485-488 (1958).
23. Paul, J., *J. biophys. biochem. Cytol.* **8,** 83-101 (1960).
24. Robineaux, R., and Pinet, J., *Ciba Foundation Symposium on Cellular Aspects of Immunity* **I,** 5 (1959).
25. Rose, G. G., *J. biophys. biochem. Cytol.* **3,** 697-704 (1957).
26. Roth, L. E., *J. Protozoology* **7,** 176-185 (1960).
27. Schumaker, V. N., *Exp. Cell. Res.* **15,** 314 (1958).
28. Siekevitz, P., *Ciba Foundation Symposium on Cell Metabolism* 17-49 (1959).
29. Straus, W., *J. biophys. biochem. Cytol.* **4,** 541-550 (1958).

Discussion

DORFMAN: I would like to mention one thing that may have some connection, somewhat far fetched, relating to the biosynthesis of the membrane, and that is in the case of our study of the synthesis of polyuronic acid in bacteria. We have been able to localize the enzyme of the final polymerization in the cells of the protoplast membrane, which can be prepared pure. There is no RNA left in them and thus this membrane is serving a function similar to the endoplasmic reticulum in the cells that Dr. Holter suggested. I just wonder whether in this question of transport if it isn't only the final polymerization of the macromolecules that is occurring at this anatomically localized site because all the other enzymic activities required to form the uridine nucleotides are all perfectly soluble and removed. It is only the final polymerizing reaction that is localized to these membranes.

CAMPBELL: I would like to ask about the possibility of whether the lysosomes are derived from the pinocytotic vesicles. I think it is shown from the work of

Coons that proteins do certainly get inside the cell intact. Now if they go in by pinocytosis then we know also from the work of Simpson and Steinberg in the States, that the breakdown of these proteins takes place by perhaps a reversal of protein synthesis, that is to say not by proteolytic enzymes. As the lysosomes are suicide squads containing proteolytic enzymes, it seems unlikely that the intact proteins are broken down in the lysosomes. On this basis the lysosomes would not be derived from pinocytotic vesicles.

HOLTER: I quite agree and I think it is one of the main objections to the whole lysosome theory, but I just wanted to present the views that have been suggested. What we really need to do is to reconcile the vacuolar membrane with the evidence for uptake of high molecular substances which have been claimed to enter the cytoplasm even without loss of their antigenic properties. To explain this we need to get rid of the membrane barrier somehow. There are people who just assume that the membrane of the pinocytic vesicles disappears, so that their contents are released into the cytoplasm. But clear evidence for this is lacking. In amoebae we have never been able to see the membrane disappear and I understand from Dr. Porter that also the other instances in which such a membrane has been reported to disappear are doubtful on technical grounds. So this is one of the many problems that are still open.

DAVIS: I would like to mention an observation which may possibly throw light on this problem. At Harvard Medical School Manfred Karnovsky has been studying the metabolic effects of phagocytosis, and has found that the process of engulfing particles markedly stimulates the rate of incorporation of phosphate into phospholipid. This suggests that the material of the membrane is turning over.

HOLTER: Yes, I know that work, and I would also like to mention that, if I remember correctly, the author regards the resynthesis of membrane as the limiting factor for the duration of the phagocytic activity. Furthermore, this paper is the only one I know of where the energetics of such processes have been considered. It is work of that kind that we badly need also in pinocytosis investigations.

LOOMIS: I was wondering if the disappearance of the nuclear membrane during mitosis casts any light on how membranes can disappear and reappear.

HOLTER: I don't know. Do you?

PORTER: Well, the observations available suggest that it simply fragments into a lot of smaller vesicles without any decrease or increase in the total area of the membrane involved.

The Ergastoplasm in the Mammary Gland and Its Tumours:
An Electron Microscope Study with Special Reference to Caspersson's and Santesson's A and B Cells

F. Haguenau and K. H. Hollmann

*Laboratoire de Médecine Expérimentale du Collège de France,
Paris, France*

To all cytologists nowadays, the ergastoplasm is a well-defined entity, the ultrastructure of which may be considered as characteristic ([1, 2], and Porter this volume). Its particular importance lies in the fact that it corresponds to the cytoplasmic nucleic acid (RNA) and is directly involved in protein synthesis. In spite of much knowledge acquired during the last few years the meaning of some ultrastructural aspects of ergastoplasm still escapes our understanding. It is our purpose, by taking the example of the mammary gland, to comment upon these aspects because though they are mentioned and acknowledged by many they have not yet sufficiently been put forward.

At the onset we wish very briefly to go back to the question of nomenclature. Contrary to what might have been expected from the confused situation which reigned at the beginning, agreement has been reached between cytologists and, most of the time, the same terms are being used now to design the same constituents:

Ergastoplasm: System of intracytoplasmic membranes characterized by the presence of granules attached to its outer surface.

"Organized" Ergastoplasm: Such a system when abundant and more or less arranged in parallel array.

"Endoplasmic Reticulum": Membrane component of this system (continuous with other intracytoplasmic membranous organelles in the cell especially the Golgi apparatus).

Ribonucleoprotein granules (RNP-granules, "Ribosomes"): The granular component of ergastoplasm either membrane-attached or isolated in the ground cytoplasm. The following diagram will be helpful:

G*

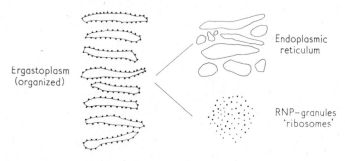

FIG. 1.

It is the relationship, if any, between one form and the other, in particular that of "organized ergastoplasm" to RNP-granules which is not clear and that we will now consider in the mammary gland and specially in its cancers.

1. Ergastoplasm in the normal mammary gland

Classic cytologists long ago discovered ergastoplasm in the mammary gland and described the strongly basophilic filaments present in great amount at the basis of the secretory cell [3, 4] and Fig. 2(a). This basophilia disappears under the action of ribonuclease and the reaction is greater during the first phase of the secretory cycle. It then decreases to appear again with reconstitution of the alveolar cells. The various changes occurring in ergastoplasm are also easily followed in the fluorescent microscope after acridine orange staining.

In the electron microscope, development of the ergastoplasm during the lactation period is remarkable (Fig. 2(b)). Its order and ultrastructure are characteristic. Ribonucleoprotein particles are regularly arranged at the surface of the membrane system of the endoplasmic reticulum which itself is organized in parallel lamellae (Figs. 3 and 4). This "organization" in parallel array is one of the essential features of the ergastoplasm at that stage. Only when ergastoplasm is found in this "organized" form does elaboration of milk occur.

The ultrastructural details of the secretion have been described in two recent studies in the rat [5] and in the mouse [6].

It has been shown that milk secretion in these species is made up of at least two morphologically distinct elements probably corresponding to protein secretion for the one and to lipid secretion for the other. The topographical relationship between lipid secretion and definite cell organelles is still under discussion while on the contrary, formation of protein granules appears clearly related to the Golgi complex. Indeed it is exclusively in the Golgi vacuoles that these granules are found before they break out into the granular lumen (see Fig. 8).

The part played by the ergastoplasm in the elaboration of these protein granules is not clear [5, 6]. All our present knowledge, however, indicates that its role is fundamental.

This interpretation is based on : (1) the continuity which exists between ergastoplasm and Golgi apparatus, the whole membrane system of which constitutes the endoplasmic reticulum; (2) the enzymic studies of the

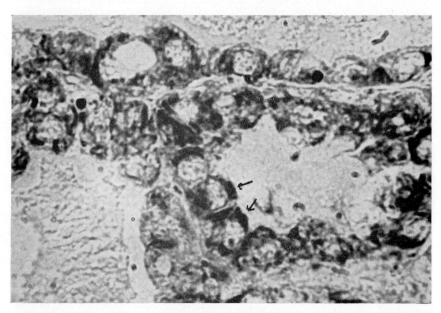

FIG. 2(*a*). Lactating mammary gland. Aspect of ergastoplasm in the light microscope. After toluidine blue staining it appears as dense basophilic masses (→) × 1600.

Rockefeller School in particular, which have shown that in the pancreas the same enzymes were present in the RNP-granules and in the final secretion granule [7a].

The first fact, the continuity of the membrane system is established now in a sufficient number of different types of mammalian cells to be considered as valid for all types of cells ([1], and Porter in this symposium).

The second fact is not yet biochemically demonstrated for glandular organs other than pancreas but the similarity of the ultrastructural pattern of all secretory cells studied up to now is strong indication that comparable mechanisms are involved in all cases.

On morphological grounds on the other hand, evidence is not easy to

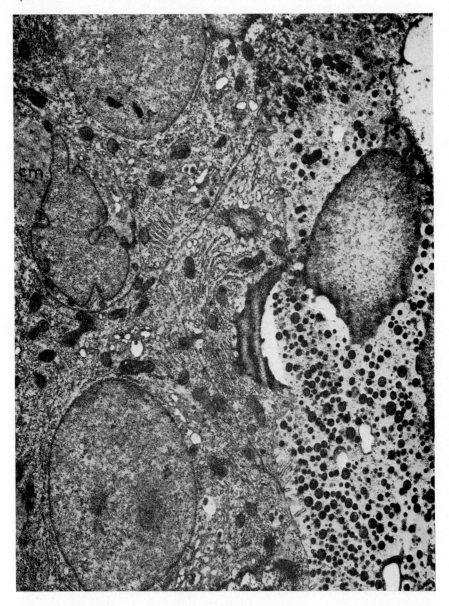

FIG. 2(b). Electron microscope aspect of a lactating mammary gland at the peak of its activity. At right glandular lumen filled with secretion product (numerous small protein granules and large lipid droplets). Note the typical parallel arrangement of the "organized" ergastoplasm in the cytoplasm of the glandular cells. In contrast, the myoepithelial cell (cm), not concerned with secretion, contains no ergastoplasm. × 7100.

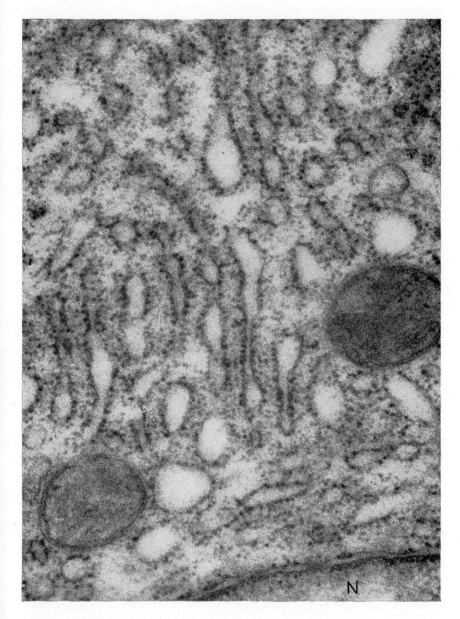

FIG. 3. Higher magnification of ergastoplasm in the cell of a lactating mammary gland. " Organized" ergastoplasm is typically made of RNP-granules attached to the surface of the endoplasmic reticulum, N = nucleus. × 51 500.

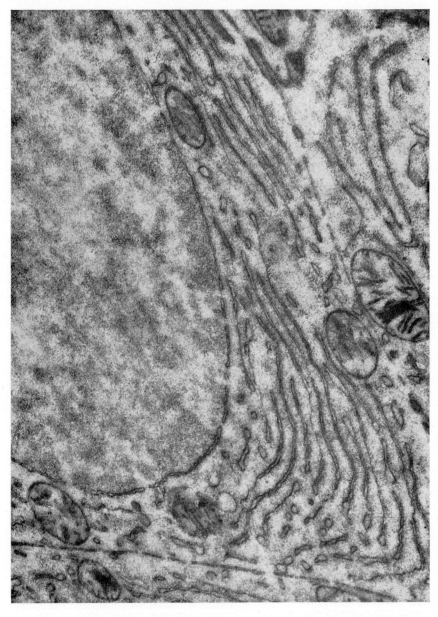

FIG. 4. Another aspect of ergastoplasm in the cell of a lactating mammary gland, to demonstrate parallel array of "organized" ergastoplasm. Here fixation with KMnO$_4$ has not preserved the RNP-granules. × 34 000.

provide. It must be pointed out that even in the case of the pancreas, the morphological demonstration of a relation between ergastoplasm and protein granules is restricted to the one example of guinea-pig pancreas [7].

Likewise in the mammary gland, aspects showing this relationship are exceptional. It is in one pathological case only that an example could be found where protein granules had accumulated in the lamellar system of the ergastoplasm (Fig. 5). When such images are found however they lead to the belief that protein elaboration may take place in the RNP-granules bordering the membrane of the endoplasmic reticulum and that secreted products then proceed towards the Golgi apparatus where they will take on their final form. Siekevitz [8, 9] has elegantly developed the matter.

When the mammary gland enters the involution phase which follows its active secretory phase, the reduction of the alveolar trunk is spectacular and similar to that of the virgin gland. Its ultrastructural counterpart, likewise is striking. The rare persisting ducts or buds are lined with mono-tonous-looking cells. The nuclei are shrunken, the cytoplasm clear, hardly containing under-developed organelles. The ergastoplasm in particular is now only represented by rare dispersed RNP-granules or isolated dotted membranes. Not only is this decrease quantitative but from the special ultrastructural point of view with which we are concerned, the ergasto-plasm has not retained the lamellar organization which was characteristic of active secretion and under this form it has disappeared together with the secretion granules themselves (Fig. 6).

Though this remarkable arrangement of the ergastoplasm has always been noted and described, its absolute relation to actual secretory activity has not been specially emphasized. Yet it is striking. If one creates con-ditions in which the physiological secretion is modified as under the influence of hormones in the case of the mammary gland this organization typical at first (Fig. 2) does not persist in the absence of sucking and is disrupted after prolonged stimulation (Fig. 8).

2. The ergastoplasm in cancer of the mammary gland

The bond between normal secretion and presence of parallel-organized ergastoplasm is further demonstrated if tumours are studied.

It is most striking that in over 100 cases of *human* breast cancer studied in the electron microscope [10, 11] none has been found where ergasto-plasm organized in parallel array was present in noticeable amount. There has been one exception to the rule only (Fig. 9), but in this case so many other features were aberrant [12] that it cannot be taken into account in the present discussion. The rarity of ergastoplasm under this form is here again linked to absence of the normal physiological secretion. Other secretion products may be found in these cancerous cells such as

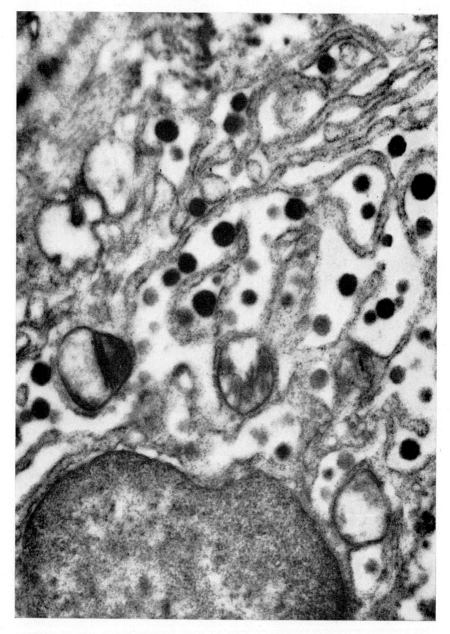

Fig. 5. Protein granules in the cisternae of ergastoplasm in a human cancer cell. This is a very rare finding. × 36 000.

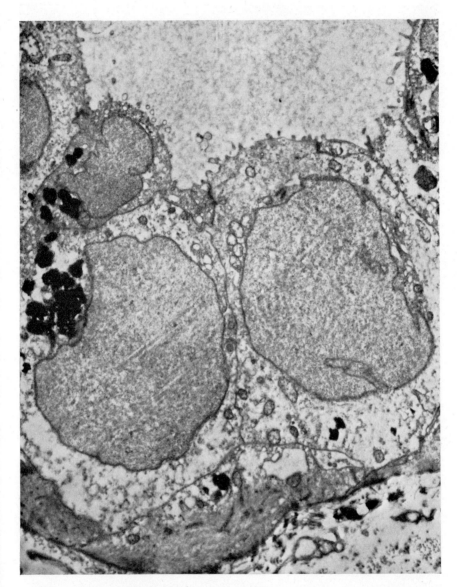

FIG. 6. Typical aspect of virgin gland cells in the mouse to show the absence of "organized" ergastoplasm and even the rarity of RNP-granules. In the upper part of the picture is the lumen whilst at the base of the glandular cells is a myo-epithelial cell. × 10 100.

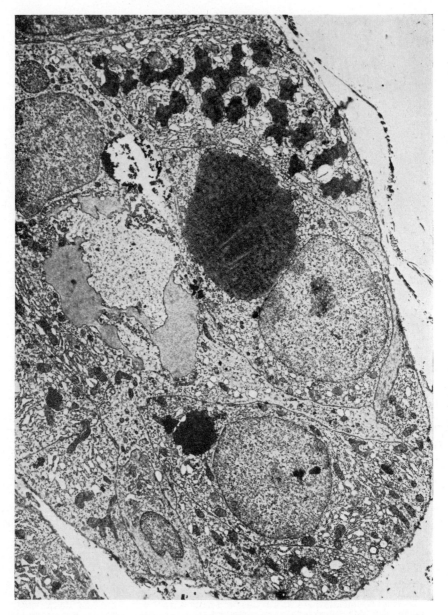

FIG. 7. Low power view of a whole acinus in a virgin mammary gland after 48 days oestrogen stimulation. "Organized" ergastoplasm is still present but lipidic storage is conspicuous. × 7000.

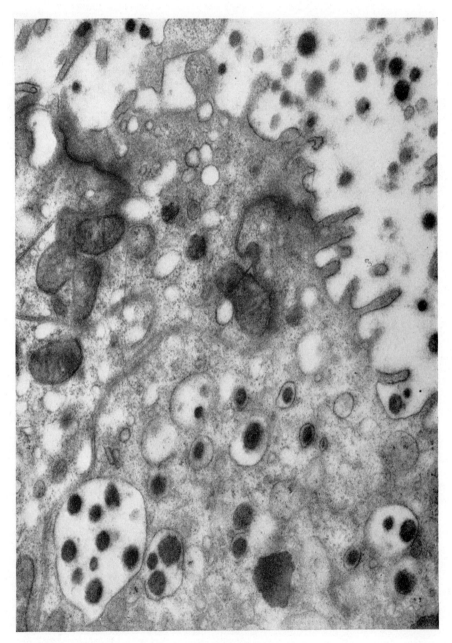

FIG. 8. Similar experimental conditions but at a later stage. "Organized" ergastoplasm has been disrupted and only RNP-granules are present. Note the typical localization of protein granules in Golgi vacuoles. × 28 250.

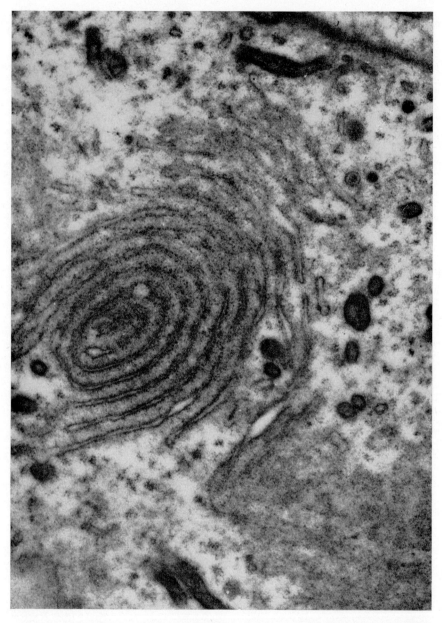

FIG. 9. Large amount of "organized" ergastoplasm in one case of human cancer, a rare finding. The granular mass at bottom right corresponds to a tangential section; only the surface RNP-granules have been concerned by it, while transverse sections show both the membrane and granular constituents of ergastoplasm. Intermediate aspects are easily followed in this picture. × 26 000.

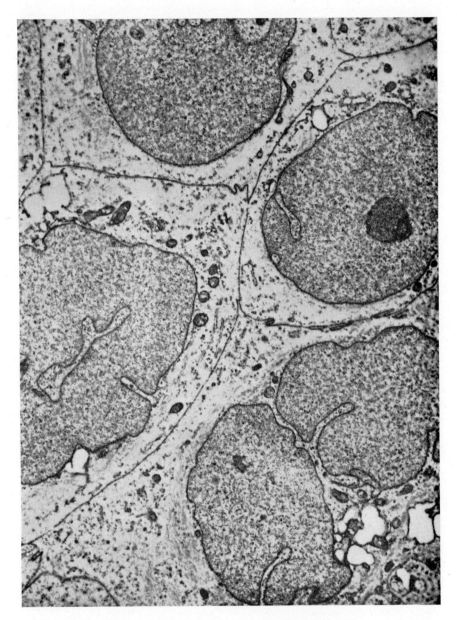

FIG. 10. Human mammary carcinoma. An example of one of the most frequent aspects. The cytoplasm is almost devoid of ergastoplasm and other organelles. These cells correspond to the B type of Caspersson and Santesson. × 3950.

lipid droplets for instance but these are not accompanied by the typical arrangement referred to here. On the whole, ergastoplasm in human breast cancer is not abundant and is not present in its "organized" form (Fig. 10).

This description, however, would lead to an erroneous representation were it not completed by another important feature directly related to the problem of nucleic acids in cancer cells. This concerns the A and B types of cells described by Caspersson and Santesson [13] in the course of their studies with ultraviolet absorption technique. These two basic types of cells were characterized by, the A cell "a well-developed cytoplasmic protein-forming system", the B cell, "a nucleolar apparatus showing signs of intense function but practically none of protein or nucleic acid formation in the cytoplasm" (Caspersson [14], pp. 142-145) (Fig. 11).

Other authors have confirmed this description though often using a different appellation for the two types of cells [15, 16, 17, 18]. Their existence is important since a relation could be established between the type of cells present in tumours and sensitivity to radiation [15, 17, 18, 19, 20, 21, 22]. The consequences of this from a prognostic as well as a therapeutic point of view would justify greater development but would lead us into the whole chapter of the relation between irradiation, growth, differentiation, ageing and death of the cell.

What matters to us here is that in the electron microscope, two types of cells corresponding roughly to those originally described by Caspersson and Santesson may be readily observed [10, 11] (Fig. 12).

Though a simultaneous spectrophotometric and electron microscopic study of the same cells has still not been achieved, parallel cytochemical studies (methyl-green-pyronin and fluorescent acridine orange stains) leave little place for doubt on the subject.

Though A cells are formed in all types of cancer studied in the electron microscope so far, they are particularly noticeable in breast cancers. Not all of these contain them nor are they present in cancers only. They can be observed in hormone-stimulated glands or in benign tumours. In this case their number is always small and their localization at the periphery of a lobule. This corresponds to the typical localization noticed by Caspersson and Santesson. In breast cancers, however, not only can their number be greatly increased but the peripheral arrangement is no longer respected.

In the electron microscope the morphological characteristics of A and

---

FIG. 11. A and B cells in human mammary cancers as seen in the ultraviolet microscope. The difference of absorption at 2570 Å wavelength is very obvious between the two types of cells. × 770 and × 550.

(By courtesy of Prof. T. O. Caspersson)

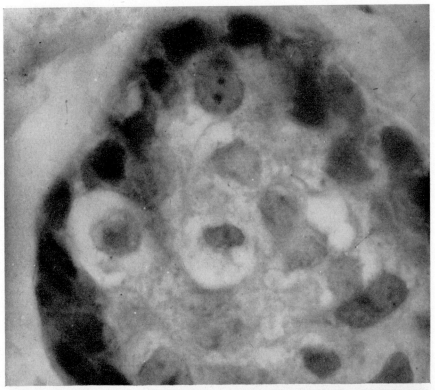

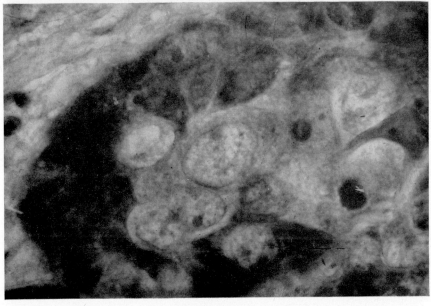

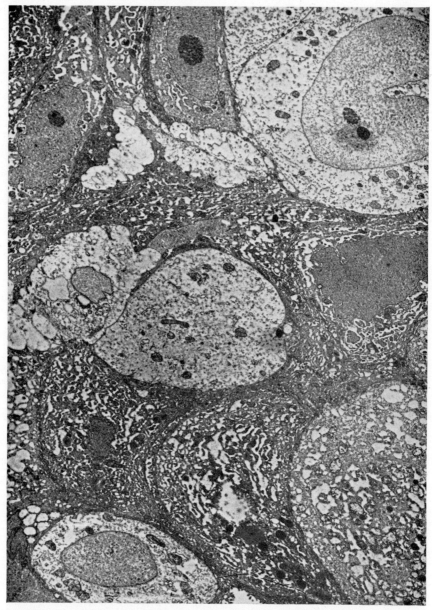

FIG. 12. Low power view of a human cancer rich in A and B cells to show their intrication. The B cells have a clear cytoplasm with almost no ergastoplasm, and a voluminous spherical-shaped nucleus with prominent nucleolus. The A cells contain a much denser nucleus with festooned limits. Ergastoplasm is abundant and totally disorganized. In the particular example here vacuolation is marked. This aspect possibly corresponds to necrosis. × 4300.

B cells correspond to Caspersson and Santesson's original description, and refinement of criteria allows better detection, better study of their repartition and lays stress on the importance of all intermediate aspects between the two A and B extreme types (Transitional T cells of Gusberg *et al.* [18] Towell [22] (Fig. 14).

Neither the B (Fig. 10) nor the intermediate (Fig. 14) type of cell which constitute the bulk of the tumour will concern us in the following description because they have been referred to in the first part of this paper and it has been shown that their ergastoplasm is not particularly developed and not typically organized.

The A type of cell, on the contrary will be described in detail because of its richness in ergastoplasm which corresponds to the high content of cytoplasmic RNA found with the ultraviolet absorption technique. Their ultrastructural appearance is striking (Figs. 12, 13, 15, 16). Usually smaller than adjacent cells they are often sharply edged, and when not at the periphery, wedged in between the other cells. They contrast with these by the remarkable density of both their nucleus and their cytoplasm.

The nucleus is characteristic, its chromatin is coarse and mottled, its limits festooned. In the cytoplasm, the ergastoplasm is densely packed and present either in its unorganized form of numerous RNP-granules or organized in a lamellar system. This latter organization, however, is distinct from that of the normal array mentioned above and related to physiological secretion. No regularity is found in the repartition of the RNP-granules along the membranes and the parallel arrangement of these is not regular either (Figs. 13, 15). Distension of the interlamellar space is often conspicuous and in many A types of cells is so marked that a lace-like pattern is outlined (Fig. 16). These cells appear vacuolated and since their nuclei are often shrunken as well, they easily evoke the picture of a degenerating necrotic cell. It is therefore impossible, on an ultrastructural basis to decide whether the typical A type of cell corresponds to a young, still undifferentiated element as believed by most or whether it is not simply a necrotic cell.

It is not the place here to argue about the matter. The important notion is that two different types of cells at least have been detected with spectrophotometric and staining techniques and are detected again in the electron microscope. Whether they are absolutely identical with the A and B cells of Caspersson and Santesson and whether they represent young or aged elements is fundamental only to explain their significance. If this could be understood, it is possible that great advances would be achieved in ultrastructural cytology of cancer because the great development of A cells in some neoplasms represents the only ultrastructural characteristic common to different types of cancer. Indeed there is no difference between some A type cells observed in adenocarcinoma of the breast and those

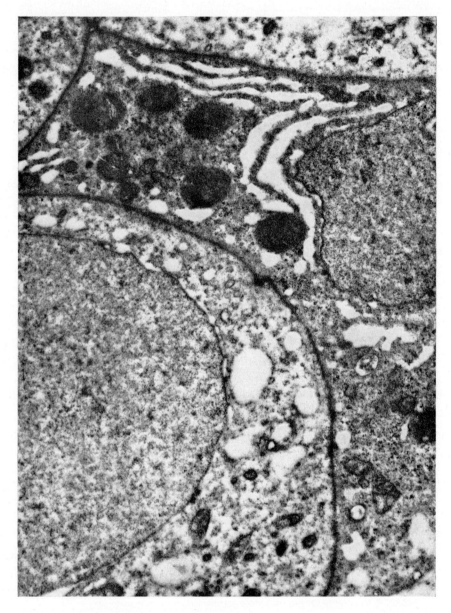

FIG. 13. Detail of an A type of cell wedged in between two "B" cells. Note the density and irregularity of ergastoplasm pattern. × 22 500.

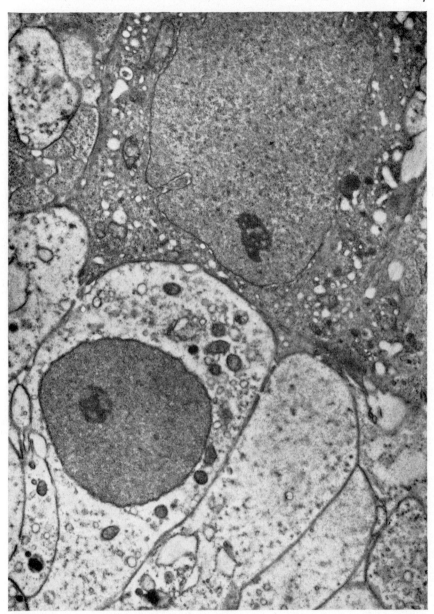

Fig. 14. Two different adjacent types of cells. At bottom a "B" cell with clear cytoplasm contrasts with a dense cell, the cytoplasm of which contains many RNP-granules. This is not a typical "A" cell, because the nucleus is not festooned and the nucleolus is still conspicuous but coarseness of chromatin is incipient. This cell may be considered as intermediate between the A and B "extreme" types. × 12 250.

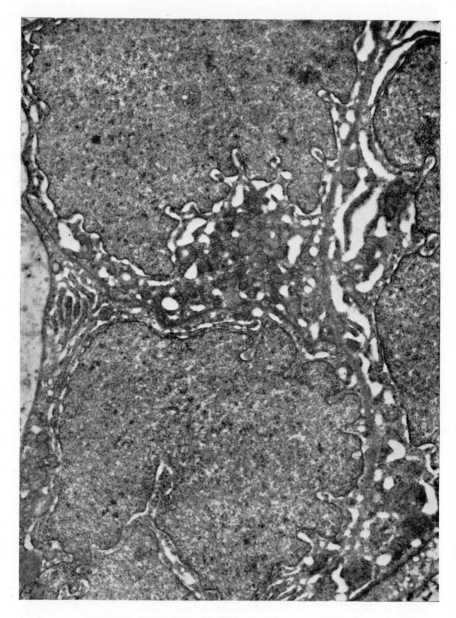

FIG. 15. "A" type of cells in human mammary cancer. Note their dense aspect, the coarseness of chromatin granules, the festooned limits of the nuclei and the abundance of peculiar ergastoplasm in the cytoplasm. × 26 000.

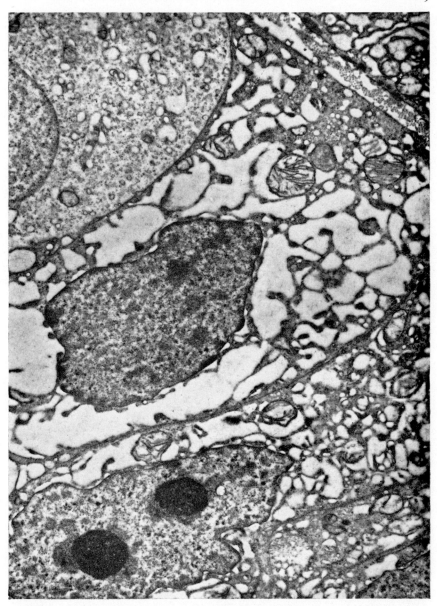

FIG. 16. Another aspect of A cells in a human mammary carcinoma. Here again the granularity of chromatin is evident. Ergastoplasm is restricted only to cytoplasmic remnants due to distension of its channels. This intense vacuolization leads to a lace-like pattern and probably corresponds as in Fig. 12 to necrosis. At upper left a "B" cell with normal cytoplasm shows that preservation of the preparation cannot be responsible for the lace-like aspect. × 7200.

observed for example in hepatoma (unpublished data) or in uterine cervix cancer (Hinglais-Guillaud, pers. comm.).

In experimentally induced mammary tumours cells of the *mouse* and of the *rat* ergastoplasm is again never found in its typical organized form as will be developed now.

The mammary neoplasms of these rodents have been studied in the electron microscope almost uniquely from the angle of their possible viral aetiology. Most of these papers, concerned with virus detection (Bittner agent in the mouse), mention only briefly if at all the general histological aspect of the tumour or the characteristics of the constituting cells.

But if one concentrates on this aspect, one observes that no "organized ergastoplasm" is to be found in these cells where no lactation occurs. Ergastoplasm is present mostly under the form of RNP-granules, abundant in some cells, sparse in others (Figs. 17, 18). Not only are these cells rapidly dividing but also they are deeply involved in virus formation as evidenced by the presence of virus particles both mature (in the acinar lumen) and in the process of formation (at the cellular membrane) (Fig. 18).

In the rat, likewise, mammary tumours are devoid of "organized ergastoplasm" (Fig. 19). There also, it is possible that virus formation occurs since elements have been discovered in the electron microscope [23] which from their morphology could be virus particles. The role they play in the aetiology of the tumour has not yet been established.

From all these observations on the ergastoplasm of the mammary gland cell the following conclusions may be drawn.

(1) In the normal gland, typical "organized" ergastoplasm is characteristically related to physiological secretion. It is an attribute of the normal lactating cell.

(2) In experimentally induced tumours, ergastoplasm is found mainly under a "non-organized" form, principally RNP-granules [1, 24].

These thus appear to be related to rapid cell replication or to forms of protein synthesis other than normal secretion, virus formation in particular. Such aspects of ergastoplasm are also characteristic of embryonic cells which produce protein but do not excrete it. These have been termed "retaining cells" by Birbeck and Mercer in a recent paper [25].

(3) In human mammary tumours, most cells also contain ergastoplasm in the form of RNP-granules or scattered dotted membranes and this ergastoplasm is not on the whole, particularly abundant (B and transitional types of cells). In some less numerous cells however (A cells of Caspersson and Santesson) ergastoplasm is remarkably dense and its pattern of a peculiar type not related to the specific tissue of origin. The significance of these cells is not yet known but they merit further intensive examination

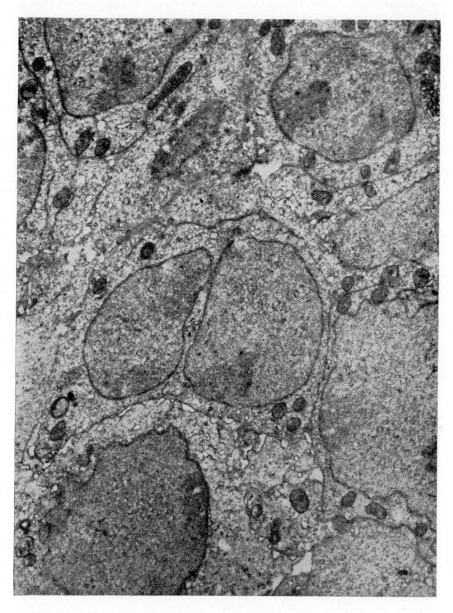

FIG. 17. Mammary tumour of the mouse. Low power view of a few cells to illustrate the absence of "organized" ergastoplasm. Free RNP-granules are widely scattered in the cytoplasm. × 21 500.

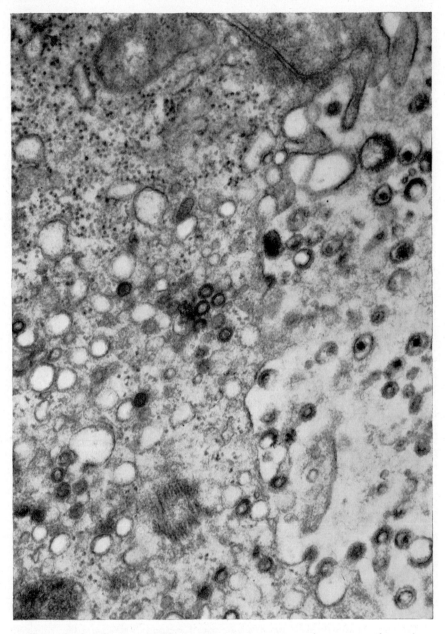

FIG. 18. Another aspect of mouse mammary tumour in an area where virus formation occurs (Bittner agent). Note at this higher magnification the numerous RNP-granules and the lack of organized ergastoplasm. × 59 000.

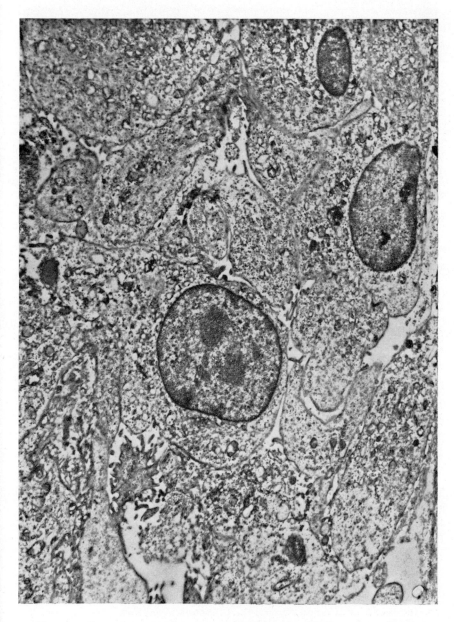

FIG. 19. General aspect of a rat mammary tumour (G.6) to show abundance of RNP-granules and absence of the membranes component of ergastoplasm. × 6400.

H

since they are found in human cancers of varied origin and thus correspond to a distinctive ultrastructural pattern common to all of these.

Furthermore a relationship exists between the presence of A cells in a tumour and its radiosensitivity. These cells thus may be of important prognostic value.

Acknowledgments

Work referred to in this paper has been aided by Grant C-4602 of the U.S. Public Health Service. Figure 11 is due to the courtesy of Prof. T. O. Caspersson.

References

1. Haguenau, F. *in* "International Review of Cytology" Vol. 7, ed. G. H. Bourne and J. F. Danielli. Academic Press, New York, 425-483 (1958).
2. Carasso, N. and Favard, P., *in* "Traité de Microscopie Electronique" (Magnan C. ed.) 1961 Paris, Hermann Publ.
3. Rauber, A., *Schmidt's Jb.* **182,** 7-8 (1879) (quoted after Dabelow *Hdb. Mikr. Anat.* III/**3,** 277-488 (1957).
4. Limon, M., *Anat. physiol.* **38,** 14-34 (1902).
5. Bargmann, W., and Knoop, A., *Z. Zellforsch.* **49,** 344-388 (1959).
6. Hollmann, K. H., *J. Ultrastruct. Res.* **2,** 423-443. (1959).
7. Palade, G. E., and Siekevitz, P., *J. biophys. biochem. Cytol.* **25,** 671-690 (1956).
7a. Siekevitz, P. and Palade, G. E., *J. biophys. biochem. Cytol.* **4,** 309-318 1958
8. Siekevitz, P., *Ciba Symp. on Cell Metabolism* 17-45 (1959).
9. Siekevitz, P., *Exp. Cell. Res. suppl.* **7,** 90-110 (1959).
10. Haguenau, F., *Bull. Cancer,* **46,** 177-211 (1959).
11. Haguenau, F., *Path. Biol.* **7,** 989-1015 (1959).
12. Haguenau, F., *C. R. Acad. Sci., Paris* **249,** 182-184 (1959).
13. Caspersson, T. O., and Santesson, L., *Acta Radiol.* XLVI *Suppl.* 5 (1942).
14. Caspersson, T. O., "Cell Growth and Cell Function. A Cytochemical Study". (1950) New York. W. J. Norton.
15. Barigozzi, C., and Dellepiane, G., *Rass. Oncologia* **22,** 1 (1948).
16. Cusmano, L., *Tumori* **21,** 107-121 (1947).
17. Cusmano, L., *Ibid.* **23,** 63-85 (1949).
18. Gusberg, S. B., Tovell, H. M. M., Long, M., and Hill, J. *Ann. N.Y. Acad. Sci.* **63,** 1147-1157 (1956).
19. Cornil, L., and Stahl, A., *C. R. Soc. Biol.* **144,** 1075-1077 (1950).
20. Cornil, L., and Stahl, A., *Pr. méd.* **59,** 933-935 (1951).
21. Gricouroff, G., *Pr. méd.* **64,** 137-139 (1956).
22. Towell, A. M. M., *Cancer. Res.* **20,** 297-306 (1960).
23. Hollmann, K. H., and Riviere, M. R., *Bull. Cancer,* **46,** 336-346 (1959).
24. Howatson, A. F., Ham, A. W., *Cancer Res.* **15,** 62-69 (1955).
25. Birbeck, M. S. C., and Mercer, E. H., *Nature, Lond.* **189,** 558-560 1961.

The External Secretion of the Pancreas as a Whole and the Communication between the Endoplasmic Reticulum and the Golgi Bodies*

GOTTWALT CHRISTIAN HIRSCH

Zoologisches Institut,
Göttingen, Germany

I have only a few remarks to make here: about logical basis of methods, about the external secretion of the pancreas as a whole, and about the "missing link" between the endoplasmic reticulum and the work of the Golgi bodies.

1. The logical basis of methods

The external secretion of the pancreas—as perhaps every kind of secretion—may be compared with the production of a factory [71, 101]: in both cases raw material comes in and products of the factory go out. Between these two events lies the synthesis of a particular product. This production flows through a cell in a way which may be compared to an "assembly line", because the synthesis of the particular product does not take place in one structure of the cell, but gradually in different places and structural parts of the cell, and in a particular order step by step. Naturally, this comparison between an "assembly line" and secretion has limitations [71]: the cell has no conveyor belts or rollers. But there is a movement of material step by step, from one cell structure to another, carrying the slowly developing product along. There are structures which, furthermore, approximately portray the workers on an assembly line: for instance the ribosomes, the endoplasmic reticulum, the Golgi field. Finally there are other cell structures which produce materials which are then moved to the place on the assembly line where they are biochemically necessary: for instance, the mitochondria and the cell nucleus.

It is the task of integrated structural and biochemical studies to observe the order of occurrence in the processes of secretion. With every new technique new observations, microscopical and biochemical are made, which have to be integrated in the scheme of a "production line". This integration is often difficult because the different investigators do not

* This work was supported by the Deutsche Forschungsgemeinschaft Bad Godesberg bei Bonn, Germany.

use the same species of animals or do not follow the same points of time in the cell production processes. And, indeed, the same species of animals show individual differences in time in their answer to the same stimulation; in other words, individuals of the same species differ in their production curves.

But in spite of all these difficulties it is possible to get a tentative scheme of the "production line" of every species and every gland cell under the following conditions:

Secretion is a long sequence of processes in time [64, 65]. I believe it may be necessary to follow this sequence by putting every qualitative and quantitative datum on a single time co-ordinate [64]. Some investigations are ill-timed because they are made with animals, whose timing of secretion is unknown. There are, so far as I know, only two ways of timing [70, 71].

First to investigate the ontogeny of gland cells during the development of many well-known stages from the first "Anlage" of the cell to the stage in which the "professional" structure and function of the cell has been constructed [2, 11, 45, 46, 70, 121, 122, 126, 145, 179, 180].

The second way may be to investigate the secretion cycle by comparing the biochemical and structural information [66, 101] first during the so-called "starvation time" in which the sequence of secretion processes is stopped or is very slow—second during the "activation time" after a certain stimulus. This "activation time" is one phase of secretion in which the extrusion of the old secretion product takes place, following the restitution and storage of the new products. This phase continues in the pancreas for about 1 to 5 hr. [66]; during the 1st hour the most important processes of restitution take place [71–72]. During this phase it is, therefore, necessary to investigate not only one point of time, but many points during the 1st hour and some points during the 2nd to 5th hours.

The number of methods of these investigations are numerous. I may say that the first necessary step is to observe the living cell, either as an isolated cell in tissue culture or preferably as one cell in living relationship with other cells inside the tissue. It is possible to observe the living tissue of the pancreas under physiological conditions during 8–10 hr. under the light microscope [66, 67]. Only in this way can an outline of the time of production processes be obtained.

The second way is the study of the life cycle of a cell [64–72]: you start your investigation with a more or less uniform stage of so-called "resting cells" during the starvation of the animal [7, 68]. Then you give the stimulus of feeding, of drugs, of nervous or of hormonal excitation always at the same time after the beginning of starvation (e.g. 1 or 2 days). Then you investigate the animals at different times after the same stimulus: e.g. 3, 5, 10, 20, 40, 60 min. and 2, 3, 4, 6, 8 hr. after stimulus. For every point of time three animals may be used. Every animal is treated by the same technique, biochemical or structural. These techniques are numerous: you can perhaps observe the living cell [66], or study the secretion product by fistula [68, 100, 101], or kill many animals in the above-mentioned times after stimulus and compare the different stages of the cell cycle [185]. The main point seems to be that all the different techniques are applied at the same points of time. In this manner you will really be able to integrate the results of different techniques. Only the integration of all the different data gives a sequence of processes and only a sequence of events gives an idea of the life of a secretion cycle [70, 71] showing us the "assembly line" during restitution of the product.

2. The life cycle of the exocrine pancreas cell

The life cycle may be divided into three phases: the ingestion of raw material, the synthesis, and the extrusion of products [69–72, 140].

The ingestion [66, 101] consists of active transport of material from the blood through the basal membrane (surrounding a whole acinus) and a cell membrane [159–161, 182]. The influx of this material in some cases seems to be changeable and higher after stimulation than during starvation of the animal. Proteins of the blood plasma are not ingested, only amino acids [100].

The synthesis of enzymes may be shown by the schematic Fig. 1 and may be divided into the following steps:

1. The ingested amino acids [15, 27, 56, 62, 88–90, 100, 104, 105, 124, 156, 162, 191] and phosphates [19, 20, 57, 101–108, 111, 125, 154, 165, 201] in the fluid basic substance and the polynucleotides from the cell nucleus [30, 47, 62, 114–116, 128, 170, 181] arrive at the ribosomes (ribonucleoprotein granules) [5, 12, 26, 58–61, 117, 120, 141–143, 188, 194–197, 200, 203, 206] and are absorbed [18, 173–177]. From the cell nucleolus ribonucleic acid reaches these granules [48–55, 73, 74, 77–80, 93, 109–113, 148]. Phosphates of high energy may be formed by mitochondria as an energy source [76, 166]. With the aid of these substances proteins are synthesized in or on the ribosomes [76, 144].

During starvation of the animal and 1 hr. after feeding, the *ribosomes* have the same size of $\sim$ 150 Å diameter and the same optical density. Their number is considerably greater, however, during the restitution period: according to the electron-microscopic pictures of Palade I would say about ten times greater. One may deduct from this that the ribosomes multiply during the 1st hour after feeding. This multiplication has also been observed during ontogenesis [2, 46]. How these granules multiply, however, is still not clear [13, 43, 44, 178]. Forms of division have not been seen. I have now come to the following hypothesis which I put up for discussion: the fluid cell plasm contains free, dissolved ribonucleic

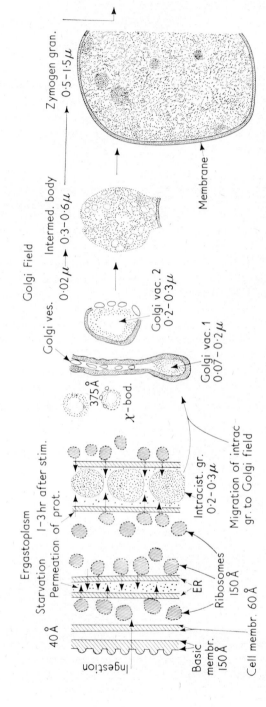

Fig. 1. Tentative outline of enzyme production seen as a "conveyor belt" in the acinus cell of the pancreas. The drawings are not correct in relative size.

acid, free amino acids, lipoproteins and synthetically active enzymes. I can imagine that through a special enzyme mechanism these parts may be building new ribosomes step by step. This restitution *de novo* may be a synthesis under controlling factors of the cell nucleus by the amount of ribonucleic acid, extruded by the nucleolus [24, 25, 37].

The origin of enzymes in ribosomes of the pancreas has been proved [32, 99, 102, 103, 106, 137, 139, 156–157, 171–177, 186, 202], and in many other cells, shown at the first Symposium of the Biophysical Society [2, 3, 4]. The ribosomes have attained, in the last 2 years, a central position in the metabolism of many different cells. It has been shown that these ribosomes have a different ribonucleoprotein ratio: first in different cells, secondly—and this is most important—in the same cell at different stages of enzyme synthesis [171–175]. The ribosomes, which appear identical under the electron microscope, are different biochemically. Step by step the amount of ribonucleic acid decreases, but the amount of proteins increases.

2. What happens with these proteins synthezised in the ribosomes? From the investigations of Siekevitz and Palade [171–177] and the Hokins [77–87] it may be concluded that the proteins are released from the ribosomes and penetrate the wall of the endoplasmic reticulum by active transport [71, 97, 129–139, 146, 149–151]. Inside the endoplasmic canals the proteins may be stored for a short time as intracisternal granules.

3. The intracisternal granules are found by Palade [136–139] in the endoplasmic reticulum of the guinea-pig only 1 to 3 hr. after feeding, but not earlier or later. They have a diameter of $0 \cdot 2$–$0 \cdot 3$ μ; they are, therefore, to be seen in the light microscope. They appear approximately homogenous inside the endoplasmic reticulum; they have no outer membrane, and differ from the zymogen granules in several respects: (*a*) The intracisternal granules originate inside the endoplasmic canals, while the zymogen granules come from the vacuoles of the Golgi bodies. (*b*) They have a diameter of at most $0 \cdot 3$ μ; the zymogen granules, however, of $0 \cdot 5$ to $0 \cdot 6$ μ. (*c*) They have no membrane; the zymogen granules, however, have one. Thus it seems that the intracisternal granules and the zymogen granules are not identical. But it is likely that both contain digestive enzymes.

4. Up to this stage of the secretion process I believe the sequence of events on the assembly line has been settled to a certain degree. A further series of arguments speaks in favour of a final condensation of the digestive enzymes as zymogen granules in the vesicles of the Golgi bodies [66, 81, 119, 183]. Sluiter confirmed this condensation statistically using a periodic count method by light microscope [185]. Also the experiments of Chésin [19–21], Marshall [116], Farquhar and Wellings [42] made this conclusion likely. The electron microscope showed a sequence of four different

vesicles and Golgi vacuoles steadily growing larger and denser. Finally the zymogen granules are surrounded by a special membrane, containing a large amount of packed enzymes. This work of condensing seems to be the general function of the Golgi bodies [67, 69, 71].

5. What is the bridge between the intracisternal granules on one hand and the condensation inside the Golgi bodies on the other ? There must be a connection which carries the enzymes from the endoplasmic reticulum to the Golgi field.

There are two possibilities. First, that the intracisternal granules are dissolved in the lumen of the endoplasmic reticulum and their parts

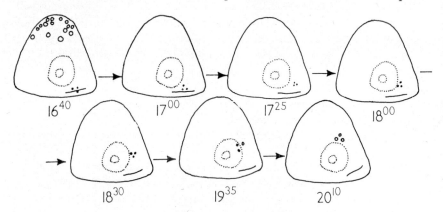

FIG. 2. A living pancreas cell of the acinus with good blood circulation. Pilocarpine stimulation 15.40 hr. First illustration at 16.40 is of entire cell, then observation of a single constellation of three granules. The mitochondrion here observed moves in a snakelike manner but was not further observed. The movement of the three granules between 17.00 and 20.10 as they moved to the Golgifield, where they disappeared. It is probable that this type of granule is identical with the intracisternal granules of G. E. Palade. (From G. C. Hirsch [66].)

(enzymes ?) are brought to the apex by currents in the canals. Secondly, that the intracisternal granules wander undissolved in the canals to the Golgi field. Both possibilities are probable in certain cases, but the dissolving of these granules on the cell base has until now not been seen in the living cell. The intracisternal granules are large and can be seen also in the light microscope. The wandering of these granules has been observed many times (Fig. 2).

This wandering was discovered by Hirsch. In the living pancreas after pilocarpine stimulation, small granules are produced on the cell base in the ergastoplasm. They have a diameter of approx. $0 \cdot 3$ to $0 \cdot 4$ μ (Hirsch's specification of $0 \cdot 03$ μ is a printing error). The endoplasmic reticulum at that time was not to be seen, but the mitochondria embedded in the reticulum were. Because of this Hirsch made the mistake that the granules were produced on the surface of the mitochondria. With the advent of the electron microscope it was discovered that these granules are not produced on the surface of the mitochondria but next to these inside the endoplasmic canals. During the 1st hour after pilocarpine stimulation the number of these granules increases. When one cuts the optical field down to a small part of the basal plasm, one sees that during the first 3 hr. ~ 10 to 40 granules appear in this field; then the number decreases to almost zero, owing to the fact that the particles move away. They show a population growth in the beginning of 100 to 150% per hour.

Hirsch could show that there is a physiological connection between these granules and the Golgi field. Figure 2 shows one of the many observations in which a single group of three granules was observed during 4 hr. The "constellation" of these three granules "twinkled" for about an hour moving irregularly to the Golgi-field where it disappeared by being dissolved. The granules followed a zig-zag course, with a velocity of 1 μ in 7 to 13 min.; the smaller granules move faster than the larger ones. As soon as a granule reaches the Golgi field it remains stationary and disappears, i.e. it dissolves. The movement of the Hirsch granules from the ergastoplasm to the cell apex was checked experimentally by three independent investigators [39].

Are these granules of Hirsch identical with the intracisternal granules ?

Size: Hirsch's granules have in the light microscope a diameter of 0·3 to 0·4 μ. The intracisternal granules have a diameter of 0·2 to 0·3 μ (Fig. 2). Both have the same size, both are visible in the light microscope.

Chemical composition: Neither are lipoid drops, but contain mostly protein, as was shown by Hirsch on his granules, and also by Siekevitz and Palade for the intracisternal granules. Thus, I believe the two types of granules are identical.

What happens to these intracisternal granules after their movement into the Golgi field ? There are some possibilities: either they develop within the Golgi field through growth directly into zymogen granules, or they dissolve, and the dissolved parts are condensed in the Golgi field. In case they are directly formed into zymogen granules then the process must be visible in the light and electron microscope. Until now, however, all investigations under physiological conditions have revealed that the intracisternal granules disappeared in the Golgi field. Their "future" in the Golgi field gave birth to several hypotheses, of which only one has been upheld: the intracisternal granules dissolve, and their components, which are more or less finished enzymes, are taken up by the Golgi bodies, and in some way "packed" into the developing and enlarging zymogen granules. This condensation of the parts of the intracisternal granules thus becomes the major function of the Golgi field.

H*

Trial and error

The communication between the endoplasmic reticulum and the zymogen granules and the way by which the enzymes are absorbed by the Golgi lamellae is not entirely clear. Recently I found in the micrographs of Palade between the endoplasmic reticulum and the Golgi lamellae many round shaped X-bodies of about 370 Å diameter. (Fig. 1.) The internal shape of these bodies is varying. It is only theoretical to say this:

1. On the end of the ER in the Golgi field, ruptures of the ER membranes are to be seen in the direction to the Golgi field. Through these ruptures the protein content of the ER seems to go out to the space between ER and Golgi lamellae.

2. These proteins may form the X-bodies (?) It is, however, only the topographical relationship that gives this idea.

3. These X-bodies may be taken up by the Golgi vacuoles and packed up to large zymogen granules. This process, however, is far from being clear.

References

1. Afzelius, B. A., *in* Wenner-Grens Institute, Festschrift (1959).
2. Ashikawa, J. K., *in* "Microsomal Particles and Protein Synthesis. 1." Symposium Biophysical Society, ed. R. B. Roberts. Pergamon Press, London, 76 (1958).
3. Askonas, B. A., Simkin, J. L., and Work, T. S., *in* " 4. Internat. Congress of Biochem.", Vol. VIII. Pergamon Press, London, 181 (1960).
4. Spooner, E. T. C., and Strocker, B. A. D. (eds.), "Bacterial Anatomy". Symposium Soc. Gen. Microbiol. Cambridge (Engl.) University Press (1956).
5. Balis, M. E., Samarth, K. D., Hamilton, Mary G., and Petermann, Mary L., *J. biol. Chem.* **233,** 1152 (1958).
6. Bargmann, W., "Histologie und mikroskopische Anatomie des Menschen". 3. Aufl. G. Thieme, Stuttgart (1959).
7. Barnum, C. P., Jardetzky, C. D., and Halberg, F. *Tex. Rep. Biol. Med.* **15,** 134 (1957).
8. Bernhard, W. *Cancer Res.* **18,** 491 (1958).
9. Bessis, M., "Die Zelle im Elekronenmikroskop." Sandoz-Monographien (1960).
10. Block, D. P., *in* "Frontiers in Cytology", ed. S. L. Palay. Yale Univ. Press, New Haven, 113 (1959).
11. Block, D. P., and Godman, G. C., *J. biophys. biochem. Cytol.* **1,** 531 (1955).
12. Brachet, J., "Biochemical Cytology". Academic Press, New York (1957).
13. Brachet, J., *in* "Mécanismes d'Autoreproduction", ed J. A. Thomas. Masson et Cie, Paris (1957).
14. Campbell, P. N., Greengard, O., and Kernot, B. A., *Biochem. J.* **74,** 107 (1960).
15. Castelfranco, P., Meister, A., and Moldave, K., *in* "Microsomal Particles and Protein Synthesis. 1." Symp. Biophysical Society, ed. R. B. Roberts. Pergamon Press, London, 115 (1958).
16. Chantrenne, H., *in* "Enzymes". Tjeenk Willink, Zwolle, 143 (1959).

17. Chauveau, J., Gautier, A., and Moulé, Y., *C. R. Acad. Sci., Paris* **241,** 337 (1955).
18. Chauveau, J., Moulé, Y., and Rouiller, C., *Exp. Cell. Res.* **13,** 398 (1957).
19. Chésin, R. B., *Biokhimiya* **17,** 664 (1952).
20. Chésin, R. B., Petrschkaite, S. K., Tolinschis, L. E., and Paulauskaite, K. P., *Akad. d. Wissensch. USSR Biochemie Moskau.* **22,** (1957).
21. Chésin, R. B., *in* "The Origin of Life on the Earth". Moscow (1957).
22. Chèvremont, M., "Notions de Cytologie et Histologie". Desoer, Liège, (149: Microsomes) (1957).
23. Ciba Foundation Symposium: "Regulation of Cell Metabolism". J. and A. Churchill, London (1959).
24. Clark, W. H., Jr., *J. biophys. biochem. Cytol.* **7,** 345 (1960).
25. Cotte, G., *Z. Zellforsch.* **50,** 232 (1959).
26. Crampton, C. F., and Petermann, M. L., *J. biol. Chem.* **234,** 2642 (1959).
27. Daly, M., Allfrey, V. G., and Mirsky, A. E., *J. gen. Physiol.* **39,** 207 (1955).
28. Davidson, J. N., *in* "Structure of Nucleic Acids". Cambridge Univ. Press, 27 (1957).
29. Decken, A. von der, and Hultin, T., *Exp. Cell Res.* **14,** 88 (1958).
30. Decken, A. von der, and Hultin, T., *Exp. Cell Res.* **15,** 254 (1958).
31. Decken, A. von der, and Hultin, T., *Exp. Cell Res.* **17,** 188 (1959).
32. Decken, A. von der, and Hultin, T., *Exp. Cell Res.* **19,** 591 (1960).
33. Dickman, S. R., and Morrill, G. A., *Amer. J. Physiol.* **190,** 403 (1957).
34. Dickman, S. R., and Morrill, G. A., *Ann. N. Y. Acad. Sci.* **81,** 585 (1959).
35. Dickman, S. R., and Trupin, K., *Arch. Biochem. Biophys.* **82,** 355 (1959).
36. Dickman, S. R., Morrill, G. A., and Trupin, K. M., *J. biol. Chem.* **235,** 169 (1960).
37. Dolley, D. H., *Amer. J. Anat.* **35,** 153 (1925).
38. Douglas, T. A., and Munro, H. N., *Exp. Cell Res.* **16,** 148 (1959).
39. Duthie, E. S., *Proc. roy. Soc.* B. **114,** 20 (1933).
40. Duthie, E. S., *Arch. exp. Zellforsch.* **15,** 352 (1934).
41. Ekholm, R., and Edlund, V., *J. Ultrastructure Res.* **2,** 453 (1959).
42. Farquhar, M. G., and Wellings, S. R., *J. biophys. biochem. Cytol.* **3,** 319 (1957).
43. Favard, P., *C. R. Acad. Sci., Paris* **247,** 531 (1958).
44. Favard, P., *C. R. Acad. Sci., Paris* **248,** 3344 (1959).
45. Ferreira, David, *J. Ultrastructure Res.* **1,** 14 (1957).
46. Ferreira, David, "A differenciação do condrioma aparelho de Golgi e Ergasto-plasma. Estudo ao Microscópio Electrónico." Lisboa (1959).
47. Ferreira, Fernandes J., and Junqueira, L. C. U., *Arch. Biochem. Biophys.* **55,** 54 (1955).
48. Ficq, A., *in* "Problèmes d'Ultrastructures et de Fonctions Nucleaires". Ed. J. André Thomas. Masson et Cie, Paris, 35 (1959).
49. Freed, J. J., *Exp. Cell Res.* **9,** 17-34 (1955).
50. Garfinkel, D., *in* "Microsomal Particles and Protein Synthesis. 1." Symposium Biophysical Society, ed. R. B. Roberts. Pergamon Press, London, 22 (1958).
52. Goldstein, L., and Plaut, W., *Proc. nat. Acad. Sci., Wash.* **41,** 874 (1955).
53. Goldstein, L., and Micou, J., *J. biophys. biochem. Cytol.* **6,** 301 (1959).
54. Goldstein, L., and Micou, J., *J. biophys. biochem. Cytol.* **6,** 1 (1959).
55. Goldstein, L., and Micou, J., *J. biophys. biochem. Cytol.* **6,** 301 (1959).
56. Greengard, O., and Campbell, P. N. *Biochem. J.* **72,** 305 (1959).
57. Grycki, S. *Ann. Univ. M. Curie-Sklodowska*, C. **8,** 193 (1953).

58. Haguenau, F. *Int. Rev. Cytol.* **7,** 425 (1958).
59. Hall, B. D., and Doty, P., *in* "Microsomal Particles and Protein Synthesis. 1." Symposium Biophysical Society, ed. R. B. Roberts, Pergamon Press, London, 27 (1958).
60. Hamilton, M. G., and Petermann, M. L., *J. biol. Chem.* **234,** 1441 (1959).
61. Hanzon, V., Hermodsson, L. H., and Toschi, G., *J. Ultrastructure Res.* **3,** 216 (1959).
62. Hecht, L. I., Stephenson, M. L., and Zamecnik, P. C., *Proc. nat. Acad. Sci., Wash.* **45,** 505 (1959).
63. Herman, L., Fitzgerald, P. J., Weiss, M., and Polevoy, I. S., *in* "Kongress für EM", Vol. 2, 372 (1960).
64. Hirsch, G. C., *Roux Arch. Entw. Mech.* **117,** 511 (1929).
65. Hirsch, G. C., *Biol. Rev.* **6,** 88-131 (1931).
66. Hirsch, G. C., *Z. Zellforsch.* **15,** 37 (1931); *Roux Arch. Entw. Mech.* **123,** 792 (1931); *Z. Zellforsch.* **14,** 517 (1931); *Z. Zellforsch.* **15,** 290 (1932).
67. Hirsch, G. C., "Handb. der Allgemeinen Pathologie", Vol. II, 1. Springer-Verlag, Heidelberg, 92-213 (1955).
68. Hirsch, G. C., Junqueira, L. C. U., Rothschild, H. A., Sesso, S. R., *Pflügers Arch. ges. Physiol.* **264,** 78 (1957).
69. Hirsch, G. C., *Naturwissenschaften* **45,** 349 (1958).
70. Hirsch, G. C., *in* "Handbuch der Biologie", Vol. 1. Athenaion-Verlag, Konstanz (1959-61).
71. Hirsch, G. C., *Naturwissenschaften* **47,** 25 (1960).
72. Hirsch, G. C., *in* "Protoplasmatologia", Vol. 3. Springer-Verlag, Wien (1961).
73. Hoagland, M. B., Zamecnik, P. C., and Stephenson, M. L., *in* "Symposium on Molecular Biology", ed. R. E. Zirkle. University of Chicago Press, Chicago, 105 (1959).
74. Hoagland, M. B., *in* "4. Intern. Congress of Biochem.", Vol. VIII, Proteins, 199 (1960).
75. Hodge, M. H., and Chapman, G. B., *J. biophys. biochem. Cytol.* **4,** 571 (1958).
76. Hogeboom, G. H., Kuff, E. L., and Schneider, W. C., *Int. Rev. Cytol.* **6,** 425 (1957).
77. Hokin, L. E., *Biochim. biophys. Acta* **8,** 225 (1952).
78. Hokin, L. E., and Hokin, M. R., *Biochim. biophys. Acta* **11,** 591 (1953).
79. Hokin, L. E., and Hokin, M. R., *Biochim. biophys. Acta* **13,** 236 (1954).
80. Hokin, L. E., and Hokin, M. R., *Biochim. biophys. Acta* **13,** 401 (1954).
81. Hokin, L. E., *Biochim. biophys. Acta* **18,** 379 (1955).
82. Hokin, L. E., and Hokin, M. R., *J. biol. Chem.* **233,** 822 (1958).
83. Hokin, L. E., and Hokin, M. R., *Gastroenterology* **36,** 368 (1959).
84. Hokin, L. E., and Hokin, M. R., *J. biol. Chem.* **234,** 1387 (1959).
85. Hokin, M. R., and Hokin, L. E., *J. biol. Chem.* **219,** 85 (1956).
86. Hokin, M. R., and Hokin, L. E., *J. biol. Chem.* **233,** 522 (1958).
87. Hokin, M. R., and Hokin, L. E., *J. biol. Chem.* **234,** 1381 (1959).
88. Hultin, T., *Exp. Cell Res.* **3,** 210 (1955).
89. Hultin, T., *Exp. Cell Res.* **11,** 222 (1956).
90. Hultin, T., and Beskow, G., *Exp. Cell Res.* **11,** 664 (1956).
91. Hultin, T., von der Decken, A., and Beskow, G., *Exp. Cell. Res.* **12,** 675 (1957).
92. Hultin, T., and von der Decken, A., *Exp. Cell Res.* **13,** 83 (1957).
93. Hultin, T., *Exp. Cell Res.* **12,** 290 (1957).
94. Hultin, T., and von der Decken, A., *Exp. Cell Res.* **15,** 581 (1958).
95. Hultin, T., and von der Decken, A., *Exp. Cell Res.* **16,** 444 (1958).
96. Hultin, T., and von der Decken, A., *Acta chem. scand.* **12,** 596 (1958).

97. Hultin, T., *in* "Wenner-Grens Institut, Festschrift" 62 (1959).
98. Ingram, V. M., *in* "4. Internat. Congress of Biochem." Vol. 8. Pergamon Press, London 95 (1960).
99. Jungblut, P. W., and Turba, F., *in* "10. Coll. Physiol. Chemie". Springer-Heidelberg, Mosbach 102 (1959).
100. Junqueira, L. C. U., Hirsch, G. C., and Rothschild, H. A., *Biochem. J.* **61**, 275 (1955).
101. Junqueira, L. C. U., and Hirsch, G. C., *Int. Rev. Cytol.* **5**, 323 (1956).
102. Keller, E. B., Zamecnik, P. C., and Loftfield, R. B., *J. Histochem. Cytochem.* **2**, 378 (1954).
103. Kirsch, J. F., Siekevitz, P., and Palade, G. E., *J. biol. Chem.* **235**, 1419 (1960).
104. Korner, A., *Biochim. biophys. Acta* **35**, 554 (1959).
105. Kurochtina, T. P., *Biochemistry, Leningr.* **19**, 16 (1954).
106. Laird, A. K., and Barton, A. D., *Biochim. biophys. Acta* **25**, 56 (1957).
107. Laird, A. K., and Barton, A. D., *Biochim. biophys. Acta* **27**, 12 (1958).
108. Lancker, J. L. van, and Holtzer, R. L., *J. biol. Chem.* **234**, 2359 (1959).
109. Leblond, C. P., Everett, N. B., and Simmons, B. *Amer. J. Anat.* **101**, 225 (1957).
110. Leuchtenberger, C., and Schrader, F., *Proc. nat. Acad. Sci., Wash.* **38**, 99 (1952).
111. Lipmann, F., *in* "4. Intern. Congress of Biochem." Vol. VIII. Pergamon Press, London, 177 (1960).
112. Littlefield, J. W., Keller, E. B., Gross, J. and Zamecnik, P. C., *J. biol. Chem.* **217**, 111 (1955).
113. Littlefield, J. W., and Keller, E. B., *J. biol. Chem.* **224**, 13 (1957).
114. Love, Robert, and Bharadwaj, T. P., *Nature, Lond.* **183**, 1453 (1959).
115. Mahlon, B., Hoagland, M. B., Stephenson, M. L., Scott, J. F., Hecht, L. I., and Zamecnik, P. C., *J. biol. Chem.* **231**, 241 (1958).
116. Marshall, A. *Lab. Invest.* **8**, 460 (1959).
117. Martin, E. M., and Morton, R. K., *Biochem. J.* **64**, 687 (1956).
118. Maurer, W. *in* "10. Coll. Physiol. Chemie" Springer-Heidelberg, Mosbach, (1959).
119. Morelle, J., *Cellule* **37**, 75 (1927).
120. Moulé, Y., Rouiller, C., and Chauveau, J., *J. biophys. biochem. Cytol.* **7**, 547 (1960).
121. Munger, B. L., *Amer. J. Anat.* **103**, 1 (1958).
122. Munger, B. L., *Anat. Rec.* **130**, 343 (1958).
123. Munger, B. L., *J. biophys. biochem. Cytol.* **4**, 177 (1958).
124. Nakano, E., and Monroy, A., *Exp. Cell Res.* **14**, 236 (1958).
125. Noback, C. R., and Montagna, W., *Amer. J. Anat.* **91**, 343 (1947).
126. Oota, Y., and Takata, Kenzo, *Physiol. Plant.* **12**, 518 (1959).
127. Oberling, Ch., *Int. Rev. Cytol.* **8**, 1 (1959).
128. Oram, V., *Acta anat. Suppl.* **23**, 1-114 (1955).
129. Palade, G. E., and Porter, K. R., *Anat. Rec.* **112**, 370 (1952).
130. Palade, G. E., *in* "Congr. Micr. électr." London (1954).
131. Palade, G. E., and Porter, K. R., *J. exp. Med.* **100**, 641 (1954).
132. Palade, G. E., *J. biophys. biochem. Cytol.* **1**, 59 (1955).
133. Palade, G. E., *J. biophys. biochem. Cytol.* **1**, 567 (1955).
134. Palade, G. E., and Siekevitz, P., *J. biophys. biochem. Cytol.* **2**, 671 (1956).
135. Palade, G. E., *J. biophys. biochem. Cytol.* **2**, *Suppl.* 85 (1956).
136. Palade, G. E., *J. biophys. biochem. Cytol.* **2**, 417 (1956).

137. Palade, G. E., *in* "Frontiers of Cytology", ed. S. L. Palay. Yale Univ. Press, New Haven, 283 (1958).
138. Palade, G. E., *in* "Microsomal Particles and Protein Synthesis. 1." Symposion Biophysical Society, ed. R. B. Roberts. Pergamon Press, London, 36 (1958).
139. Palade, G. E., *in* "Subcellular Particles" ed. T. Hayashi. Ronald Press Co., New York, 64 (1959).
140. Palay, S. L., *in* "Frontiers of Cytology" ed. S. L. Palay. Yale Univ. Press, New Haven, 305 (1958).
141. Petermann, M. L., Hamilton, M. G., and Mizen, N. A., *Cancer Res.* **14**, 360 (1954).
142. Petermann, M. L., and Hamilton, M. G., *J. biol. Chem.* **224**, 725 (1957).
143. Petermann, M. L., Hamilton, M. G., Balis, M. E., Samarth, K., and Pecora, P., *in* "Microsomal Particles and Protein Synthesis. 1." Symposium Biophysical Society, ed. R. B. Roberts. Pergamon Press, London, 70 (1958).
144. Peters, T., Jr., *J. Histochem. Cytochem.* **7**, 224 (1959).
145. Pipan, N., *Dissert. Bonn* (1960).
146. Policard, A., and Bessis, M., *Pr. méd.* **64**, 2153 (1956).
147. Policard, A., and Baud, C. A., "Structures inframicroscopiques normales et pathologiques des Cellules et des Tissus". Masson et Cie, Paris (1958).
148. Pollister, A. W., *in* "Dynamics of Growth Processes" ed. A. J. Boell. Princeton University Press, 33 (1954).
149. Porter, K. R., *J. Histochem. Cytochem.* **2**, 346 (1954).
150. Porter, K. R., *Fed. Proc.* **14**, 673 (1955).
151. Porter, K. R., *in* "The Harvey Lectures", Series 51 (1955-56). Academic Press, New York, 175 (1957).
152. Porter, K. R., and Bruni, C., *Anat. Rec.* **136**, 260 (1960).
153. Quastler, H., *in* "Information Theory in Biology", ed. H. Quastler. Univ. of Illinois Press, Urbana, 170 (1958).
154. Rabinovitch, M., Valeri, V., Rothschild, H. A., Camara, S., Sesso, A., and Junqueira, L. C. U., *J. biol. Chem.* **198**, 815 (1952).
155. Rashevsky, N., *Bull. math. Biophys.* **21**, 309 (1959).
156. Rendi, R., and Hultin, T., *Exp. Cell Res.* **19**, 253 (1960).
157. Rendi, R., and Hultin, T., *Exp. Cell Res.* **18**, 542 (1959).
158. Rhodin, J., *Verh. dtsch. Ges. Pathol.* G. Fischer, Stuttgart, 275 (1958).
159. Robertson, J. D., *Biochem. Soc. Symp.* **16**, 3 (1959).
160. Robertson, J. D., *Anat. Rec.* **136**, 266 (1960).
161. Robertson, J. D., *in* "Kongress für Elektronenmikroskopie", Vol. 2, 159 (1960).
162. Rothschild, H. A., Hirsch, G. C., and Junqueira, L. C. U., *Experientia* **13**, 158 (1957).
163. Runnström, J., *in* "Modern Trends in Physiology and Biochemistry". Academic Press, New York, 47 (1952).
164. Ruska, H., *Studium gen.* **12**, 133 (1959).
165. Schapot, V. C., *Adv. mod. Biol., Moscow* **37**, 255 (1954).
166. Schneider, W. C., and Hogeboom, G. H., *Ann. Rev. Biochem.* **25**, 201 (1956).
167. Schucher, R., and Hokin, L. E., *J. biol. Chem.* **210**, 551 (1954).
168. Schulz, Heribert, and de Paola, D., *Z. Zellforsch.* **49**, 125 (1958).
169. Schwarz, W., and Hofmann, M., "Vierter Internationaler Kongress für Elektronenmikroskopie", **2**, 369 (1958).
170. Sesso, A., and Valeri, V., *Exp. Cell Res.* **14**, 201 (1958).
171. Siekevitz, P., and Palade, G. E., *J. biophys. biochem. Cytol.* **4**, 203 (1958).

172. Siekevitz, P., and Palade, G. E., *J. biophys. biochem. Cytol.* **4**, 309 (1958).
173. Siekevitz, P., and Palade, G. E., *J. biophys. biochem. Cytol.* **4**, 557 (1958).
174. Siekevitz, P., and Palade, G. E., *J. biophys. biochem. Cytol.* **5**, 1 (1959).
175. Siekevitz, P., *Exp. Cell Res. Suppl.* **7**, 90 (1959).
176. Siekevitz, P., and Palade, G., *J. biophys. biochem. Cytol.* **7**, 619 (1960).
177. Siekevitz, P., and Palade, G. E., *J. biophys. biochem. Cytol.* **7**, 631 (1960).
178. Simkin, J. L., and Work, T. S., *in* "Symp. Soc. Exper. Biol". XII. Cambridge (Engl.) Univ. Press, 164 (1958).
179. Sirlin, J. L., and Waddington, C. H., *Exp. Cell Res.* **11**, 197 (1956).
180. Sirlin, J. L., and Edwards, R. G., *Exp. Cell. Res.* **18**, 190 (1959).
181. Sirlin, J. L., *Exp. Cell Res.* **19**, 177 (1959).
182. Sjöstrand, F. S., and Hanzon, V., *Exp. Cell Res.* **7**, 393 (1954).
183. Sjöstrand, F. S., and Hanzon, V., *Exp. Cell Res.* **7**, 415 (1954).
184. Sjöstrand, F. S., *Int. Rev. Cyto.* **5**, 455 (1956).
185. Sluiter, J. W., *Z. Zellforsch.* **33**, 187 (1944).
186. Stephenson, M. L., Hecht, L. I., Littlefield, J. W., Loftfield, R. H., and Zamecnik, P. C., *in* "Subcellular Particles", ed. T. Hayashi. Ronald Press Co., New York, 160 (1959).
187. Stich, H., *in* "Developmental Cytology", ed. D. Rudnick. Ronald Press Company, New York, 105 (1959).
188. Straub, F. B., *Chem. Tech.* **9**, 460 (1957).
189. Strugger, S. *Naturw. Rdsch.* **1**, 7 (1960), and **2**, 51 (1960).
190. Swift, Hewson, *in* "Symposium on the Chemical Basis of Development", ed. W. D. McElroy, B. Glass. Johns Hopkins Univ. Press, 175 (1958).
191. Szabó, M. T., and Garzó, T., *Acta physiol. hung.* **12**, 303 (1957).
192. Tamaki, M., and Iwashige, K., *Folia. anat. Jap.* **23**, 1 (1950).
193. Tandler, C. J., *Exp. Cell Res.* **17**, 560 (1959).
194. Tashiro, Y., Sato, A., and Furuta, Y., *Cytologia* **22**, 136 (1957).
195. Tashiro, Y., *Acta Sch. med. Univ. Kioto* **34**, 238 (1957).
196. Tashiro, Y., Ogura, M., Sato, A., Shinagawa, Y., Imai, Y., Hirakawa, K., and Hirano, S. *in* "International Symposium on Enzyme Chemistry, Tokyo", 436 (1958).
197. Ts'o, Paul O. P., *in* "Microsomal Particles and Protein Synthesis. 1." Symposium Biophysical Society, ed. R. B. Roberts. Pergamon Press, London, 156 (1958).
198. Ullmann, A., and Straub, F. B., *Acta physiol. hung.* **8**, 279 (1955).
199. Ullmann, A., Garzó, T., and Straub, F. B., *Acta physiol. hung.* **13**, 179 (1958).
200. Vendrely, C., Vendrely, R., *in* "Handbuch der Histochemie", **3**, 2. Teil: Nucleoproteide, ed. W. Graumann and Neumann, K. Gustav Fischer-Verlag, Stuttgart, 84 (1959).
201. Vorbrodt, A., *Exp. Cell Res.* **15**, 1 (1958).
202. Webster, G. C., *J. biol. Chem.* **229**, 535 (1957); *Fed. Proc.* **18**, 348 (1959).
203. Weiss, J. M., *J. exp. Med.* **98**, 607 (1953).
204. Wilson, J. W., *J. Histochem. Cytochem.* **2**, 317 (1954).
205. Ycas, M., *in* "Symposium on Molecular Biology", ed. R. E. Zirkle. University of Chicago Press, Chicago, 115 (1959).
206. Zalockar, M., *Nature, Lond.* **183**, 1330 (1959).

Discussion

PORTER: I think it is appropriate to mention to the audience at this point that Palade has been interested in this topic and has published or has in press observations which would indicate that the intracisternal granules do not have to enter the matrix phase of the cytoplasm to get to the Golgi components, but that intermittent continuity is made between the cavities of the ER and those of the Golgi. It is probable that the granules break down into less condensed forms in making this migration.

Immunological Studies of Microsomal Structure and Function

PETER PERLMANN AND WINFIELD S. MORGAN*

*The Wenner-Gren Institute for Experimental Biology,
University of Stockholm, Sweden*

In a number of publications it has been shown that specific antibodies can be used as tools for studying the intracellular distribution of anti-genically distinct macromolecules of rat liver [1, 15, 20]. In this paper, the immunological properties of microsomal fractions from various organs will be described, and some of our recent findings will be discussed with regard to microsomal function in protein synthesis. In the present context, the term microsomes refers to the ribonucleic acid rich fraction, sedimen-ted in the ultracentrifuge when a cell-free homogenate is subjected to differential centrifugation under certain standard conditions [14, 1, 10]. This definition does not involve any particular implications as to the cyto-logical homogeneity of this fraction which consists of ribonucleoprotein particles and different types of endoplasmic membranes. It may contain a good number of subcellular elements which are functionally unrelated and of different origin [13]. The enzymic or electron microscopic criteria applied for the characterization of the microsomal fractions in this type of work are the same as those available in other biochemical studies, e.g. [14, 28, 7].

Antigens in microsomes of liver and other organs of the rat

So far, rat livers have constituted the most thoroughly studied material. The analytical reagents are antisera obtained from rabbits injected either with total microsomes or with microsomal subfractions, with the final supernatant after removal of the microsomes ("cell sap"), or with rat serum proteins. Details may be found elsewhere [1, 10]. When such antisera are reacted on agar diffusion plates according to Ouchterlony [12] one obtains complicated patterns of antigen–antibody precipitates. Most of

* Parts of this work were carried out during a tenure of a Special Research Fellowship granted by the National Cancer Institute, U.S. Public Health Service. —Permanent address: *Department of Pathology, Massachusetts General Hospital, Boston, 14, Mass., U.S.A.*

the antigens are both immunologically and chemically different from the serum proteins. All subcellular fractions contain a number of these "liver" antigens in common. These antigens may either be present physiologically or their presence in a certain fraction may be an artefact of fractionation. However, in addition, there also exists a considerable number of antigens typical of various fractions. Thus, the microsomal fraction of rat liver is characterized primarily by five to six strongly antigenic proteins which can be extracted with sodium deoxycholate, non-ionic detergents such as lubrol W (cetyl alcohol polyoxyethylene condensate) [11, 5], or with phospholipase A [1, 20]. These antigens seem to be lipoproteins. They are difficult to characterize electrophoretically. However, it has been possible to isolate two of these antigens in an immunologically pure form. A lubrol extract of microsomes was separated by chromatography on DEAE cellulose [23], using constant pH (0·035 M tris-buffer, pH 7·8) and a gradient of KCl for elution. The presence of 0·2% lubrol in all reagents was necessary for fractionation (unpublished results).

The microsomal subfraction which remains insoluble after treatment of the microsomes with detergent (ribonucleoprotein particles) contains some additional weak antigens. These antigens can be visualized in the diffusion plates after extraction with chelating agents at pH 7·4 [1, 20]. Their chemistry is so far unknown.

The microsomal antigens described above are different from the antigens typical of liver cell sap. Moreover, when extracts of the liver fractions are compared with microsomal extracts or cell sap from other rat organs, additional differences are found. This is illustrated in Fig. 1. This shows the reactions obtained when lubrol extracts of microsomes from liver, kidney, pancreas, testis, spleen and brain were reacted with the corresponding anti-microsomal sera. Each line in these photographs represents the precipitate formed by one, or sometimes several antigens, with their corresponding antibodies. Fusion of precipitates from neighbouring containers suggests an immunological identity of the antigens, while the precipitates of unrelated antigens cross. The formation of spurs in certain cases indicates either cross reactions or an immunological heterogeneity of the precipitates [12].

None of the antigens appearing in Fig. 1 is due to serum proteins, since antibodies against these had been removed in advance by means of absorption of the antisera with rat serum. Roughly, Fig. 1 demonstrates that the microsomal extracts of liver, kidney, and pancreas are highly organ-specific in the sense that they give the greatest number of precipitates with their homologous antisera. The anti-liver microsomal serum contains the largest number of antibodies reacting with antigens present in extracts from other organs. In contrast, lubrol extracts of microsomes from testis contain only a few components; in common with liver microsomes spleen

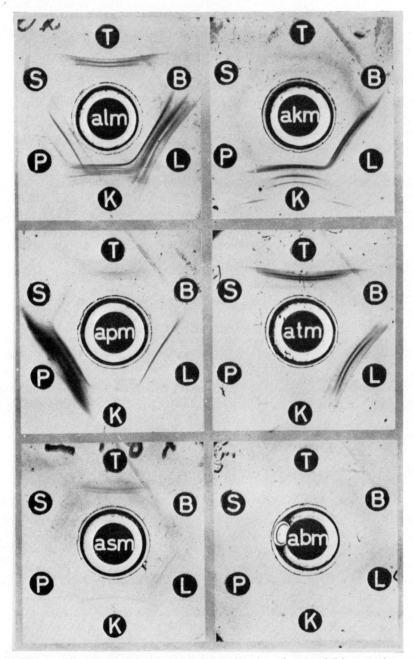

Fig. 1. Photograph of six agar plates showing the precipitin reactions of lubrol extracts of microsomes from different rat organs, and the corresponding antisera. The antigen solutions labelled with the same letters in the different plates were aliquots of the same extracts. The extracts were diluted to contain 350–400 μg. protein/ml. T, B, L, K, P, S: microsomal extracts of testis, brain, liver, kidney, pancreas, spleen, respectively; *alm, akm, apm, atm, asm, abm*: antisera against microsomes of liver, kidney, pancreas, testis, spleen, brain, respectively. For details see [19].

and brain microsomes seem to be more or less devoid of lubrol-extractable antigens specific for these organs.

A somewhat different picture emerges when the cell saps from these organs are compared in similar experiments. In this case, the number of common antigens in the different organs is greater. In general, it may be stated that the "organ specificity" of the cell sap is less than that of the microsomes, although organ specific antigens are present in these fractions also.

A full description of these results will be given elsewhere [19]. Obviously, no immediate conclusions can be drawn from experiments such as these, since the various homogenates are histologically heterogenous, the cytology of some of the microsomal preparations is badly known, and the chemistry of the antigens has not yet been studied. However, it appears that further studies along these lines should render important information regarding the chemistry and genetics of microsomal structures in different types of cells.

The presence of transitory antigens in microsomal fractions

While the aim of the above-mentioned studies is to investigate the chemical composition and relationship of subcellular structures, the immunology of the microsomes has another important aspect. Microsomes are believed to be important sites of protein synthesis. While the synthesis of protein is assumed to take place in or on the ribonucleoprotein particles, the endoplasmic membranes of the microsomal fractions are often believed to possess a regulatory function and to be involved in transportation of freshly formed protein out of the cells. (See [25] for references and discussion.) During recent years, there has accumulated evidence indicating that microsomes can be characterized immunologically by the antigens which are believed to be the transitory products of their synthetic or transporting activities. Thus, in a number of animal species, serum albumin can be extracted from the microsomes of the liver, where it is synthesized [4, 21, 22]. Similarly, antibody-active proteins have been extracted from microsomes of lymph nodes or spleen of immunized animals [2, 6]. It has also been reported that ribosomes from *Escherichia coli* can be precipitated specifically by means of an antiserum against beta galactosidase [8].

Certain results obtained in our laboratory also point in that direction. Thus, injection of rat liver microsomes into rabbits leads to a strong production of antibodies, not only against the "liver" antigens shown above, but also against a great number of serum proteins of the rat [1, 20]. Antisera against microsomes of spleen contained antibodies against rat gamma globulin, in very high concentration. In contrast, the antisera against microsomal fractions of the other organs shown in Fig. 1 contained none, or only trace amounts, of such antibodies [19].

Although other explanations cannot be excluded, the antibody-inducing potencies of the microsomes from various organs may be a reflection of their synthetic activities. More direct indications for such activities have recently been obtained in human patients suffering from ulcerative colitis. In this disease, there occur autoantibodies against a substance of the colon, and the colonic lesions found seem to be of an immunological nature [3]. In regional colonic lymph glands of these patients, antibody-active microsomes could be detected in a remarkably high concentration, whereas microsomes from lymph glands of the ileal region of the same patients were devoid of antibody activity [17].

Finally, as the last example, in the chick embryo, one can detect an organ specific lens antigen in the microsomal fraction at a very early age, just before lens formation is initiated [18]. Later during embryogenesis, when lens differentiation is going on, and in the adult, this lens antigen occurs both in the microsomal fraction and in the cell sap. Electron microscopy of these microsomal fractions indicates that both ribonucleoprotein particles and membranous elements are present.

In conclusion, serum proteins, including antibody-active globulins, as well as the lens antigen, are most likely first synthesized in the microsomes. Assuming these products remain attached to any one of the microsomal substructures for a measurable period of time, it can also be expected that they are available for detection with immunological tools. It has already been shown that this is true in certain cases where proteins are temporarily bound to the endoplasmic membranes before being exported [22]. Definite proof for the immunological recognition of ribonucleoprotein particles by means of antibodies against their synthetic products is so far lacking. It is not at all clear whether or not such transitory products already possess an immunological specificity while being attached to the particles. The fact that ribonucleoprotein particles of the pancreas may carry freshly synthesized chymotrypsin suggests that this could be possible [27].

Incorporation of isotopes into antigens of rat liver homogenates

It should be emphasized once more that the mere presence of these transitory antigens in microsomal fractions only provides indirect evidence for the assumption that they are products of microsomal activity. The microsomal fractions mentioned above are all isolated from heterogenous cellular populations. Moreover, they may contain both the ribosomal and membranous machinery involved in protein synthesis, as well as subcellular elements of a completely different functional significance. However, questions related to the problem of microsomal activity in protein synthesis can be studied by combining immunological techniques with the study of isotope incorporation. This has been done in several of the cases referred to above, as in the case of the serum albumin [4, 21, 22], or in the case of the beta galactosidase in *E. coli* [8]. In the following, this will be exemplified briefly with some experiments from this laboratory. A detailed discussion of the results will be published elsewhere [10]. The purpose of these experiments was to study, qualitatively and under various experimental conditions, the pattern of *in vitro* incorporation of isotopes into the bulk of immunologically distinct proteins of fractionated homogenates.

Figure 2 shows the results of an experiment with rat liver slices, incubated for 30 min. with ^{14}C amino acids. After incubation, the slices were

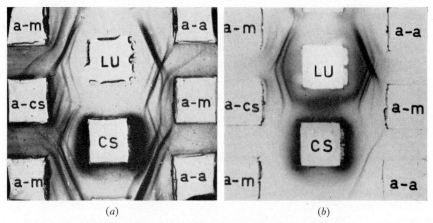

(a)   (b)

FIG. 2. (a) Photograph, and (b) autoradiograph, of precipitin reactions of lubrol extracts of microsomes (*LU*) and of a cell sap (*CS*), from rat liver, with various antisera (*a-m*: antiserum against liver microsomes; *a-cs*: antiserum against liver cell sap; *a-a*: antiserum against rat serum albumin). The antigen solutions were obtained from a fractionated homogenate of liver slices, previously incubated for 30 min. with [^{14}C]-L-leucine, -L-isoleucine, and -L-valine. The radioactivity of the TCA-precipitated protein of an aliquot of the total homogenate was 425 c.p.m./mg. protein and of an aliquot of the isolated cell sap 311 c.p.m./mg. protein. From Morgan *et al.* [10].

homogenized, and a lubrol extract of the microsomes and the cell sap was reacted with antiserum on agar plates. After completion of the immunological reactions, the agar plate was dried and covered with an X-ray film for 3 weeks (cf. also [16, 20]).

Figure 2(a) is a photograph of the precipitin reactions. As can be seen, the two antigen solutions were reacted with an anti-liver microsomal serum, an anti-liver cell sap serum, and an antiserum against rat serum albumin. Both anti-liver sera had been absorbed with rat serum and were free of precipitating antibodies against serum proteins. The antiserum against serum albumin contained antibodies against the albumin, and in small concentrations, against two alpha globulins and one beta globulin. The photograph shows that the lubrol extract of the microsomes gives four distinguishable precipitates with these antibodies. These serum protein-like antigens are immunologically different from other microsomal antigens, reacting with the anti-microsomal serum. Moreover, a considerable amount of serum proteins had also accumulated in the cell sap. This also contained additional antigens, some specific for cell sap, and some in common with the microsomal extract.

From the autoradiograph of Fig. 2(b), it can be seen that an appreciable number of the precipitates were distinctly labelled. As described elsewhere [10], several lines of evidence, and control experiments such as addition of unrelated precipitin systems to the solutions before agar plating, or dilution with unlabelled amino acids after incubation with ^{14}C amino acids, all suggest that the labelling in the autoradiograph is not due to an unspecific adsorption of radioactive material to the precipitates. Rather, we may assume that the labelling of the precipitates indicates a true incorporation of ^{14}C amino acids into the antigens. The autoradiograph shows that the albumin and other serum protein-like antigens which were solubilized from the microsomes were heavily labelled, as well as some additional microsomal antigens of unknown significance. In contrast, in the cell sap, only the serum albumin carried enough of the label to be easily detected. This is in spite of the fact that the concentration of the serum proteins in this fraction probably was higher than in the microsomal extract, as indicated by the relative positions and the appearance of the precipitates. Other cell sap antigens were more or less inactive.

Experiments of this type make it possible to follow the distribution, under various experimental conditions, of the radioactive label in immunologically identical proteins, *recovered from different cellular fractions*. Thus, the results of the experiment of Fig. 2 confirm other work reporting the first appearance of the radioactive label in the microsomal serum albumin followed by an increasing specific activity of this protein in the cell sap. This is taken to indicate that freshly synthesized molecules are transferred from the microsomes to this fraction [21, 22].

A great number of specific precipitates appearing in Fig. 2(a), particularly those formed by the antigens of the cell sap, were hardly labelled at all. However, as we do not know their chemical nature or their antibody combining ratios, we cannot use the degree of labelling of precipitates as the basis for comparison of the metabolism of *immunologically different antigens*. Problems of this type can be approached in a different way. Figure 3 shows a series of four autoradiographs, made from four experiments with slices of rat liver, incubated with ^{14}C amino acids. The four experiments were made with aliquots of the same preparation, and the only difference between them was the time of incubation with the isotopic amino acids; for details see [10]. The Ouchterlony reactions of all four agar plates were practically identical and very similar to those shown in Fig. 2(a). Figure 3 demonstrates again that the radioactive label first appears in the microsomal serum proteins, reacting with an antiserum against rat serum, and in some additional microsomal antigens, reacting

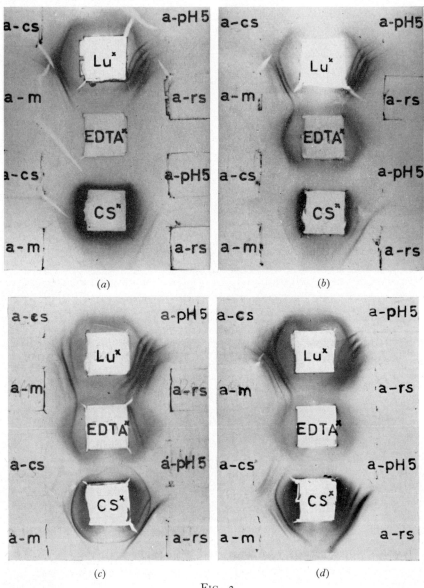

FIG. 3

with anti-microsomal serum. In the cell sap, the appearance of labelled serum proteins is again slower. Nevertheless, after a long period of incubation, the cell sap also contained a complete spectrum of strongly labelled serum proteins. It should be emphasized that the concentration of the serum proteins was practically the same in the cell saps of all four experiments. Moreover, Fig. 3(d) shows, that even additional antigens in the cell sap finally become considerably labelled, provided the period of incubation with the isotope is sufficiently long. Thus, experiments of this type suggest that the rate of isotope incorporation in the serum proteins is faster than that of most other liver antigens reacting in our systems.

When the pattern of incorporation of ^{14}C amino acids into liver antigens is studied after incubation of mitochondria-free homogenates, or of isolated microsomal particles [24], a number of interesting differences are observed. Even in these systems, a reasonable labelling is obtained, both of serum protein-like antigens, and of other antigens extracted from the microsomal fraction. However, only trace amounts of radioactive serum proteins can be detected in the cell sap. Instead, this fraction, and, to a still higher extent, the ribonucleoprotein particles, contain radioactive material which precipitates in the agar around the basins, but without reacting with antibodies. The nature of this material is unknown. The significance of these findings will be discussed elsewhere [9].

FIG. 3. Autoradiographs of precipitin reactions of lubrol extracts (*Lu*) and EDTA-extracts (*EDTA*) of microsomes, and of the cell sap (*CS*), of rat liver, with various antisera (*a-m*: antiserum against liver microsomes; *a-cs*: antiserum against liver cell sap; *a-pH 5*: antiserum against cell sap fraction precipitated at pH 5; *a-rs*: antiserum against rat serum). The antigen solutions were obtained from four separately incubated ([^{14}C]-L-leucine, L-isoleucine, and L-valine) and subsequently fractionated aliquots of a preparation of rat liver slices.

(a) 15 min. incubation with isotope. Time of exposure of autoradiograph: 3 months. The radioactivity of the TCA-precipitated protein of an aliquot of the total homogenate was 135 c.p.m./mg. protein and that of an aliquot of the isolated cell sap 68 c.p.m./mg.

(b) 30 min. incubation with isotope. Time of exposure of autoradiograph: 6 weeks. Radioactivity: total homogenate 402 c.p.m./mg. protein; cell sap: 280 c.p.m./mg. protein.

(c) 60 min. incubation with isotope. Time of exposure of autoradiograph: 6 weeks. Radioactivity: total homogenate 478 c.p.m./mg. protein; cell sap: 380 c.p.m./mg. protein.

(d) 120 min. incubation with isotope. Time of exposure of autoradiograph: 3 weeks. Radioactivity: total homogenate 2190 c.p.m./mg. protein, cell sap 1510 c.p.m./mg. protein.

(Autoradiographs obtained after 6 months exposure of the plates corresponding to the experiments of Figs. 3(a)–(c) did not show a greater number of labelled precipitates.) The reactions obtained with the EDTA extracts and with *a-pH 5* as well as other details are discussed elsewhere. From Morgan *et al.* [10].

Summary

The microsomal fraction isolated from rat liver homogenates by differential centrifugation contains a number of antigens which are typical for this fraction. Extracts of microsomes of other organs of the rat contain antigens which are typical for these fractions but are different from the microsomal liver antigens. In addition to such "microsomal" antigens, microsomes sometimes contain transitory antigens which are only temporarily bound to microsomal particles or membranes. Examples of such antigens are serum proteins in liver microsomes, antibody-active proteins in microsomes of spleen or lymph nodes, and lens antigen in microsomes of early chick embryos. The presence of these transitory antigens in the microsomes may be an expression of their synthetic function. This function can be studied by combining immunological techniques with isotope incorporation. Examples are given, where the *in vitro* incorporation of ^{14}C amino acids into various antigens of rat liver homogenates was studied. After 30 min. of incubation of liver slices, serum albumin and other serum protein-like antigens of the microsomes were more strongly labelled than similar antigens in the cell sap. After longer periods of incubation, strongly labelled serum proteins also appeared in the cell sap. Under the same conditions the labelling of most other liver antigens was weaker than that of the serum proteins. Incubation of cell-free systems also led to the labelling of the different antigens.

Acknowledgments

This work has been supported by grants from the Swedish Cancer Society. The technical assistance of Miss Margareta Engdahl is gratefully acknowledged.

References

1. D'Amelio, V., and Perlmann, P., *Exp. Cell Res.* **19,** 383 (1960).
2. Askonas, B. A., *in* "Mechanisms of Antibody Formation", eds. M. Holub and L. Yarošková, Publishing House of the Czechoslovak Academy of Sciences, Prague, 231 (1960).
3. Broberger, O., and Perlmann, P., *J. exp. Med.* **110,** 657 (1959).
4. Campbell, P., Greengard, O., and Kernot, B. A., *Biochem. J.* **74,** 107 (1960).
5. Cohn, P., and Butler, J. A. V., *Biochem. J.* **70,** 254 (1958).
6. Feldman, M., Elson, D., and Globerson, A., *Nature, Lond.* **185,** 317 (1960).
7. Hanzon, V., and Toschi, G., *Exp. Cell Res.* **16,** 256 (1959).
8. Kameyama, T., and Novelli, G. D., *Biochem. Biophys. Res. Comm.* **2,** 393 (1960).
9. Morgan, W. S., Hultin, T., and Perlmann, P. (in preparation).
10. Morgan, W. S., Perlmann, P., and Hultin, T., *J. biophys. biochem. Cytol.* (in press).
11. Ord, N. G., and Thompson, R. H. S., *Biochem. J.* **49,** 191 (1951).
12. Ouchterlony, Ö., *in* "Progress in Allergy", Vol. V, ed. P. Kallos. S. Karger, Basel, 1 (1958).

13. Palade, G. E., "First Symposium Biophysical Society". Pergamon Press, London, 36 (1958).
14. Palade, G. E., and Siekevitz, P., *J. biophys. biochem. Cytol.* **2,** 171 (1956).
15. Perlmann, P., and D'Amelio, V., *Nature, Lond.* **181,** 491 (1958).
16. Perlmann, P., and Hultin, T., *Nature, Lond.* **182,** 1530 (1958).
17. Perlmann, P., and Broberger, O., *Nature, Lond.* **188,** 749 (1960).
18. Perlmann, P., and De Vincentiis, M., *Exp. Cell Res.* (in press).
19. Perlmann, P., and Morgan, W. S., *Exp. Cell Res.* (in press).
20. Perlmann, P., Hultin, T., D'Amelio, V., and Morgan, W. S., *Exp. Cell Res. Suppl.* **7,** 279 (1959).
21. Peters, T., Jr., *J. biol. Chem.* **229,** 659 (1957).
22. Peters, T., Jr., *J. Histochem. Cytochem.* **7,** 224 (1959).
23. Peterson, E. A., and Sober, H. A., *J. Amer. chem. Soc.* **78,** 751 (1956).
24. Rendi, R., and Hultin, T., *Exp. Cell Res.* **19,** 253 (1960).
25. Siekevitz, P., *Exp. Cell Res., Suppl.* **7,** 90 (1959).
26. Siekevitz, P., and Palade, G., *J. biophys. biochem. Cytol.* **4,** 203 (1958).
27. Siekevitz, P., and Palade, G., *J. biophys. biochem. Cytol.* **7,** 619 (1960).
28. Toschi, G., *Exp. Cell Res.* **16,** 232 (1959).

Discussion

SIEKEVITZ: In your autoradiographs did you see any protein which would be labelled in the supernatant without first being labelled in the microsomes ?

PERLMANN: We know that some of the typical "liver" antigens in the cell sap will become labelled after a long period of incubation but we have not been able to identify them since there are so many antigens in this fraction. We only know that these labelled antigens are immunologically different from the serum proteins. So far, we cannot exclude their presence in the microsomal extract.

MARSHALL: I wonder if you or anyone you know of has tried labelling similar antigenic systems with an isotope which goes not into the proteins but into phospholipids for example ? Also I should like to ask whether you have any indication that lipid rather than protein constituents are responsible for antigenic specificity in any of these cases ?

PERLMANN: I don't think these methods have been used for the study of incorporation into the phospholipids or of the immunological properties of the lipid fractions. Up to now, we have only used ^{14}C amino acids and have followed their incorporation into the proteins.

Amino Acid Incorporation by Liver Microsomes and Ribonucleoprotein Particles

Tore Hultin, Alexandra von der Decken,
Erik Arrhenius and Winfield S. Morgan*

*The Wenner-Gren Institute for Experimental Biology,
University of Stockholm, Sweden*

Experiments ranging over widely different groups of organisms have shown that at least in the cytoplasm, but probably in all parts of the cell [24, 25], the synthesis of proteins is intimately connected with a class of submicroscopic particles (cf. [10]) remarkably rich in RNA.† By means of isolated particles it has been possible to reconstruct, at the subcellular level, essential parts of the protein-synthesizing mechanism, and model experiments of various kinds have already yielded a rich supply of information about the enzymic pathways involved in the synthetic process. However, in spite of the remarkable prosperity of the approach, the basic function of the particles is still very vaguely understood, i.e. the reaction by which individual, activated amino acids become linked together in a predetermined order to polypeptide chains of specific configuration, precursors of the final proteins. Neither has any definite answer been given to the question of how the completed protein molecules are eventually released from the active sites on the particles.

From the point of view of cell function a particularly important problem pertaining to protein metabolism is how this fundamental process is quantitatively and qualitatively regulated in growth and differentiation. Unfortunately, our possibilities of reaching concrete answers to this particular problem are even more limited at present, since no model experiments have yet been devised which unambiguously reproduce such regulatory mechanisms *in vitro*.

In experiments with cell-free amino acid incorporation systems it is often observed that the incorporation activity under optimal conditions is approximately proportional to the amounts of RNP-particles present [5].

---

* Permanent address: *Department of Pathology, Massachusetts General Hospital, Boston, Mass., U.S.A.*

† Abbreviations: ATP, adenosine triphosphate; GTP, guanosine triphosphate; PEP, phosphoenolpyruvate; RNA, ribonucleic acid; RNP-particles, ribonucleoprotein particles.

One might therefore assume that after the break-down of the gross structural organization of the cells the activity of the particles rapidly reaches a uniform level, independently of the previous functional state. If this were always the case, it would seem doubtful whether the effects of rate-regulating factors would ever become accessible to experimental study by cell-free systems.

In the following some experimental evidence will be discussed, indicating that under certain conditions *the actual rate of amino acid incorporation* in vitro *is determined not only by the concentration of potentially active RNP-particles*. The incorporation activity may also be influenced by other factors, including some which depend on physiological (or pathological) conditions in the living tissues before the preparation of the homogenates.

Microsomes and RNP-particles in incorporation systems

According to the picture obtained by electron microscopy RNP-particles may occur in the cytoplasm either in a free state, or associated with the membranes of the endoplasmic reticulum [23, 27, 31]. Especially in the cells of highly differentiated animal tissues which have become specialized for protein secretion or protein accumulation, the majority of RNP-particles may appear in a membrane-bound form. It has been suggested that in such cells the membranes are directly or indirectly concerned with the anabolic functions of the particles [11, 29].

In rat liver a high proportion of the RNP-particles are firmly attached to the endoplasmic membranes. Membrane fragments with adhering particles can be isolated from liver homogenates by differential centrifugation, accumulating in the microsome fraction. Rat liver microsomes, as is well known, has become a classical material in the study of protein metabolism by cell-free systems [28, 33].

It has recently been observed that the membrane components of microsomes are not necessarily required for the function of the particles in amino acid incorporation [4, 17, 26]. Liver systems containing purified enzyme preparations in combination with isolated RNP-particles have, for instance, the same ability as systems with whole microsomes to incorporate labelled amino acids into interior sites of protein molecules [22]. Nevertheless, there are certain potential differences between incorporation systems with whole liver microsomes and such ones with isolated RNP-particles.

This fact is illustrated by the experiment shown in Fig. 1. The particles used in this experiment were prepared by treating rat liver microsomes with a mixture of detergents (deoxycholate and Lubrol W) in a solution of fairly high ionic strength [26]. The detached particles were then separated from the digestion mixture by centrifugation through a density gradient [6, 26]. The experiment shows a characteristic difference between the system with whole microsomes and that with isolated RNP-particles: With the isolated particles there was a considerably longer period of active incorporation.

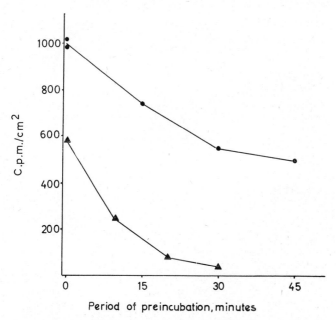

FIG. 1. Life-span of incorporation systems with microsomes or RNP-particles from rat liver. ● RNP-particles and cell sap [26]. ▲ Microsomes and cell sap (mito-chondria-free homogenate) [5]. At the indicated periods of incubation (35°) the following components were added: 0·08 μmole [^{14}C]-L-leucine (5·75 mC/mmole), 10 μmoles PEP, 1 μmole ATP and 0·2 μmole GTP. Final volumes 1·0 ml. Incuba-tion period after these additions 15 min. Proteins were purified and counted as described previously [5].

Effects of liver poisons on the activity of microsome systems

The tendency of the membrane fragments of liver microsomes to exert an unfavourable influence on the incorporation activity becomes con-siderably more pronounced in experiments with liver preparations from certain kinds of pretreated animals. The experiment illustrated by Fig. 2 [8] was carried out with liver microsomes from guinea-pigs which had been treated for 2 hr. with the liver poison phalloidin [32] (0·5 μg./kg., intravenous injection). The activity of these microsomes in amino acid in-corporation was determined at a series of increasing concentrations by use of a standard assay system containing excess amounts of soluble fraction from normal guinea-pig liver. Incubation tubes with microsomes from normal guinea-pig liver at the same concentrations were run in parallel.

Irrespective of whether [¹⁴C]-L-leucine or [¹⁴C]-L-lysine was used as labelled component in the system, a considerably reduced incorporation activity was observed with the microsomes from the phalloidin-treated animals.

That this effect on the activity of the microsomes was mediated in some way by the membrane components was suggested by the fact that isolated RNP-particles from the same animals showed no significant

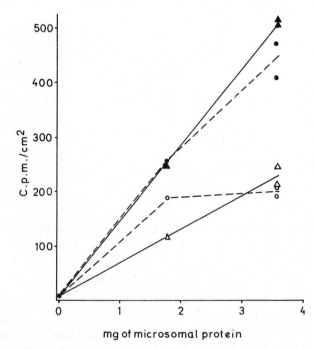

FIG. 2. Incorporation activity of liver microsomes from normal and phalloidin-treated guinea-pigs. Incorporation system as in Fig. 1, with 9 mg. of soluble proteins from normal liver. Incubation period 15 min. (35°). After the addition of TCA the tubes were adjusted to equal protein contents [5]. *Upper curves:* normal microsomes. *Lower curves:* microsomes from phalloidin-treated animals (0·5 μg./kg, 2 hr.). *Solid curves:*[¹⁴C]-L-leucine (0·08 μmole, 5·75 mC/mmole). *Broken curves:* [¹⁴]C-L-lysine (0·04 μmole, 13·5 mC/mmole).

inhibition under these conditions (Table I). Not until later, when the phalloidin-effect had become more manifest (or under the influence of a higher phalloidin concentration) did the isolated particles give evidence of irreversible damage, as indicated by the incorporation data. The RNA/protein ratio of the microsomes was not influenced by the early phalloidin-effects described here.

In this connection it should be noted that in the early stages of the phalloidin treatment no impairment could be demonstrated of a number

TABLE I

EFFECT OF PHALLOIDIN-TREATMENT *in vivo* ON THE ACTIVITY OF INCORPORATION
SYSTEMS WITH MICROSOMES AND RNP-PARTICLES

From livers of control and phalloidin-treated guinea-pigs microsomal fractions
[5] and RNP-particles [26] were isolated in parallel. The activities of these preparations were compared in the same way as in Fig. 2.

μg. phalloidin per g. body weight	Incorporation in per cent of controls	
	Microsomes	RNP-particles
0·4	72	96
0·6	45	94
1·0*	53	63

* Macroscopic effects on liver.

of mitochondrial functions, including P/O-ratio, respiratory control and
latent ATP-ase.

It may be of some interest that the inhibitory effect of phalloidin on
the incorporation of labelled amino acids into protein was not confined
only to the cell-free systems. Similar effects were readily obtained with
liver slices under conditions when there is no histological evidence of any
appreciable intracellular disorganization (Table II).

TABLE II

EFFECT OF PHALLOIDIN ON THE INCORPORATION OF [^{14}C]-DL-VALINE INTO PROTEIN
BY GUINEA-PIG LIVER SLICES

Incubation at $35°$ in O_2–CO_2 (95 : 5) gas phase. The tubes contained 80 mg.
of liver slices [12] in 2 ml. of a Krebs-Henseleit medium [18] including 0·025 M
glucose. Addition of 1·34 μmoles of [^{14}C]-DL-valine (0·14 mC/mmole) at the
beginning of incubation or after 60 min. of preincubation.
Incubation after the addition of [^{14}C]-DL-valine 45 min.

Concentration of phalloidin	Without preincubation		60 min. preincubation	
	c.p.m./cm².	% Inhibition	c.p.m./cm².	% Inhibition
0	73	—	106	—
3 × 10^{-6} M	46	37	74	30
10^{-5} M	40	45	64	40

It is not known yet by which modification of the membrane functions
phalloidin exerts its inhibitory effects on the incorporation activity of the
microsomes. The effect seems not to be due to an induction of ATP-ase
in the membranes. As is shown by Table III about 25% of the ATP and
PEP added to the incorporation system was broken down to orthophosphate
in the course of the incubation, but no increased phosphate formation was

I

TABLE III

Release of orthophosphate from ATP (11 μmoles) or ATP (1 μmole) and PEP (10 μmoles) in incorporation systems containing liver microsomes from control and phalloidin-treated guinea-pigs. Incubation system otherwise as in Fig. 2. ATPase activity [19] of the control liver microsomes: 1·5 μmoles orthophosphate/ 15 min./mg. microsomal protein.

	μmoles P_i formed in 15 min. per mg. microsomal protein		% Inhibition of [^{14}C]-L-leucine incorporation
	1 μmole ATP + 10 μmoles PEP	11 μmoles ATP	
Control liver	2·6	3·1	—
Phalloidin liver	1·9	2·0	20

observed in the presence of microsomes from phalloidin-treated guinea-pigs.

Effects of a somewhat similar kind have been obtained in rat liver with the liver carcinogen, dimethylnitrosamine [12, 13], and to some extent also with 2-aminofluorene [1]. Taken together these experiments indicate that the incorporation *in vitro* of amino acids into protein by liver microsomes is influenced by factors acting in the membrane components of the microsomes. Such factors may be predetermined by conditions prevailing already in the living cells.

Evidence of stimulation effects in cell-free systems

The experiments discussed above serve to illustrate the fact that under certain conditions the activity of cell-free incorporation systems may be abnormally low in proportion to their content of microsomal RNA, owing to the influence of factors induced already *in vivo*.

The opposite situation may also be met with in the study of cell-free systems of this type, i.e. that the incorporation activity shows a marked enhancement which cannot be explained on the basis of a proportional increase in the total content of RNP-particles. The first observation of this kind was made in sea urchin eggs in connection with their fertilization [14]. Only a few minutes after fertilization when the total number of RNP-particles still must have been very nearly the same as in the unfertilized eggs, the activity of whole egg homogenates in amino acid incorporation was considerably increased (Table IV). The same was true with "mitochondria-free homogenates" (centrifuged for 8 min. at 12 000 × **g**). The fertilization reaction rapidly seemed to make the individual RNP-particles more active in amino acid incorporation, in such manner

TABLE IV

INCORPORATION OF [¹⁴C]-L-LEUCINE INTO PROTEIN BY CELL-FREE PREPARATIONS
FROM UNFERTILIZED AND FERTILIZED *Psammechinus* EGGS

Preparation of cell fractions essentially as in Fig. 1. The incubation system contained 0·4 ml. of whole homogenate or 0·6 ml. of 12 000 **g** supernatant fraction from equal egg samples in combination with 0·6 ml. of rat liver cell sap [5], or RNP-particles from 0·7 ml. of packed eggs in combination with 0·65 ml. of the liver cell sap. System otherwise as in Fig. 1. Incubation period (20°) 30 min.

	c.p.m./cm.²	
	Unfertilized	Fertilized
Whole homogenate	29	71
12 000 **g** supernatant	28	74
RNP-particles	45	58

that this effect persisted also in preparations from disrupted cells. However, with RNP-particles isolated from the homogenates by the detergent treatment and layering procedure briefly mentioned in a previous section this fertilization effect was less marked.

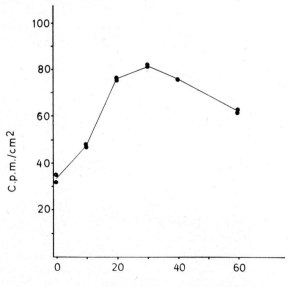

FIG. 3. Incorporation activity of a mitochondria-free rat liver homogenate at different periods of incubation (20°). At the periods indicated 0·08 μmole [¹⁴C]-L-leucine, 10 μmoles PEP, 15 μg. pyruvate kinase, 1 μmole ATP and 0·2 μmole GTP were added. Incubation period after these additions 5 min.

It may be relevant in this connection to mention some characteristic properties of cell-free incorporation systems containing mitochondria-free homogenates from liver [7]. Contrary to what would reasonably be expected in view of the limited life-span of these systems, the incorporation rate is not optimal just after the beginning of the incubation, but attains a fairly distinct maximum after some period of preincubation, the duration of which varies with temperature (Fig. 3). This lag is not due to the time

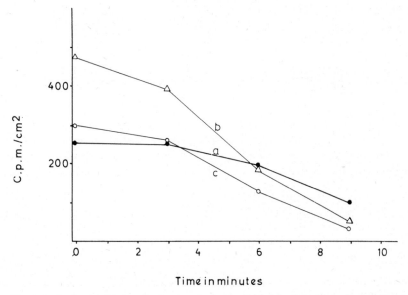

Time in minutes

FIG. 4. Amino acid incorporation by mitochondria-free liver homogenates from normal (*a*) and phalloidin-treated (*b*, *c*) guinea-pigs. Doses of phalloidin 0·4–0·5 μg./kg. System as in Fig. 1. [^{14}C]-L-leucine was added at the indicated periods of incubation, and TCA at 15 min. (35°).

required for the labelled amino acids to become activated, since in the illustrated experiment the nucleoside triphosphate-generating system was added to the system together with the labelled amino acid at the different periods indicated.

When mitochondria-free homogenates were prepared from phalloidin-treated mice or guinea-pigs, the preincubation effect was less pronounced or absent. The incorporation then proceeded at a maximal rate from the beginning of the incubation. With animals treated with small doses of phalloidin the paradoxical situation therefore sometimes occurred that over a 15 min. incubation period the total incorporation became higher in liver homogenates from the phalloidin-treated animals than in those from the controls (Fig. 4).

Stimulation effects in liver systems with relationship to the action of cortisone

As was briefly mentioned in a previous section the treatment of rats with liver carcinogens may lead to a *reduced* activity of the isolated microsomes in amino acid incorporation. After a single dose of 2-aminofluorene (2·5 mmoles per kg.) this effect is usually observed most easily 4–6 hr. after the administration.

Only a few hours later a strikingly different picture develops. As is shown by Table V, 20 hr. after the administration of 2-aminofluorene the

TABLE V

EFFECT OF *in vivo* TREATMENT WITH 2-AMINOFLUORENE (AF) OR 2-AMINOAPHTHALENE (AN) ON THE INCORPORATION OF [^{14}C]-L-LEUCINE INTO PROTEIN BY CELL-FREE LIVER SYSTEMS

The carcinogens (2·5 mmoles/kg. body weight) were administered 21 hr. prior to sacrifice. Incorporation system as in Fig. 1. Incubation period (35°) 10 min.

| | Incorporation in per cent of controls | | |
| | Rats | | Guinea-pigs |
	AF	AN	AF
Mitochondria-free homogenates	490*	220	144
Microsomes†	242	222	143
RNP-particles†	128	142	100

* RNA/protein ratio 120 per cent of that of normal homogenate [3].
† Primary values expressed as c.p.m./cm². per 100 μg. of particle-bound RNA added to system (cf. Fig. 2).

activity of mitochondria-free rat liver homogenates in amino acid incorporation was *increased* far above the normal level. At the same time there was some increase of the RNA-content in the homogenates, but this increase (usually less than 25%) was not nearly so great as the sometimes several-fold rise in incorporation activity.

Owing to the lack of proportionality between the activity of these liver homogenates in amino acid incorporation and their RNA contents it seemed possible that the activity increase might depend on a more efficient amino acid activation. It turned out, however, that this was not the main reason of the effect. Liver microsomes were prepared in parallel from aminofluorene-treated and normal rats and their incorporation activities were determined at different concentrations in a system containing standard amounts of normal soluble liver fraction. The microsomal activities were then compared at equal RNA or protein concentrations in the same way as in the phalloidin experiments described before. As is shown in Table V the microsomes from aminofluorene-treated animals showed a considerably higher incorporation activity per unit amount of RNA than did normal microsomes. With isolated RNP-particles, however, the stimulation effect was less pronounced.

There may be some relationship between the effects of 2-aminofluorene and its carcinogenic potency. In guinea-pigs, a species refractory to the carcinogenic action of 2-aminofluorene, the activation after 20 hr. was smaller than in rats (Table V). On the other hand, a significant stimulation was repeatedly observed after 4–6 hr., i.e. at a period when rat liver microsomes showed a definite inhibition. This species difference may possibly be due to the more rapid disposal of aminofluorene by metabolic detoxication in the guinea-pig liver. It may be of some interest that the well-known bladder carcinogen 2-aminonaphthalene, which has some potency also in liver, had about the same effects in rat liver as 2-aminofluorene (Table V).

TABLE VI

Effect of *in vivo* Treatment with 2-Aminofluorene or X-Rays on the Glycogen Content of Rat Liver

Dose of 2-aminofluorene 2·5 mmoles/kg. body weight, and of X-rays (all body irradiation, 45 min.) 2500 r. Glycogen content [16] in per cent of liver dry weight.

Treatment of rats	Glycogen content
Fed *ad libitum*	9·1
Fasted 20 hr.	0·53
Fasted 45 hr.	0·43
Fasted 24 hr. Aminofluorene 4 hr.	1·51
Fasted 45 hr. Aminofluorene 21 hr.	3·26
Fasted 45 hr. X-rays 21 hr.	6·1

As a routine the experiments were carried out with animals which had been kept without food for 16–20 hr. By this brief period of starvation the glycogen content in the liver is greatly reduced, a fact of practical advantage in the preparation of microsomes and RNP-particles. In the animals treated with 2-aminofluorene it was observed that the content of liver glycogen was higher than in the controls, without reaching, however, the level characteristic of normal, fed animals (Table VI). A similarly increased glycogen content has been observed by Kay and Entenman [15] in X-ray irradiated rats. In view of this striking similarity it seemed pertinent to find out whether X-ray treatment would also evoke an increased activity of amino acid incorporation *in vitro* As is shown by Table VII the incorporation activity of mitochondria-free rat liver homogenates was in fact increased 21 hr. after the exposure of the animals to an X-ray dose of 2500 r.

TABLE VII

Effect of X-Irradiation or Prednisolone Treatment *in vivo* on RNA-Content and [¹⁴C]-L-Leucine Incorporation Activity of Mitochondria-Free Rat Liver Homogenates

X-rays (all body irradiation, 45 min. 2500 r) and prednisolone (50 mg/kg. body weight, intraperitoneal injection) 21 hr. prior to decapitation. Incubation as in Table V.

	Incorporation and RNA content in per cent of controls	
	X-irradiation	prednisolone
[¹⁴C]-L-leucine incorporation	282	455
RNA content	110	120*

* Cf. [20].

Experimental evidence has been advanced by Mole [21] that the effect of irradiation on the content of liver glycogen depends on an increased susceptibility of the liver cells to corticoids. The following facts indicate that the increased incorporation activity described in this section has a similar relationship to corticoid functions: (*a*) The activation normally observed 20 hr. after aminofluorene treatment was absent in adrenalectomized animals (Table VIII). As a matter of fact, an inhibition was

TABLE VIII

Effect of 2-Aminofluorene-Treatment *in vivo* on the Incorporation of [¹⁴C]-L-Leucine into Protein by Mitochondria-Free Homogenates from Adrenalectomized Rats

The rats were adrenalectomized 48 hr. before the incorporation experiment. Experimental conditions as in Table V, 2-aminofluorene (AF) being administered 21 hr. prior to decapitation.

Pre-treatment *in vivo*	c.p.m./cm²
Adrenalectomized controls	441
Adrenalectomized, AF (0·5 mmole/kg.)	389
Adrenalectomized, AF (1·0 mmole/kg.)	308

usually observed; (*b*) Activation effects similar to those obtained in the rat with 2-aminofluorene, 2-aminonaphthalene or X-irradiation were obtained after the intraperitoneal administration of prednisolone (Table VII). These experiments are consistent with the recent observations by Feigelson *et al.* [9] that cortisone enhances the amino acid incorporation by rat liver *in vivo*.

Not very much can be said at present about the working mechanisms behind the activation effects described. It may be recalled from the previous section that unexpectedly high incorporation values were often obtained in systems containing mitochondria-free liver homogenates from animals treated with sublethal doses of phalloidin (Fig. 4). This effect could be related to a characteristic modification of the normal time course of the incorporation. In liver systems from animals recovering after amino-fluorene treatment the maximal rate of incorporation may possibly be reached slightly earlier than usual (Fig. 5), but the quantitative importance

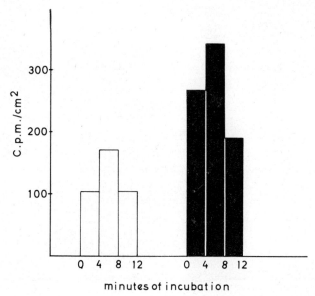

FIG. 5. Incorporation of [^{14}C]-L-leucine into protein by mitochondria-free guinea-pig liver homogenates. At zero time, or after 4 or 8 min. of incubation (35°C) 0·08 μmole of [^{14}C]-L-leucine, 10 μmoles of PEP and 1 μmole of ATP were added. Incubation was interrupted 4 min. later by the addition of TCA. *Open bars:* control livers. *Solid bars:* livers from animals given 2-aminofluorene (2·5 mmoles/kg.) 21 hr. prior to decapitation.

of this tendency must be fairly limited. As is evident from the time-course curve shown in Fig. 1, stimulation effects of the kind discussed here could in principle be due to a prolongation of the active life-span of the micro-somes. However, with the liver preparations from the aminofluorene-treated animals there was no indication of any appreciably longer active period. As is shown by Fig. 5, the increase in incorporation activity was equally pronounced in the period with maximal incorporation rate as in any other incubation period.

In cell-free liver systems from adult animals only a limited part of in-corporated, labelled amino acids becomes distributed to the proteins of the soluble fraction. It seemed possible, therefore, that the increased in-corporation rates described here might be due to a facilitated release of already labelled proteins from the anabolic sites on the RNP-particles. The distribution of incorporated ^{14}C-amino acids in different subfractions of the incubation mixture was therefore studied in experiments with mitochondria-free homogenates from normal and aminofluorene-treated animals. An experiment of this kind is shown in Table IX. When the

TABLE IX

INCORPORATION OF [^{14}C]-L-LEUCINE INTO PROTEIN BY MITOCHONDRIA-FREE RAT LIVER HOMOGENATES FROM NORMAL AND AMINOFLUORENE-TREATED ANIMALS. DISTRIBUTION OF ISOTOPE BETWEEN THE PROTEINS OF DIFFERENT SUBFRACTIONS OF THE INCUBATION SYSTEM.

Experimental conditions as in Table V, 2-aminofluorene (AF, 2·5 mmoles/kg. body weight) being administered 21 hr. prior to decapitation.

Fraction	c.p.m./cm².		AF/Controls
	AF	Controls	
Unfractionated	1048	449	2·33
Whole microsomes	3000	1650	1·82
Microsomes, DOC-extract	563	221	2·50
Cell sap, pH 5 precipitate	510	104	4·90
Cell sap, pH 5 supernatant	185	37	5·0

incorporation system from the aminofluorene-treated animals is compared with the control system, it appears in fact that an especially high increase in specific activity was obtained in the soluble fraction. A significantly smaller increase was observed in the proteins of the microsomes.

Discussion

The experiments described above indicate that under certain con-ditions the activity of RNP-particles in cell-free incorporation systems may be determined by factors, established in the intact cells and still retaining their influence in the disintegrated preparations. According to the experimental evidence, positive effects of this kind may be observed as well as negative. The examples which were given of negative after-effects in cell-free systems are most easily explained on the basis of a decreased functional stability of the microsomal membranes. In the experiments mentioned, this effect was induced under the action of a characteristic group of liver poisons which also includes some potent carcinogens. The experiments clearly illustrate the general importance of the metabolic

1*

state of the microsomal membranes for the functional abilities of the attached RNP-particles.

The stimulation effects described in the previous sections cannot yet be properly interpreted. It has been shown, particularly by experiments with regenerating liver, that growth stimulation may be accompanied by an increase in the total amount of RNP-particles in the cytoplasm [2, 5]. This process, by which the total capacity of the protein synthesizing machinery rapidly increases, may, however, constitute a rather late link in the reaction chain of growth stimulation, since, at least in regenerating liver, it demands a fairly long induction period (12–14 hr.). There reasonably must be a demand for more direct regulation mechanisms, by which the production of individual protein species can be adapted to current needs in a more rapid and flexible way (cf. [30]). The anabolic capacity of an average cell is probably not fully utilized under normal physiological conditions. It seems very likely, therefore, that the early stages of growth induction are characterized by an intensified utilization of the anabolic units already available.

The experiments described here may have some bearing on stimulation effects of the latter kind. They all suggest that even in cell-free incorporation systems the protein-synthesizing units are not always working at full speed. There apparently may still be room for some influence of modifying factors. In the experiments which were described these factors were physiological in the sense that they could be induced at will already in the living cells by treatments *in vivo* with agents such as hormones, carcinogens and, in the case of the sea urchin egg, the fertilizing sperm. There is some indication that the effects are related to a facilitated release of labelled proteins from the metabolic sites on the microsome particles. In view of this it will be of importance to attain a more detailed knowledge about the mechanisms by which this release is mediated.

Summary

Some experimental evidence has been collected in favour of the possibility that factors which influence the protein metabolism in the living cells may survive the disintegration of the cell structure and continue to influence the anabolic activity of the RNP-particles even in cell-free amino acid incorporation systems. Both negative and positive after-effects of this kind are discussed. The negative effects are illustrated by the action of certain liver poisons, including potent carcinogens. A treatment *in vivo* with these agents reduces the activity of isolated liver microsomes in cell-free incorporation systems. The effect is not entirely due to a direct and irreversible damage to the RNP-particles of the microsomes. Apparently a decreased functional stability of the microsomal membranes, which secondarily influences the activity of the attached particles, is a factor of importance in this reduction of activity.

The positive after-effects described have been observed in experiments with just fertilized sea-urchin eggs, and with liver directly or indirectly influenced by corticoids. In this case the activity of the cell-free incorporation systems becomes abnormally high in proportion to the amount of RNP-particles present. There are some indications that these effects are related to a facilitated release of labelled proteins from the particles.

The possibility is considered that effects of this kind may reflect simple intracellular regulation mechanisms, which to some extent may continue to operate also when the gross structural organization of the cells has been destroyed.

References

1. Arrhenius, E., and Hultin, T., *Exp. Cell Res.* **22**, 476 (1961).
2. Bernhard, W., and Rouiller, C., *J. biophys. biochem. Cytol.*, Suppl. **2**, 73 (1956).
3. Ceriotti, G., *J. biol. Chem.* **214**, 59 (1955).
4. Cohn, P., *Biochim. biophys. Acta* **33**, 284 (1959).
5. Decken, A. von der, and Hultin, T., *Exp. Cell Res.* **14**, 88 (1958).
6. Decken, A. von der, and Hultin, T., *Exp. Cell Res.* **15**, 254 (1958).
7. Decken, A. von der, and Hultin, T., "Progress in Biophysics and Biophysical Chemistry" (in press).
8. Decken, A. von der, Löw, H., and Hultin, T., *Biochem. Z.* **332**, 503 (1960).
9. Feigelson, P., Feigelson, M., and Greengard, O., "1st Internatl. Congr. Endocrinology", Abstracts 823 (1960).
10. Hanzon, V., Hermodsson, L. H., and Toschi, S., *J. Ultrastructure Res.* **3**, 216 (1959).
11. Hirsch, G. C., *Naturwissenschaften* **47**, 25 (1960).
12. Hultin, T., Arrhenius, E., Löw, H., and Magee, P. N., *Biochem. J.* **76**, 109 (1960).
13. Hultin, T., Magee, P. N., and Arrhenius, E., "4th Internatl. Congr. Biochem", Abstracts 185 (1958).
14. Hultin, T., and Bergstrand, Å., *Developmental Biol.* **2**, 61 (1960).
15. Kay, R. E., and Entenman, C., *Proc. Soc. exp. Biol.* **91**, 143 (1956).
16. Kemp, A., and Kits van Heijningen, A. J. M., *Biochem. J.* **56**, 646 (1954).
17. Korner, A., *Biochim. biophys. Acta* **35**, 554 (1960).
18. Krebs, H. A., and Henseleit, K., *Hoppe-Seyl. Z.* **210**, 33 (1932).
19. Löw, H., *Biochim. biophys. Acta* **32**, 1 (1959).
20. Lowe, C. U., Rand, R. N., and Venkataraman, P. R., *Proc. Soc. exp. Biol.* **98**, 696 (1958).
21. Mole, R. H., *Brit. J. exp. Path.* **37**, 528 (1956).
22. Morgan, W. S., von der Decken, A., and Hultin, T., *Exp. Cell Res.* **20**, 655 (1960).
23. Palade, G. E., *J. biophys. biochem. Cytol.* **1**, 59 (1955).
24. Rendi, R., *Exp. Cell Res.* **17**, 585 (1959).

25. Rendi, R., *Exp. Cell Res.* **19,** 489 (1960).
26. Rendi, R., and Hultin, T., *Exp. Cell Res.* **19,** 253 (1960).
27. Selby, C. C., *J. biophys. biochem. Cytol.* **1,** 429 (1955).
28. Siekevitz, P., *J. biol. Chem.* **195,** 549 (1952).
29. Siekevitz, P., *Exp. Cell Res. Suppl.* **7,** 90 (1959).
30. Spiegelman, S., *in* "Symposia of the Society for Experimental Biology", ed. F. Danielli and R. Brown. University Press, Cambridge, 286 (1948).
31. Ts'O, P. O. P., Bonner, J., and Vinograd, J., *J. biophys. biochem. Cytol.* **2,** 451 (1956).
32. Wieland, T., *in* "Festschrift Arthur Stoll", ed. P. Karrer *et al.* Birkhäuser, Basel, 582 (1957).
33. Zamecnik, P. C., and Keller, E. B., *J. biol. Chem.* **209,** 337 (1954).

Discussion

WILLIAMS: Korner has reported effects of insulin and growth hormone on amino acid incorporation, and I was wondering if you had confirmed these effects.

HULTIN: No. I do not think that Korner's experiments say very much about whether a high content of ribonucleoprotein particles has been induced or whether the particles already available work more efficiently in the system, but I should like to test that possibility.

SIEKEVITZ: One other explanation of your results is this: In the liver cells some RNP particles are on the membrane and some others are free, and when you measure the incorporation you measure the protein radioactivity in these mixed kind of particles. These particles are possibly synthesizing proteins at different rates and are perhaps also synthesizing different kinds of proteins. So that when you think you are making these particles increase they synthetic ability, what you might be really doing is changing the ratio from the normal state, the ratio of bound to free particles. You, therefore, might be switching over the synthesis from one kind of protein to another kind of protein which has a higher rate of synthesis.

HULTIN: I have also been considering that kind of possibility and also the possibility that particles may be released from the membrane and therefore work better. I am not quite convinced that a major change in the population pattern of the particles would be the right explanation in the case of the just fertilized sea urchin egg.

PACKER: Both you and Dr. Siekevitz are implying that what has happened is that changes in structure are simultaneously occurring, and I was wondering whether it would not be possible to devise an experiment, at least in an *in vitro* system, where you could simultaneously follow a parameter in physical structure and one in the function activity, such as viscosity determinations, light scattering determinations and sedimentation velocity.

HULTIN: Yes, perhaps under certain conditions what you call ergastoplasm may form some sort of sandwich which may become released, so that particles attached to this open sandwich may act more rapidly by becoming more easily supplied with energy and amino acids.

ZAMECNIK: There is another possible site of operation of a regulator of protein synthesis. Data of Dr. Tissieres *et al.* (*Proc. nat. Acad. Sci., Wash.* **46,** 1450-1463

(1960)) suggest that the 70 S ribonucleoprotein particle is actively engaged in protein synthesis, but that the 30, 50 and 100 S particles are not. Since a 30 S and a 50 S particle aggregate to form the active 70 S particle, it is possible that factors (such as Mg^{++} concentration) which influence the aggregation and disaggregation of these particles, may regulate the number of active sites available at a single moment for protein synthesis.

PACKER: Detergents are one clear way by which one can dissociate microsomes; another clear way is the type which has just been put on the board and this type has been documented quite nicely for microsomes of pea seedlings. Recently we have been examining suspensions of liver microsomes by adding anions and cations and chelating agents such as ATP, and following the changes in scattered light in the suspensions, and we find very large changes in light scattering accompany the addition of these reagents; so I would like to suggest that these normal chemical substances which are present in the cell are capable of affecting the state of structure of particles and perhaps the reaction system you employ for measuring the incorporation of labelled amino acids.

HULTIN: Perhaps I should point out again that we always have a good deal of magnesium present, and the magnesium content, as shown by Dr. Peterman, is very important in determining the aggregation of the particles. I think that factor is under control as we use a little more than the physiological concentration of magnesium.

PACKER: I feel that this sort of approach must be considered if you are to evaluate properly the structural-functional relationships especially as the types of changes in light scattering which I have mentioned occur very rapidly.

HULTIN: We agree that this has something to do with structure because when we treat the particles with detergents in a solution of high ionic strength we find the effects fade off.

PORTER: I would like to ask what you think happens to the microsomal membrane when you detach the RNP particle from the microsomes with DOC or any other of these reagents. Does a fragment go with the particle?

HULTIN: No. The particles we obtain in this way are absolutely free from all the enzymes which are typical of the microsomes. For example, from glucose-6-phosphatase, from DPNH-cytochrome c reductase, from TPNH-cytochrome c reductase, from cytochrome $5b$, etc. This means that they have very little impurities from the membrane.

CAMPBELL: Have you any idea what happens to the microsome pellet when you incubate it, when it loses its ability to incorporate?

HULTIN: I am very interested in this point but unfortunately I can't say very much about it yet.

The Effects of Spermine on the Ribonucleoprotein Particles of Guinea-Pig Pancreas*

PHILIP SIEKEVITZ

The Rockefeller Institute, New York, U.S.A.

Introduction

Our laboratory has been interested in the RNP† particles of the pancreas for the past few years [1–7]. Particularly pure preparations of these particles can now be obtained, having a diameter of 150 Å [1, 6, 7]. These particles have an RNA content of from 35 to 45% [1, 7], a sedimentation coefficient of 85 S [7] and a molar amount of Mg^{++} equivalent to about one tenth that of the phosphate groups in the RNA [7]. The particles as isolated have bound amylase, RNase and TAPase activities [6, 7]. Indeed, after the injection of radioactive leucine, the chymotrypsinogen which can be isolated from these particles has a higher specific radioactivity, at the early time points after injection, than the chymotrypsinogen isolated from other parts of the cell [6]. This finding indicates that these particles synthesize chymotrypsinogen, and possibly other secretory enzymes of the pancreas.

When the Mg^{++} of the particles is removed by chelating agents such as versene, ATP, GTP, and P-P, all of the above-named enzymes are concomitantly removed together without about 25% of the total protein and about 80% of the RNA of the particles [7]. It was calculated [7] that a good deal of the protein removed was made up of these bound enzymes. The particles are still recognizable as such, but their diameter has been increased about twofold [7]. We believe that the proteins synthesized on the particles are there for a finite period of time and have to be removed to complete the process of soluble protein synthesis. We were therefore interested in finding conditions under which only the enzymes are released

* This work was made possible by grant (A-1635) from the National Institute of Arthritis and Metabolic Diseases, National Institutes of Health, U.S. Public Health Service.

† Abbreviations used are: RNA, ribonucleic acid; RNA-P, ribonucleic acid phosphate; RNP, ribonucleoprotein; P-P, inorganic pyrophosphate; ATP and GTP, adenosine and guanosine triphosphates; tris, tris (hydroxymethyl) aminomethane; RNase, ribonuclease; TAPase, trypsin-activateable proteolytic activity; TCA, trichloracetic acid.

from the particles, without removal of the RNA from the particles, since the total RNA of these particles has a very low rate of turnover *in vivo* [5]. This preliminary report notes one of these conditions. In brief, it has been found that the polyamines, putrescine, cadaverine, and particularly spermine, will effect a release of the bound enzymes from the particles. In addition, spermine replaces the Mg^{++} of the particles, and in doing so, confers a stability on the particles in the absence of Mg^{++}, so that very little or no release of the RNA occurs under these conditions. The consequence of these findings on the nature of the bindings among the RNA, protein, and enzymes of the particles is discussed.

Methods

The RNP particles of the pancreas were isolated from pancreatic microsomes by the detergent, deoxycholate, as already described [6, 7]. The measurements of amylase, RNase, and TAPase activities, and the conditions for measurements of the release of these activities from the particles has already been given [7]. Also, the estimations of RNA, protein, and Mg^{++}, and the estimations of the release of these from the particles, has been detailed [7]. RNA-P was calculated as being 9% of the RNA. The incubations conditions for the experiments were as follows: The surface of the pellets of the RNP particles was washed, and the particles resuspended by homogenization in 30% sucrose. Particles from 250 mg. wet weight pancreas were incubated for 30 min. at 35° in a total volume of 2·0 ml., containing the various compounds to be tested, and with the final sucrose concentration being 15%. After incubation, the contents of two tubes were pooled, cold distilled water was added, to make the final sucrose concentration 5%, and the suspension was then spun for 90 min. at 105 000 × **g** in a Spinco Co. refrigerated centrifuge. Enzymic activities were tested on the original particle suspension before incubation, and on the supernatant and sometimes on the pellet after incubation and sedimentation. In other experiments, the RNA, protein, and Mg^{++} contents of the original particle suspension and of the re-sedimented particles were measured. In some cases, where duplicate assays were particularly desirable, as in the Mg^{++} determinations, more of the incubated particles were pooled for sedimentation. In the cases where radioactive spermine was used, the spun-down pellet was washed several times with cold distilled water to remove possible contamination by unbound spermine and then resuspended in water. In these experiments, one-half of the suspension was used for RNA, protein, and Mg^{++} determinations, while the other half was dried down on aluminum planchets, kept in a desiccator, and counted with a Nuclear-Chicago gas-flow counter, with a counting error of less than 1%. In these radioactive experiments, about 10 000 c.p.m.

spermine was used in each experiment, and from 250 c.p.m. to 1000 c.p.m. were recovered in the particles in the various experiments; this is much more than would be expected from contamination, since the particles were well washed after centrifugation. In the experiments in which the release of radioactive spermine from the particles was followed, the following conditions were used: The particles were incubated with radio-active spermine as given above. They were then centrifuged, washed extensively, and resuspended by homogenization in cold distilled water. An aliquot of this suspension was then removed for immediate chemical and radioactive analyses, while another aliquot was incubated at 35° for 30 min. with various additions in a total volume of 1·0 ml. After incuba-tion, water was added, the suspension centrifuged at 105 000 × **g** for 90 min., and the pellet was resuspended in water and assayed as above. All the compounds used in the experiments were brought to pH 7·0. The radioactive spermine, specific activity approximately 0·1 $\mu c/\mu$mole, was labelled with ^{14}C in the 1 and 4 positions of the butane part of the mole-cule ([1,4-^{14}C]-1,4-di-(1′,3′-diamino propyl) butane) and was obtained through the generosity of Drs. H. Waelsch and D. Clarke.

Results

In a previous paper [7], it was reported that P-P, or even ATP or GTP, at a conc. of 5 × 10^{-4} M, could release from 80 to 100% of the bound amylase, RNase, and TAPase activities of the RNP particles, after incuba-tion of the particles at 35° for 30 min. Table I shows, again as a com-parison, the results of further experiments with P-P and also the results of experiments with various amines and other compounds. Spermine, even at 5 × 10^{-5} M, could release the amylase activity from the particles. In experiments not shown, spermine at 10^{-4} M was equivalent to P-P at 5 × 10^{-4} M in releasing also the RNase and TAPase activities of the particles. Putrescine and cadaverine, while effective, could not release the amylase activity as well as spermine, and it would seem that the ability to release the enzymic activity is related to the number of amine groups and hence the charge on the molecule. As can be seen, histamine, lysine, and ornithine had some effect, while even tris buffer had an effect, but a marked one only at 5 × 10^{-3} M. It is noteworthy that pilocarpine, car-bamylcholine, and acetylcholine have very little, if any, effect on the amylase release, as compared to incubation in water.

The P-P release of the bound enzymic activities of the particles is probably a consequence of the concomitant release of all the Mg^{++} and most of the RNA of the particles [7]. Table II shows, again further experiments with P-P, and with various amine compounds, on the dis-charge of Mg^{++} and of RNA from the particles. However, unlike P-P,

TABLE I

Release of Amylase Activity from RNP Particles by Spermine, Various other Amines, and Various other Compounds

Incubation conditions are given in the text. Per cent release is that percentage of amylase activity which was rendered soluble after spinning the incubated particles for 90 min. at 105 000 × **g**. Each figure represents one experiment.

Compound added	Conc. (M)	Per cent release	Compound added	Conc. (M)	Per cent release
Spermine	5×10^{-5}	83, 88	Tris, pH 7·0	5×10^{-4}	33
Spermine	10^{-4}	86, 90,	Tris, pH 7·0	10^{-3}	63, 41§
		82, 93	Tris, pH 7·0	5×10^{-3}	71, 46, 86
Spermine	5×10^{-4}	97, 100,	In. Pyrophos.	5×10^{-4}	91, 80, 100,
		99, 100*			81, 99
Spermine	5×10^{-3}	100†	Serotonin	5×10^{-4}	29
Putrescine	10^{-3}	68‡	Carbamylcholine	5×10^{-4}	23
Putrescine	10^{-2}	72	Pilocarpine	5×10^{-4}	19
Cadaverine	10^{-3}	66	Acetylcholine	5×10^{-4}	15
Histamine	10^{-3}	48	Liver glycogen	1 mg.	8
L-Lysine	10^{-3}	30	Water	—	8, 9, 15
L-Ornithine	10^{-3}	32			18, 0, 21
L-Arginine	10^{-3}	10			

* Incubated at $0° = 83$.
† Plus 10^{-3} M $Mg^{++} = 96$.
‡ Plus 10^{-3} M $Mg^{++} = 77$.
§ Incubated at $0° = 32$.

spermine only discharges a small amount of the RNA of the particles, and in fact, the ratio, RNA/protein, of the spermine-treated particles is the same or even higher than that of the particles incubated in water. In contradistinction, the P-P treated particles have an RNA/protein ratio of one-half (Table II), or even lower [7] than, that of the control particles. However, spermine, like P-P, releases nearly all the Mg^{++} of the particles into solution. Putrescine, at 10^{-3} M, behaves similarly to spermine at 5×10^{-4} M or at 10^{-4} M, but at 2×10^{-3} M putrescine begins to disrupt the particles so that some of the RNA is released.

The reason given previously for the action of the pyrophosphate compounds was that these compounds effectively compete with the phosphate groups of the RNA for the Mg^{++} complexed to these groups. Thus, the addition of Mg^{++} to the incubation medium along with the pyrophosphate compounds nullifies the effect of these compounds [7]. However, when Mg^{++} was added with the spermine, it did not counteract the effect of spermine on amylase release (cf. footnote, Table I). In fact, it was uniformly found that in the presence of both Mg^{++} and spermine,

TABLE II

EFFECT OF VARIOUS AMINES AND INORGANIC PYROPHOSPHATE
ON THE RELEASE OF RNA, PROTEIN, AND Mg^{++} FROM RNP PARTICLES

Incubation conditions are given in the text.

Exp. No.	Compound added	Left in RNP particles after spinning incubated particles for 90 min. at 105 000 × **g**			
		RNA (μg.)	Protein (μg.)	RNA/ Protein	Mg^{++} (μmoles)
1	None	362	728	0·50	—
	Inorg. Pyrophos. (5 × 10^{-4} M)	140	515	0·27	—
	Spermine (10^{-4} M)	355	555	0·64	—
	Tris, pH 7·0 (10^{-3} M)	353	555	0·63	—
2	None	351	550	0·64	0·08
	Spermine (5 × 10^{-4} M)	260	419	0·62	0·00
	Putrescine (5 × 10^{-3} M)	179	506	0·35	0·00
3	None	915	1250	0·73	0·30
	Inorg. Pyrophos. (5 × 10^{-4} M)	456	1190	0·38	0·04
	Spermine (10^{-4} M)	935	1300	0·72	0·05
	Putrescine (10^{-3} M)	920	1270	0·73	0·11
4	None	142	350	0·41	0·04
	Spermine (10^{-4} M)	143	287	0·50	0·00
	Putrescine (10^{-3} M)	111	281	0·40	0·01
5	None	112	256	0·44	0·03
	Spermine (10^{-4} M)	102	237	0·43	0·00
	Putrescine (2 × 10^{-3} M)	51	237	0·22	0·00
6	None	289	—	—	0·08
	Spermine (10^{-4} M)	272	—	—	0·02
	Spermine (10^{-4} M) plus Mg^{++} (10^{-3} M)	321	—	—	0·10

the RNA/protein ratios of the incubated particles were the same or in
most cases higher than those of either the untreated particles or the
particles treated with spermine alone (Table III). This might be related to
the observation that in the presence of Mg^{++} in the medium, spermine
did not release the Mg^{++} from the particles (Table II, Exp. 6).

From the results of the above experiments, it would appear that the
action of the various amines, particularly spermine, can be described as
follows. Spermine replaces the Mg^{++} complexed to the phosphate groups
of the RNA of the particles by forming a strong salt bond between its
charged amine groups and the charged phosphate groups of the RNA.
This salt bond is stronger than the Mg^{++}-phosphate complex. The

TABLE III

EFFECT OF SPERMINE AND OF Mg^{++} ON RELEASE OF RNA AND
PROTEIN FROM RNP PARTICLES

Incubation conditions are given in the text.

Exp. No.	Additions	Left in RNP particles after spinning incubated particles for 90 min. at 105 000 × **g**		
		RNA (μg.)	Protein (μg.)	RNA/ Protein
1	None	229	341	0·67
	Spermine (10^{-4} M)	209	278	0·75
	Spermine (10^{-4} M) plus Mg^{++} (10^{-3} M)	273	319	0·85
2	Spermine (10^{-4} M)	188	272	0·69
	Spermine (10^{-4} M) plus Mg^{++} (10^{-3} M)	246	275	0·89
3	Spermine (10^{-4} M)	116	250	0·47
	Spermine (10^{-4} M) plus Mg^{++} (10^{-3} M)	156	271	0·58
4	None	211	315	0·67
	Spermine (10^{-4} M)	154	282	0·55
	Spermine (10^{-4} M) plus Mg^{++} (10^{-3} M)	176	287	0·62

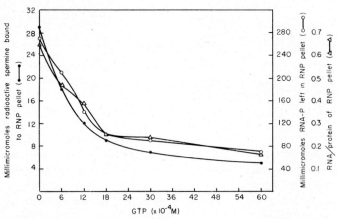

FIG. 1. Effect of GTP concentration on the bound radioactive spermine, on the RNA, and on the RNA/protein ratio of the RNP particles. Methods are given in the text.

addition of Mg^{++} along with the spermine results in a very weak Mg^{++}-spermine complex and hence has no effect on the salts formed between the spermine and the phosphate groups. Since the spermine would appear

TABLE IV

BINDING OF RADIOACTIVE SPERMINE TO RNP PARTICLES, AND
THE EFFECT OF Mg^{++} ON THIS BINDING

Incubation conditions are given in the text.

Exp. No.	Additions	Spermine bound (μmoles)	μmoles spermine bound per 10 μmoles RNA-P
1	Spermine (5×10^{-4} M)	0·022	0·29
2	Spermine (10^{-4} M)	0·014*	0·31
	Spermine (10^{-4} M) plus Mg^{++} (10^{-3} M)	0·031	0·74
3	Spermine (10^{-4} M)	0·009†	0·30
	Spermine (10^{-4} M) plus Mg^{++} (10^{-3} M)	0·036	1·20
4	Spermine (10^{-4} M)	0·034	0·55
	Spermine (10^{-4} M) plus Mg^{++} (10^{-3} M)	0·039	0·49
5	Spermine (10^{-4} M)	0·058	1·05
	Spermine (10^{-4} M) plus Mg^{++} (10^{-3} M)	0·061	0·87
6	Spermine (10^{-4} M)	0·049	1·49
	Spermine (10^{-4} M) plus Mg^{++} (10^{-3} M)	0·049	1·09
7	Spermine (10^{-4} M)	0·050	1·12
	Spermine (10^{-4} M) plus Mg^{++} (10^{-3} M)	0·014	0·26

 * When pellet was treated with 5% TCA, then re-spun, and pellet recounted, 0·002 μmoles radioactive spermine remained bound.

 † When pellet was treated with 5% TCA, then re-spun, and pellet recounted, 0·0018 μmoles radioactive spermine remained bound.

to replace the Mg^{++} from the particles, and since the Mg^{++} seems to be one of the principal instrumentalities in stabilizing these particles (cf. ref. in [7]), it should follow that spermine also helps to bind the RNA to the protein of the particles, and as Tables II and III indicate, it seems to do so.

Since we were doubly fortunate to be in New York City and knew of certain experiments performed by Dr. Waelsch and his associates, and were also friends of Dr. Waelsch and his associates, we were able to test the above possibility by obtaining radioactive spermine from them. The results are shown in Tables IV and V and Fig. 1. Table IV shows, indeed, that spermine is bound to the particles, while Table V shows that by far the greatest part of the bound spermine cannot be washed off the particles by further water incubation of the particles. Previously [7], we had found

TABLE V

EFFECT OF GTP AND OF Mg^{++} ON THE RELEASE OF RADIOACTIVE SPERMINE, AND OF PROTEIN AND RNA FROM RNP PARTICLES

The RNP particles were labelled with radioactive spermine as described in the text. These particles were then re-suspended and re-incubated at 35° for 30 min. under the conditions given in the text and with additions given below. After re-incubation, the particles were spun at 105 000 × **g** for 90 min., and radioactivity, protein, and RNA determined as described in the text.

Exp. No.	Additions	Left in RNP particles after spinning re-incubated particles for 90 min. at 105 000 × **g**				
		Protein (μg.)	RNA (μmoles RNA-P)	RNA/ Protein	Spermine (μmoles)	μmoles spermine per 10 μmoles RNA-P
1	None	—	—	—	0·018	—
	Mg^{++} (10^{-2} M)	—	—	—	0·018	—
2	Control (no re-incubation)	250	0·33	0·47	0·049	1·49
	None	150	0·25	0·58	0·028	1·12
	Mg^{++} (10^{-2} M)	—	—	—	0·023	—
	GTP (5 × 10^{-4} M)	—	—	—	0·016	—
	GTP (5 × 10^{-4} M) plus Mg^{++} (3 × 10^{-3} M)	—	—	—	0·022	—
3	Control (no re-incubation)	282	0·44	0·55	0·050	1·12
	None	259	0·37	0·49	0·034	0·92
	GTP (2 × 10^{-3} M)	122	0·04	0·12	0·004	1·00
	GTP (2 × 10^{-3} M) plus Mg^{++} (3 × 10^{-3} M)	188	0·23	0·44	0·026	1·13
4	Control (no re-incubation)	275	0·54	0·67	0·069	1·28
	None	231	0·37	0·56	0·045	1·22
	GTP (2 × 10^{-3} M)	187	0·14	0·27	0·014	0·97
	GTP (2 × 10^{-3} M) plus Mg^{++} (3 × 10^{-3} M)	253	0·32	0·43	0·036	1·12
	ATP (2 × 10^{-3} M)	228	0·18	0·28	0·019	1·08
	ATP (2 × 10^{-3} M) plus Mg^{++} (3 × 10^{-3} M)	250	0·27	0·38	0·034	1·26

that the ratio, μmoles Mg^{++}/10 μmoles RNA-P, in the RNP particles was approximately one. In Table IV it can be seen that this ratio for spermine varied from 0·29 to 1·49 in the various experiments; or, if put in another way, from 0·6 to 3·0 μmoles primary amine/10 μmoles RNA-P, or from 1·2 to 6·0 μmoles total amine group/10 μmoles RNA-P. It can be noticed that these experiments of Table IV fall into three classes; one in which relatively low binding of spermine occurred but the addition of Mg^{++} increased it (Exps. 1, 2, 3); one in which an intermediate uptake of spermine occurred and Mg^{++} had little effect (Exps. 4, 5); and one in which high binding of radioactive spermine occurred but the addition of Mg^{++} decreased this binding (Exps. 6, 7). The possible reasons for these variations will be discussed below.

That the binding of the spermine is primarily due to the RNA of the particles can be inferred from the concluding data. First, washing of the particles with TCA releases most of the spermine counts (cf. footnote, Table IV), indicating a non-covalent bond. Secondly, it can be seen (Table V and Fig. 1) that the radioactive spermine which is bound to the particles can be largely removed by treating the particles with either GTP or ATP, and in doing so the RNA is also removed. Figure 1 shows that as the bound spermine is removed from the particles, the RNA is proportionally removed, whereas very little protein is lost. Hence, the ratio, RNA/protein, follows the removal of the spermine and of the RNA, as the GTP concentration is increased. Table V also indicates that when Mg^{++} is incubated along with the GTP or ATP, the removal of spermine by GTP or ATP is largely prevented, indicating that the added Mg^{++} effectively forms a complex with the added GTP or ATP and prevents its action in removing the spermine and the RNA. Thus it can be deduced that the amine groups of the bound spermine were salt-bonded to the phosphate groups of the RNA, and the addition of the pyrophosphate compounds, GTP or ATP, effectively competes with the phosphate groups of the RNA, for the bound spermine. When Mg^{++} was present, the pyrophosphate groups were complexed with it, and hence had little effect.

Discussion

Firstly, it should be understood that the pancreatic RNP particles do not seem to be quite the same as the bacterial and yeast or even the liver particles. Their size is different; 150 Å for the 85 S pancreatic particles [7], and 200 Å for the 80 S yeast particles [8] and for the 70 S Escherichia coli particles [9, 10]. Furthermore, it appears that the E. coli particles are made up of sub-units of 30 S and 50 S particles [9, 10, 11, 12] and of 100 S dimers [9, 10, 11]. There is no evidence as yet, either morphologically or with the analytical centrifuge, that the pancreatic particles are made up of smaller units. There is evidence, though, that this might be the case for the 80 S pea seedling particles [13] and the 80 S liver particles [14], but even in these cases the sub-units seem to be 60 S and 40 S particles [13, 14]. In all the cases mentioned, except for pancreas, a decrease in the Mg^{++} content of the particles results in their disruption, so that the smaller sub-units have the same RNA/protein ratios, indicating that the Mg^{++} is involved in RNA to RNA binding and not in RNA to protein binding. The reasons for this apparent discrepancy between these results and ours is not known (cf. [7]); it could be that while in the pea seedling particles there is about 1 mole Mg^{++} for every four phosphates in the RNA [13] and while the Mg^{++} requirement for the *E. coli* particles seems to be very high [11], in the pancreatic particles there is only about 1 Mg^{++} for every ten phosphates [7].

In our view, there are three components to be considered in the pancreatic RNP particles; the RNA and proteins themselves, and the sub-divisions of the latter into the so-called "structural" proteins of the particles, and into the proteins which are being synthesized by the particle and some of which still reside there, on the "template" if you wish. The reason for the latter part of the statement are the earlier findings [7] and the present ones, that Mg^{++} chelators and replacers can release some of the proteins of the particle without releasing the bulk of them. Even the RNA of the particle might not be homogeneous, for we have never been able to remove all the RNA from the protein of the particle, either by Mg^{++} chelators [7] or by the removal of the spermine in the present experiments. Thus it could be that a small proportion of the RNA is more tightly bound to the protein, and could be metabolically different, than is the bulk of the RNA.

What are the probable bindings between RNA and proteins in the pancreatic particles? There is evidence that hydrogen bonding [15, 16], electrostatic bonding [17] and Mg^{++} complexing (cf. literature cited in [7]) are all somehow involved. I will just discuss the Mg^{++} binding and the effects of spermine on this binding. We must look to two possibilities; that the Mg^{++} ties together various RNA chains in the RNP and thus stabilizes the hydrogen and electrostatic bonds between the RNA and the protein of the RNP [15], or that Mg^{++} links the RNA chains both to the structural and to the newly synthesized proteins of the RNP (cf. [7]). It is difficult to decide between these two not mutually exclusive propositions, for it is conceivable that if Mg^{++} complexes adjacent RNA chains, the removal of this Mg^{++} so weakens the hydrogen and electrostatic bonds between RNA and protein that these groups become separated from each other. It is thus clear that no one binding force seems adequate by itself to explain the structural stability of the particles. However, it would appear that the Mg^{++} complexing is of utmost importance, at least in the pancreatic particles. Once the Mg^{++} is removed, and not replaced by other binding agents, such as spermine, then any hydrogen bonds or ionic forces which might hold the RNA to the protein are weakened, and the particle loses identity as an RNP particle. In the case of the particles from other sources, it would appear as mentioned, that Mg^{++} links together the RNA chains within one particle. There is no reason to disbelieve that the same does not also hold for the pancreatic particles. For example, when spermine is added to a suspension of these particles, they immediately begin to aggregate, as if the spermine is providing more groups, in this case the positively charged amine groups, for attachment to any negatively charged groups in the vicinity, be they the phosphate groups in the RNA of a single particle or the phosphate groups in the RNA of adjacent particles, the latter explaining the aggregation.

The experiments mentioned in this paper, while clarifying some aspects of the RNP particle structure, also add some complexities to the picture, for which no adequate answer is available at present. It is clear, for example, that in replacing the Mg^{++} of the particle, spermine discharges only some of the proteins from the particles. A theory based on this finding is as follows. The Mg^{++} is complexed to the phosphate groups of adjacent RNA chains; but it is possible that the amino groups of adenine and guanine also contribute to the binding energy of the complex [18]. When spermine is added, Mg^{++} is removed, and the salt linkages formed by the spermine amine groups and the RNA phosphate groups are strong enough to stabilize the particle in the absence of Mg^{++}, by also preserving any hydrogen and ionic bindings between the RNA and protein. However, some of the proteins, namely, the secretory enzymes, presumably the newly synthesized proteins [6], are discharged from the particle. It is our contention that these particular proteins are held on to the RNA ("template"?) by the bridging, by some of the Mg^{++}, between the phosphate groups of the RNA and the amino groups of the peptide bond or the free amine groups of the basic amino acids. The amine groups of spermine cannot replace the co-ordination bonds of Mg^{++} in such a situation and the enzymes are discharged from the particles. Since there is only one Mg^{++} for every ten phosphates of the RNA, it is conceivable that all of the Mg^{++} is involved in holding these newly synthesized proteins on to the particle. For, since Mg^{++} has a co-ordination number of four and possibly six [19], it is possible that some of these co-ordination bonds are involved in only phosphate complexing, while others are involved in complex formation between the phosphate groups and the carbonyl groups of the structural protein or the amino groups of the synthesized proteins.

However, it appears that the binding of the RNA molecules to each other or to the proteins is not as secure as might be assumed for a stable configuration. It had been previously found that when all the Mg^{++} and most of the RNA of the particles are removed, the remainder of the particle has a diameter almost twice that of the original particle [7]. Even when the RNA is not removed, as in the present experiments with spermine, the particle diameter becomes twice that of the original particle, as found in electron micrographs by G. E. Palade. This could be explained by assuming that the particle is somewhat an open structure,* and the compactness of the particle can be changed by the availability of bonding forces, in this case, the amine groups of the spermine and the phosphate groups of the RNA (cf. [20]). These variations in the compactness of the particles can explain the variations noted in Table IV. Firstly, it is probable that at pH 7 all the basic groups of the spermine are charged (cf. [21]). The amount of spermine binding to the particles could be determined by the availability of phosphate groups open to salt linkage. The farther apart are the available phosphate groups, then the greater the number of *molecules* of spermine which are bound, for only one amino group per spermine can be bound.† When the phosphates are closer together, the less spermine *molecules* will be bound, because all the available phosphate groups in the vicinity can be linked to the amine groups of the same spermine molecule. It thus might be of significance that the amount of spermine bound per RNA goes up by factors of approximately two and four (Table IV), as if one, two, or all four of the amine groups in spermine are becoming involved. Thus, in the various experiments cited in Table IV, the RNP particles as isolated may be greatly different in their compactness of structure. When this structure is loose, more spermine can be bound (Table IV, Exps. 5, 6, 7). In the presence of Mg^{++}, the intermolecular distances might become smaller owing to the formation of Mg^{++}-spermine-phosphate complexes (cf. [19]). Hence the available phosphate groups can be linked to more than one amine groups of the spermine molecule, thus less spermine molecules are bound in the presence of Mg^{++} (Table IV, Exps. 6, 7). When the structure is tight, less spermine is bound (Table IV, Exps. 1, 2, 3). In the presence of Mg^{++}, again Mg^{++}-spermine-phosphate complexes can be formed, but in this case these complexes can open up a resilient structure, allowing more spermine to be bound (Table IV, Exps. 1, 2, 3). As disclosed in Table III, and has been found previously [22] with *E. coli* particles, the particles have higher RNA/protein ratios in the presence of both spermine and Mg^{++} than in the presence of either alone. Also, when the particles are incubated in the presence of both spermine and Mg^{++}, the spermine becomes bound, and no Mg^{++} or RNA leaves the particle. Furthermore, nucleotide incorporation into RNA by liver preparations can be stimulated by the addition together of spermine

---

* The mean diameter of the particles under the experimental conditions mentioned, as found by G. E. Palade, is as follows: As isolated, 150 Å; after incubation in sucrose, 180 Å; after incubation in ATP, P-P, or versene, 250–300 Å; after incubation in spermine, 400 Å; after incubation in spermine plus Mg^{++}, 300 Å. In some cases, when the RNA is removed from the particles, a less dense centre appears, giving the particle a doughnut appearance [7].

† It has been estimated [20] that the distance between the terminal primary amines in spermine is approximately 16·5 Å.

and Mg^{++} [23]. These findings are not in disagreement with the existence within the particles of Mg^{++}-spermine-phosphate complexes.

The finding that spermine could release the enzymes from the particles without disrupting them prompted us to look for this polyamine in the particles. We were encouraged by a report [24] that in *E. coli* and in liver particles there exist some of these polyamines, namely putrescine, cadaverine, and spermidine. We have used the electrophoretic and chromatographic methods mentioned [24] and have tentatively identified spermine and perhaps spermidine in rat liver, guinea-pig liver, and guinea-pig pancreas particles.* Contrary to the above, we could find no cadaverine nor spermidine in the rat liver particles using the methods mentioned; but we also found another compound (cf. [24]) which gave a ninhydrin colour and was positively charged, but whose mobility was different from that of the polyamines mentioned and the basic amino acids. Thus, these polyamines could well be the physiological agents which might effect a release of synthesized enzymes, leaving the RNP structure intact. A possible physiological mechanism regulating this release would thus have to do with Mg^{++} availability and displacement by spermine.

However, it could be that spermine acts in these particles as a stabilizing agent, helping to hold the particle together, as it has been found to preserve nucleic acid structure [25, 26], to preserve bacterial [27, 28] and protoplast [27, 29] structure, as well as conferring stability on mammalian mitochondria [29] and nuclei [20]. Also, it has been found that these polyamines can bind strongly to polynucleotides [30] and to phage [21], and thus to stabilize and neutralize the DNA of the latter [21].

There have been reports that the total proteins of the RNP particles from liver [31, 32], reticulocytes [31] and pea seedlings [31] contain relatively large amounts of basic amino acids, but other findings suggest that this is not the case for *E. coli* particles [15], nor for liver particles [33]. If this be the case, it is hard to see, from the discussion above, how these basic amino acids contribute to the binding of the RNA to the protein, particularly in light of the finding that even histidine does not bind strongly to certain synthetic polynucleotides [30].

References

1. Palade, G. E., and Siekevitz, P., *J. biophys. biochem. Cytol.* **2**, 671 (1956).
2. Siekevitz, P., and Palade, G. E., *ibid.* **4**, 203 (1958).
3. Siekevitz, P., and Palade, G. E., *ibid.* **4**, 309 (1958).
4. Siekevitz, P., and Palade, G. E., *ibid.* **4**, 557 (1958).
5. Siekevitz, P., and Palade, G. E., *ibid.* **5**, 1 (1959).

* However, it is possible that *in vivo* the particles do not contain these polyamines, for their presence in the isolated particles may be a result of redistribution during homogenization, from a soluble state to that of being bound to any available phosphate groups of the RNA.

6. Siekevitz, P., and Palade, G. E., *ibid.* **7,** 619 (1960).
7. Siekevitz, P., and Palade, G. E., *ibid.* **7,** 631 (1960).
8. Chao, F.-C., and Schachman, H. K., *Arch. Biochem. Biophys.* **61,** 220 (1956).
9. Hall, C. E., and Slayter, H. S., *J. mol. Biol.* **1,** 329 (1959).
10. Huxley, H. E., and Zubay, G., *J. mol. Biol.* **2,** 10 (1960).
11. Tissières, A., Watson, J. D., Schlessinger, D., and Hollingsworth, B. R., *J. mol. Biol.* **1,** 221 (1959).
12. Report of Biophysics Section, Dept. Terr. Mag., Carnegie Inst. Wash. Year Book (1959).
13. Ts'o, P. O. P., Bonner, J., and Vinograd, J., *Biochim. biophys. Acta* **30,** 570 (1958).
14. Hamilton, M. G., and Petermann, M. L., *J. biol. Chem.* **234,** 1441 (1959).
15. Elson, D., *Biochim. biophys. Acta* **36,** 362 (1959).
16. Hall, B. D., and Doty, P., *J. mol. Biol.* **1,** 111 (1959).
17. Tashiro, Y., and Inouye, A., *J. Biochem., Tokyo,* **46,** 1625 (1959).
18. Zubay, G., *Biochim. biophys. Acta* **32,** 233 (1959).
19. Chaberek, S., and Martell, A. E., "Organic Sequestering Agents". J. Wiley Sons, New York (1959).
20. Anderson, N. G., and Norris, C. B., *Exp. Cell Res.* **19,** 605 (1960).
21. Ames, B. N., and Dubin, D. T., *J. biol. Chem.* **235,** 769 (1960).
22. Cohen, S. S., and Lichtenstein, J., *J. biol. Chem.* **235,** 2112 (1960).
23. Chung, C. N., Mahler, H. R., and Enicore, M., *J. biol. Chem.* **235,** 1448 (1960).
24. Zillig, W., Krone, W., and Albers, M., *Hoppe-Seyl. Z.* **317,** 131 (1959).
25. Doctor, P. B., and Herbst, E. J., *Fed. Proc.* **17,** 212 (1958).
26. Fraser, D., and Mahler, H. R., *J. Amer. chem. Soc.* **80,** 6456 (1958).
27. Mager, J., *Biochim. biophys. Acta* **36,** 529 (1959).
28. Herbst, E. J., Weaver, R. A., and Keister, D. L., *Arch. Biochem. Biophys.* **75,** 171 (1958).
29. Tabor, C. W., *Biochem. Biophys. Res. Comm.* **2,** 117 (1960).
30. Felsenfeld, G., and Huang, S., *Biochim. biophys. Acta* **37,** 425 (1960).
31. Ts'O, P. O. P., Bonner, J., and Dintzis, H., *Arch. Biochem. Biophys.* **76,** 225 (1958).
32. Crampton, C. F., and Petermann, M. L., *J. biol. Chem.* **234,** 2642 (1959).
33. Butler, J. A. V., Cohn, P., and Simson, P., *Biochim. biophys. Acta* **38,** 386 (1960).

Discussion

HULTIN: Did you say that if you treated these particles with spermine then they would swell up ? If you now treat these gels with magnesium, what happens ?

SIEKEVITZ: Yes, they do swell up. We haven't done what you suggested, but we have incubated them with spermine + magnesium and they looked the same way as with spermine alone.

BERGERON: Did the aggregates seen in the electron micrographs of the pellets precede fixation or arise in the course of fixation ?

SIEKEVITZ: This is a visible aggregation during the centrifugation. In the absence of spermine when you centrifuge these particles they form a nice pellet on the bottom. In all these other cases they precipitated on the side of the tubes indicating that they were aggregating during centrifugation, and in the case of the spermine, they aggregated before centrifugation.

HUNTER: I was just thinking that if manganese had a greater affinity than magnesium, that would help to get the spermine out.

SIEKEVITZ: Actually I should say that we only looked for magnesium in these particles. There might be manganese there or even calcium. Dr. Ts'O has found that in pea seedling particles there was five times as much magnesium as calcium.

HUNTER: Even if manganese were not present physiologically, it still might be useful for getting spermine out.

SIEKEVITZ: Yes.

The Correlation Between Morphological Structure and the Synthesis of Serum Albumin by the Microsome Fraction of the Rat Liver Cell

P. N. Campbell

Courtauld Institute, Middlesex Hospital, London, England

Our interest in serum albumin is based on the assumption that it is typical of the soluble proteins synthesized by the liver. It happens to be a rather convenient protein to study since it is homogeneous and not too difficult to isolate in a pure form. I should like to describe some experiments we have done in an attempt to determine the role of the various morphological structures that go to make up the microsome pellet in the synthesis and secretion of serum albumin.

Peters [3] has shown in his work with slices of chick liver that the microsome fraction is the most active site in the cell for the synthesis of albumin. We have for some time been working with the isolated microsome fraction from rat liver. We now have good evidence that such a fraction is able to synthesize serum albumin. Initially we demonstrated the incorporation of [14C]-amino acids into the serum albumin released from the microsome pellet by ultrasonics. The albumin was characterized by immunological, electrophoretic and solubility criteria [1]. More recently we have been studying the pattern of incorporation of [14C]-leucine under *in vivo* and *in vitro* conditions. We hope by this means to determine whether there is *de novo* synthesis under *in vitro* conditions. So far the results obtained are consistent with this concept.

Although the above experiments show that the microsome fraction is an active site for albumin synthesis they do not preclude such synthesis by other organelles such as the mitochondria. This fraction contains significant amounts of serum albumin and may also be a site for synthesis.

As explained by Dr. Porter in his paper the predominant structure seen in electron micrographs of the microsome fraction of rat liver is the so-called rough endoplasmic reticulum. As Dr. Porter has shown, this consists of vesicles bearing ribonucleoprotein (RNP) particles on the outside.

The experiments of Peters, and those on the isolated microsome fraction, show that the albumin that is synthesized in the reticulum is at first retained. In fact with the isolated microsome system the synthesized albumin is not released into the soluble fraction of the incubation medium.

The newly synthesized albumin can be released from the membranes either by treatment with deoxycholate (DOC) or by breaking them up with ultrasonic vibrations. Our first idea was to determine whether the protein released by DOC which appeared to be serum albumin by its immunological properties, had in fact all the properties of serum albumin.

We have examined extracts of the microsome pellet obtained either by DOC extraction or ultrasonics. Immunoelectrophoresis on agar gel was used with an antiserum prepared against a purified preparation of rat serum albumin. We can find no evidence for the existence of precursors of albumin with a molecular weight of less than that of the whole molecule. This finding is of special relevance in the case of serum albumin since Lapresle [2] and Porter [4] have both shown that degradation products of serum albumin retain some of the immunological properties of the native protein.

What can be learned from the nature of the binding between the membranes and serum albumin? As already mentioned, if the microsome pellet is treated with ultrasonics there is a certain release of serum albumin. If we centrifuge down the residue and treat with deoxycholate we get a further release of albumin. The comparable amounts are approximately two-thirds by ultrasonics and a further one-third by DOC. We are at present carrying out studies with the electron microscope to determine the nature of the action of ultrasonics. These studies are far from complete but we are accepting as a working hypothesis that the ultrasonic vibrations disrupt the membranes of the vesicles and permit the soluble contents to be released. The albumin which is only released by DOC we assume to be particularly closely associated with the lipid substances that go to make up the fabric of the membranes.

In order to determine whether there was any metabolic difference between the albumin in the two fractions we injected a rat with a mixture of [^{14}C]-labelled amino acids and killed it after 3 min. We homogenized the liver, isolated the microsome fraction and washed it free of the cell sap (105 000 **g** supernatant). We then determined the specific activity of the albumin in the two fractions. We found that the DOC albumin was 40% more active than the ultrasonic albumin whereas at this short time after injection the cell sap albumin was not significantly radioactive. We have also done similar estimations after the incubation of isolated liver microsomes with [^{14}C]-leucine. In this case the DOC albumin was about four times as radioactive as the ultrasonic albumin.

We cannot at present interpret these results with certainty but they are consistent with the idea that some stage of the synthesis of albumin involving incorporation of amino acids takes place in the lipid membrane.

Next we must turn to the ribonucleoprotein (RNP) particles. Dr. Siekevitz has described in his paper experiments with guinea-pig pancreas that suggest strongly that the RNP particles attached to the endoplasmic reticulum are the site of synthesis of the completed molecules of chymotrypsinogen and other hydrolytic enzymes of the pancreas. We have naturally been interested to determine whether the same holds true for the rat liver so far as albumin synthesis is concerned.

Two aspects of this problem have occupied us. First we wanted to know if the RNP particles contained any serum albumin. We have prepared many batches of such particles after treating the microsome pellet with DOC, extensive centrifugation at 105 000 **g** for $2\frac{1}{2}$ hr., washing free of DOC and further centrifugation. Such particles have the usual RNA/protein ratio of about 0·4. We have treated the particles with a variety of agents and compared the amounts of soluble albumin in the supernatants with that obtained by suspension in water. We have incubated the particles in each of the following: pyrophosphate (5×10^{-4} M), ATP (5×10^{-4} M), NaCl (0·5 M), ethylenediaminetetra-acetic acid (2%), ribonuclease (0·5 mg./ml.) and, finally, 70% aq. acetic acid. None of these reagents had any detectable effect on the immunological properties of serum albumin. We have not obtained a consistent release of serum albumin from the particles by any of these treatments. With ribonuclease the RNA/protein ratio was reduced to about 0·1, which may be taken to indicate a considerable degree of disruption of the particle. So far, therefore, we have no evidence of the presence of serum albumin in the RNP particles.

The other aspect of our work has been an attempt to obtain a synthesis of serum albumin with the isolated RNP particles. We have studied the conditions for the incorporation of amino acids into the protein of such preparations. Like others, we find that provided the deoxycholate is removed from the particles it is possible to obtain preparations which are consistently active. It is not necessary to go into details, for our results are very similar to those already described by Dr. Hultin. As with our experiments on the synthesis of serum albumin by the isolated microsome system, our initial aim was to demonstrate the incorporation of amino acid into the purified serum albumin. The difficulty with the RNP particles is that the cell sap is required for optimum activity and this contains large amounts of serum albumin. Unlike the microsome preparation the particles would not be expected to retain the newly synthesized albumin so that the latter would be diluted with the inactive albumin already present in the cell sap. We have in fact failed to demonstrate an energy-dependent incorporation of amino acid into the serum albumin on incubation of the particles.

To summarize therefore we have no evidence that the RNP particles of rat liver are the site for the synthesis of the complete albumin molecule. At present the results are consistent with the idea that in the liver the initial incorporation of amino acids is into the RNP particles and that an

K

albumin precursor then moves to the lipid membranes where there is a further addition of amino acids to complete the albumin molecule. The albumin then moves to the internal medium of the vesicles where it is securely retained until it is passed through the cell membrane.

I am grateful for the expert assistance of Miss Barbara Kernot in all the experiments described which were carried out in our laboratory. I am also grateful for the encouragement of Professor F. Dickens. The work described was made possible by a grant to the Medical School from the British Empire Cancer Campaign.

References

1. Campbell, P. N., Greengard, O. and Kernot, B. A. *Biochem. J.* **74,** 107 (1960).
2. Lapresle, C., *Ann. Inst. Pasteur* **89,** 654 (1955).
3. Peters, T., Jr., *J. Histochem. Cytochem.* **7,** 224 (1959)
4. Porter, R. R., *Biochem. J.* **66,** 677 (1957).

Discussion

PORTER: I was impressed by the rate at which serum albumin was synthesized after the intravenous injection of labelled amino acids and I wondered how much synthesis took place during homogenization and fractionation of the particles of the microsomes.

CAMPBELL: This seems unlikely for the conditions which exist during the homogenization and fractionation procedure are not favourable for the incorporation of much [^{14}C]-amino acid. The concentration of amino acid would be very small owing to the addition of medium, the concentration of ATP and other energy-rich compounds would be low, and the temperature is also low. We hope that the finger-print method may prove to be a useful technique. A mere demonstration of radioactivity in a protein after injection should not really be taken as evidence of complete synthesis. We think that by this method it would be possible to demonstrate a synthesis of complete molecules.

DAVIS: I wonder whether the fact that you find uniform distribution of radioactive leucine in serum albumin after only 3 min. might not be compatible with the following alternative interpretation. The individual amino acid molecules might line themselves up at random times, with no one site having a preferential position compared with another in relation to time. That is, the first few amino acids might just as well go on at one end as at the other or even in the middle. When the entire set of slots were filled peptide bond formation would be completed and the polypeptide chain would zip off. Therefore during that 3 min. the radioactive leucine might have found some templates which were almost completed but missing a few leucines here, and other templates missing a few leucines there. All the proteins that did get produced at that time would average out a random distribution of radioactive leucine.

CAMPBELL: Yes, that is a most interesting possibility. If it were true we should not find any change in the pattern even when the animal was killed at a very short time after injection. The problem is of course to get enough radioactivity incorporated at the very short times for without this it is not possible to study the pattern of labelling.

HOLTER: I think that we need not be afraid of the short time of 3 min. The group at the Department of Terrestrial Magnetism of the Carnegie Institution in Washington found in *E. coli* incorporation times of the order of seconds, so I don't expect there is any reason to believe that in higher organisms it should go so much slower than in *E. coli*.

CAMPBELL: There is only one snag, it is presumably easier for the amino acids to get to the site of protein synthesis in *E. coli* than it is in this case.

ALLFREY: I think that one answer to Dr. Davis's question comes from the work of Dr. Friedrich-Frekse's department at Tübingen. In this department they have shown that exposure to U.V. or X-irradiation affects protein synthesis and they have deduced that the laying down of protein proceeds from one end of the chain; if it is interrupted by irradiation at any stage, then the synthesis of that particular chain is stopped.

PORTER: It is an extraordinary thing but I do not believe anyone has observed in electron micrographs of liver cells any evidence of accumulation of material within the extremely flat cysternae of the ER. I imagine that it could be brought out by physiological experiments.

WILLIAMS: I wonder whether you could tell us anything about the serum albumin in the mitochondria. Firstly, is it readily released and secondly, does it incorporate amino acids rapidly?

CAMPBELL: The answer to the second question is that we don't know. As to the serum albumin being readily released, once again Peters has done a considerable amount of work on this with the chick liver and we have worked on the rat. Serum albumin is released with DOC so it is certainly held in quite nicely.

MITCHELL: Can you tell us more about the lipid membrane that you mentioned. I believe that Dr. Siekevitz in his very nice Ciba Foundation review said that he did not think that the membrane of the reticulum had very much lipid in it.

SIEKEVITZ: If you isolate liver microsomes and test for phospholipid you find a great deal, but if you isolate the pancreas microsomes you find very little, using the same methods of extraction.

Amino Acid Transport and Early Stages in Protein Synthesis in Isolated Cell Nuclei

VINCENT G. ALLFREY

The Rockefeller Institute, New York, U.S.A.

The application of tracer techniques to the study of nuclear protein synthesis dates back to 1948, to the exciting experiments of Bergstrand, Eliasson, Hammarsten, Norberg, Reichard and von Ubisch; they showed that, after the injection of $[^{15}N]$-glycine, the ^{15}N concentration in the proteins of the liver cell nucleus was just as high as that of proteins in the cytoplasm [1]. This great disclosure of the dynamic state of protein metabolism in the interphase nucleus is now a classic observation in nuclear biochemistry and it has become a point of departure for many subsequent experiments on protein synthesis in the nuclei of intact organisms.

Until 1954, virtually all tracer work on nuclear protein synthesis was based on similar experiments carried out *in vivo*, in which nuclei or nuclear protein fractions were isolated from the tissues of animals previously injected with isotopic amino acids. (This procedure is still clearly the method of choice for studying many aspects of the physiology of the nuclear proteins (e.g. [2, 3].)

However, in 1954 the surprising synthetic potentialities of the isolated thymocyte nucleus came to light [4], and it became possible to study the chemical mechanisms employed by the isolated nucleus in incorporating free amino acids into polypeptide chains. This aspect of nuclear protein synthesis has held our interest for the past five years, and some of the reactions and sites involved in amino acid incorporation are now known. Part of this work, done in collaboration with Drs. A. E. Mirsky, J. W. Hopkins, and J. H. Frenster, will now be described. It presents our current views of the protein synthetic pathway in the cell nucleus. The treatment of previously published work will omit details in order to permit the description of some newer aspects of nuclear amino acid and protein metabolism.

Pathways in nuclear protein synthesis

AMINO ACID UPTAKE BY ISOLATED CELL NUCLEI

Suspensions of nuclei possessing a high degree of purity can be obtained by differential centrifugation of homogenates of calf thymus tissue.

We have shown that if thymus nuclei are isolated under isotonic conditions in a medium containing 0·25 M sucrose and 0·003 M CaCl$_2$, they are able to retain their nucleic acids [5, 6], soluble enzymes [7], and low-molecular weight compounds such as mononucleotides [8] and free amino acids [9].

The isolated thymocyte nucleus also retains a surprising number of its original synthetic capabilities. These include the synthesis of ATP by an aerobic phosphorylating mechanism [8], the incorporation of thymidine into deoxyribonucleic acid [10], and the utilization of a variety of purine and pyrimidine precursors for ribonucleic acid synthesis [5, 6, 11, 12] and partial turnover [11].

Nuclear activity in amino acid incorporation experiments is especially striking [4, 5]. The latter process is illustrated by the uptake curves shown

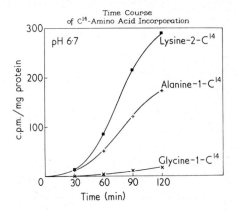

FIG. 1. The time course of incorporation of [^{14}C]-labelled amino acids into the total proteins of isolated thymus nuclei during incubation *in vitro*.

in Fig. 1; these show the time course of labelling of the nuclear proteins during incubations in the presence of either [1-^{14}C]-alanine, [1-^{14}C]-glycine, or [2-^{14}C]-lysine.

There are two aspects of this incorporation process which mark it as characteristically nuclear. First, amino acid uptake is sodium-ion dependent. (The reasons for this are discussed below.) Secondly, amino acid uptake does not take place if the nuclei are first treated with crystalline pancreatic deoxyribonuclease. This evidence for the DNA-dependence of nuclear amino acid incorporation is further supported by observations that added DNA always restores uptake to DNAase-treated nuclei [5]. (The reason for this is now clear, since recent experiments have shown that nuclear ATP synthesis is DNA-dependent [13]; removal of the DNA stops nuclear phosphorylation, and without the necessary ATP, nuclear protein synthesis cannot proceed [5, 8]. Restoring the DNA (or substituting other large polyanionic molecules for it) restores nuclear ATP synthesis; as a result, other energy-dependent synthetic reactions in the nucleus can resume [14].

These two facets of amino acid incorporation in the intact isolated nucleus (sodium ion requirement and DNA-dependence) set it apart from protein synthesis in the cytoplasm, which requires potassium, not sodium ions [15], and is sensitive to ribonuclease [16] and not to deoxyribonuclease. Yet a detailed study of the mechanism of protein synthesis in sub-nuclear fractions leads to the conclusion that the protein synthetic pathway in the nucleus is essentially the same as that found in the cytoplasm (and previously discussed in this symposium by Drs. Zamecnik, Hultin, Siekevitz, and Campbell).

AMINO ACID ACTIVATION

In the nucleus, as in cytoplasmic and bacterial systems, the primary step in protein synthesis appears to be an activation reaction requiring the participation of ATP. The reaction is mediated by activating enzymes similar to those originally described by Hoagland [17], according to the equation:

$$\text{amino acid} + \text{ATP} + \text{activating enzyme} \rightleftharpoons \text{enzyme-AMP} \sim \text{amino acid} + \text{PP}$$

A convenient method of assay for this activity is based on the reverse reaction, in which pyrophosphate is incorporated into ATP. Using ^{32}P-labelled pyrophosphate and measuring the production of radioactive ATP [18] it was possible to show that extracts of isolated thymus nuclei will form ^{32}ATP, but only if amino acids are present in the incubation mixture [19].

The ATP-pyrophosphate exchange reaction is promoted by the addition of mixtures of amino acids or by individual amino acids tested separately. Neutral extracts of highly purified thymus nuclei contain activating enzymes for at least fifteen L-amino acids; the D-isomers of these amino acids are not acted upon (Table I).

Many of the activating enzymes can be precipitated from solution by lowering the pH of the nuclear extract to $5 \cdot 2$, as was observed previously in cytoplasmic systems.

Many tests have been made to verify that the amino acid activating activity is actually present in the cell nucleus and is not an artefact due to the adsorption of cytoplasmic enzymes during the isolation procedure. The most reliable evidence in this connection is that obtained from a study of nuclei isolated in non-aqueous media by techniques which preclude any exchange of water-soluble enzymes between nucleus and cytoplasm [20, 21]. Two types of "non-aqueous" nuclei were selected for analysis because their purity had been established by chemical, enzymic, and immunological tests for cytoplasmic contamination; these were the nuclei prepared from

TABLE I

Amino acids promoting exchange	Amino acids without effect in this system
L-Alanine	L-Arginine*
L-Aspartic acid	Glycine*
L-Cysteine	L-Phenylalanine*
L-Glutamic acid	All D-amino acids
L-Histidine	
L-Isoleucine	
L-Leucine	
L-Lysine	
L-Methionine	
L-Proline	
L-Serine	
L-Threonine	
L-Tryptophan	
L-Tyrosine	
L-Valine	

* Found in low concentration in 0·05 M KCl supernatant before precipitation of pH 5 fraction.

lyophilized calf thymus and chicken kidney tissues [21]. It was found that the "non-aqueous" thymus nuclei contained slightly more activating activity (in units per mg. dry weight) than the equivalent weight of whole tissue. In kidney nuclei the enzyme concentration (in units per mg.) is about half that of the whole tissue. In both instances, the high purity of the preparations make it certain that the activating enzymes are of nuclear origin and are not due to cytoplasmic contamination.

Amino acid activating enzymes have also been detected in calf liver nuclei following an isolation in dense sucrose solutions by the method of Chauveau et al. [22]. These nuclei are characterized by a high degree of morphological purity (but other tests have shown that the adsorption of soluble cytoplasmic enzymes can occur in heavy sucrose solutions). In a recent communication, Webster [23] has described the properties and partial purification of an alanine-activating enzyme from pig liver nuclei. Considering the variety of nuclear types successfully tested for activating activity, the occurrence of amino acid activating enzymes in the cell nucleus promises to be a widespread phenomenon.

Ultracentrifugation experiments have shown that the activating enzymes of the thymus nucleus tend to remain associated with the nuclear ribosome fraction. As a result, they can be sedimented from neutral nuclear extracts by centrifuging under conditions which bring down the ribonucleoprotein particles of the nucleus. The association of the activating enzymes with particles which have been proven to be intranuclear (see below) is additional evidence for the conclusion that the nucleus itself carries out the amino acid activation reaction.

AMINO ACID TRANSFER TO NUCLEAR RIBONUCLEIC ACID

Studies of many cytoplasmic and bacterial systems have shown that the sequel to amino acid activation is a transfer reaction in which the

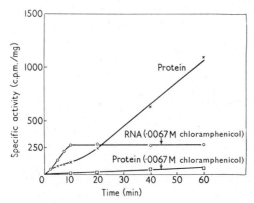

FIG. 2. The time course of uptake of [1-^{14}C]-leucine into the protein and "carrier" RNA of isolated thymus nuclei. The specific activity of the total nuclear protein (c.p.m./mg.) is plotted in the upper curve. The incorporation into protein is greatly inhibited by the presence of chloramphenicol (lower curve). The uptake of amino acid into the RNA is the same in chloramphenicol-treated nuclei as in "controls".

activated amino acid is coupled to a soluble ribonucleic acid, according to the equation:

enzyme—amino acyl $\sim$ AMP + sRNA $\rightleftharpoons$
$$\text{amino acyl—sRNA} + \text{enzyme} + \text{AMP}$$

[24–28]. A similar process occurs in the isolated thymocyte nucleus [19, 29]. The transfer of amino acid to RNA in the nucleus can be shown directly by isolation of radioactive "carrier" RNA after incubating nuclei in the presence of a radioactive amino acid and chloramphenicol [19] or puromycin [29, 30]. The addition of either of these antibiotics blocks amino acid incorporation into nuclear protein, but does not interfere with the formation of the amino acyl-RNA complex [29]. The RNA can then be prepared by the phenol method [31, 32] without risk of contamination by radioactive protein. The results of such an experiment are summarized in Fig. 2, in which the specific activities of nuclear protein and nuclear "phenol"

K*

RNA are plotted against the time of incubation in the presence of [1-^{14}C]-leucine. It is clear that the addition of chloramphenicol effectively stops amino acid uptake into protein (as first pointed out by Breitman and Webster [33]); despite the presence of the antibiotic, leucine enters the ribonucleic acid fraction at a very high initial rate.

Similar results have recently been obtained with puromycin [29]. Yarmolinsky and de la Haba have called attention to the fact that the structure of puromycin closely resembles that of the proposed amino acyl-RNA complex [30]. Considering its structure, the effectiveness of puromycin as an inhibitor of nuclear protein synthesis can be interpreted as due to a close competition between the antibiotic and the natural amino acyl-RNA complex. This would then be strong presumptive evidence that most of the incorporation of amino acids into nuclear proteins proceeds through an amino acyl-RNA intermediate.

In the experiments described above, the formation of leucyl-RNA took place in the intact thymus nucleus. An alternative method allows the preparation of the amino-acid-carrier RNA complex in sub-nuclear fractions. This procedure employs the nuclear activating enzymes (the nuclear pH 5 fraction), ATP, RNA, and the radioactive amino acid [29, 34].

It is of interest that much of the "transfer" or "carrier" RNA in the thymus nucleus occurs in association with the nuclear ribosome fraction and can be centrifuged down together with the ribosomes in the spinco. (This differs from the usual observation that in cytoplasmic extracts, the "carrier" RNA occurs in a relatively low-molecular weight, soluble form.) The pH 5 fraction as usually prepared from neutral extracts of thymus nuclei contains a few per cent of RNA which readily accepts activated amino acids. The addition of more nuclear RNA (prepared by the phenol method) results in a higher level of amino acid transfer.

In this connection, it should be mentioned that not all nuclear RNA fractions can function as leucine acceptors in the transfer reaction. For example, there is good evidence that the high molecular weight RNA of the nucleolus does not take part in this transfer process [19, 29]. (This RNA also fails to go into solution during the usual phenol extraction procedure.) Similar tests for amino acid transfer to DNA in the nucleus have led to negative results [19].

The transfer reaction in sub-nuclear fractions provides a convenient method for the preparation of leucyl-RNA. That the ^{14}C-uptake observed under these conditions actually represents a true incorporation of amino acid into RNA has been shown in several ways: (1) all of the radioactivity can be removed from the labelled pH 5 fraction by treatment with ribonuclease; (2) the presence of traces of ribonuclease during the reaction effectively prevents any uptake of isotope. (This is of interest because amino acid uptake in the intact nucleus cannot be blocked by adding RNA-ase to the incubation medium. This result fits in with other observations that added RNAase does not attack the ribosomal RNA as long as it remains within the nucleus (see below).) (3) The RNA can be prepared by the phenol isolation method and shown to contain bound ^{14}C-amino acid; (4) all the counts are removed by alkaline digestion of the RNA or by treatment with hot 5% trichloroacetic acid to remove nucleic acids; the protein residue after these treatments is not radioactive.

PROPERTIES OF THE AMINO ACYL-RNA COMPLEX

The chemical nature of the leucyl-RNA complex has been studied using the *in vitro* system of labelling the RNA associated with the nuclear pH 5 fraction. The product of the reaction (nuclear leucyl-RNA) has many properties which show its similarity to the amino acyl-RNA complexes studied in cytoplasmic systems. It is non-dialyzable and stable in dilute acids (e.g. 2 per cent $HClO_4$). On the other hand, a brief exposure to dilute alkali (0·005 N NaOH) removes all the radioactivity from leucyl-RNA, and subsequent chromatography on paper separates the counts as free [^{14}C]-leucine.

A short ribonuclease digestion of the nuclear leucyl-RNA complex (adding 10 μg. of RNAase for 15 min. at 37°) separates the radioactivity in an acid-soluble form. It has been shown that the action of ribonuclease releases the amino acid bound to a nucleoside [29, 34]. By following the procedure described by Zachau *et al.* [35], we have isolated the amino acyl-nucleoside by ionophoresis on filter paper. At pH 3·2 the leucyl-nucleoside differs in its mobility from any of the free nucleosides in the RNA digest and it can be located on the paper as a radioactive, u.v.-absorbing spot. Alternatively, the leucyl-nucleoside separates nicely in the paper chromatographic system described by Preiss *et al.* [36]. In both cases treatment of the radioactive, u.v.-absorbing spot with dilute alkali releases the radioactivity as free ^{14}C-leucine and leaves the nucleoside. Both components are readily separable by chromatography or electrophoresis [34].

In order to get sufficient material for identification of the nucleoside, a large-scale preparation of leucyl-RNA was carried out, using the pH 5 fraction from over 500 g. of isolated nuclei. The product was digested with ribonuclease, and the amino acyl-nucleoside separated by ionophoresis. Alkaline treatment then released the nucleoside, which, in its mobility, R_f, and ultraviolet absorption spectrum appears to be adenosine [34].

It follows that the receptor group in nuclear "carrier" RNA is a terminal adenylic acid, as was found earlier in the s-RNA of cytoplasmic systems [35].

AMINO ACID INCORPORATION INTO NUCLEAR RIBOSOMES

Much of the protein synthesis in the intact nucleus occurs in its ribonucleoprotein components [5, 37]. These are readily extractable from the nucleus in dilute salt solutions or neutral buffers. Recent fractionation studies of such nuclear extracts has revealed a heterogeneous population of ribonucleoprotein particles which can be separated into classes of different chemical composition and biosynthetic activity [37].

When the different fractions are examined under the electron microscope, one observes the presence of large numbers of dense particles of about 100 Å diameter. Particles of this size are clearly discernible in electron micrographs of sections of intact thymus nuclei, and in tissue sections. Similar particles have also been reported in nucleoli [38, 40], chromosomal loops [41], in the Balbiani rings of certain chromosomes [42], and throughout the nuclear sap in other tissues [43]. Dr. J. H. Frenster has made some attempts at further morphological characterization of these nuclear ribonucleoprotein particles (ribosomes), but problems of resolution make this very difficult [37].

Tracer studies have shown that the nuclear ribonucleoprotein particles, like those of the cytoplasm, are actively engaged in protein synthesis. Their activity within the thymus nucleus has been followed by incubating isolated nuclei in the presence of [14C]-labelled amino acids and subsequently isolating the various RNP fractions [37]. The results of such experiments indicate that the different particle fractions, separated on the basis of differing sedimentation properties, also differ greatly in their metabolic activity [37].

There is convincing evidence that amino acid uptake takes place in ribosomal particles within the nucleus. (1) The incorporation of amino acids requires the presence of sodium ions in the nuclear suspension. (As will be shown later, this requirement for sodium, rather than potassium ions, is a sure indication of nuclear localization.) (2) Preincubation of the nuclei with deoxyribonuclease effectively inhibits the subsequent uptake of [14C]-labelled amino acids into the proteins of the RNP particles. This evidence for DNA dependency, apart from establishing nuclear localization, also reflects the need for the nuclear phosphorylating system as a source of ATP [13].

The synthetic activity of the nuclear ribosomes can also be studied outside of the cell nucleus because, if they are properly supplemented, free RNP particles prepared from thymus nuclei can incorporate [14C-]amino acids *in vitro* [37, 44]. The process requires, in addition to the particles, ATP and an ATP-regenerating system, the nuclear pH 5 enzymes, and guanosine triphosphate (GTP) [37, 44]. The time course of incorporation of [1-14C]-leucine into the proteins of isolated nuclear ribosomes is depicted in Fig. 3. It is of special interest that amino acid incorporation can take place only in particles which were prepared under isotonic conditions (upper curve); ribonucleoprotein particles isolated in, or exposed to hypertonic sucrose solutions are completely inert (lower curve). This finding is in agreement with earlier experiments on intact nuclei showing that amino acid uptake proceeds best in isotonic sucrose solutions and is impaired when nuclei are exposed to either hypertonic or hypotonic conditions [44].

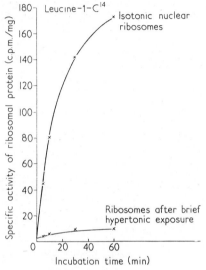

FIG. 3. The time course of incorporation of [1-^{14}C]-leucine into isolated ribonucleoprotein particles prepared from thymus nuclei. The incubation medium contained (in addition to the particles), nuclear pH 5 enzymes. ATP + an ATP-regenerating system, and GTP. The upper curve shows the specific activity of the proteins of the ribosomes under isotonic conditions. A brief exposure to hypertonic sucrose solutions destroys the capacity for amino acid uptake under these conditions (lower curve).

The incorporation of amino acids by isolated nuclear ribosomes is inhibited if ribonuclease is added to the incubation medium. This effect is of interest because it contrasts with findings on intact nuclei. It has been shown that ribonuclease does not affect amino acid uptake into the ribosomes of the intact isolated nucleus [37]. The results indicate that the RNA of the ribosome fraction is immune to attack by RNAase as long as it remains inside the nucleus. This is one of the unique properties of the protein synthetic pathway in the nucleus.

Some characteristically nuclear aspects of amino acid incorporation

On the whole, the study of sub-nuclear fractions has shown that the protein synthetic mechanism in the cell nucleus is very much like that of the cytoplasm. It involves (1) amino acid activation, (2) transfer of the amino acid to the terminal adenylic acid of a carrier RNA, and (3) incorporation into the proteins of the ribosome fraction by a reaction sequence requiring GTP. Yet there are some striking differences between nuclear and cytoplasmic incorporation systems. The first of these is the specific requirement of the nucleus for sodium ions.

Why is protein synthesis in the nucleus sensitive to the presence or absence of sodium ions ? This question has been studied in suspensions of isolated cell nuclei by tracer methods, and the answer is now clear. Sodium ion dependency reflects the operation of a transport system for bringing amino acids into the cell nucleus.

NUCLEAR AMINO ACID TRANSPORT

The effect of sodium ions on the overall process of amino acid incorporation into nuclear proteins was discovered (largely by accident) at

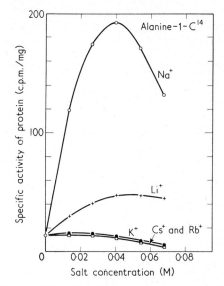

FIG. 4. The effect of adding different monovalent cations (as chlorides) on the incorporation of [1-¹⁴C] alanine into the proteins of intact isolated thymus nuclei. The specific activity of the nuclear protein after 60 min. incubation is plotted against the salt concentration of the medium.

the very beginnings of our study of uptake processes in the nucleus [5, 45]. The magnitude of the effect is strikingly demonstrated in Fig. 4, which compares the uptake of [1-¹⁴C]-alanine in a medium containing sodium ions with that observed in the presence of equivalent amounts of potassium (or other monovalent cations). The stimulatory effect of added sodium is particularly large in the case of alanine uptake [46] but it is easily demonstrated for other amino acids as well. Lithium is partly effective as a sodium substitute, but caesium, rubidium or potassium are without effect.

A number of quaternary ammonium ions were also tested because Lorente de No [47] had shown them to be effective sodium substitutes in maintaining membrane potentials in isolated nerve. However, neither hydrazinium, guanidinium, or tetraethyl ammonium ions could promote alanine incorporation into the proteins of sodium-deficient thymus nuclei.

The reason for the sodium-dependence of the incorporation process was sought for but could not be found in studies of the individual reactions in the nuclear synthetic pathway. There was no specific sodium ion requirement for amino acid activation, or for transfer to nuclear RNA, and a 50% reduction in sodium ion concentration had no effect on amino acid incorporation into isolated nuclear ribosomes [44]. This led us to test the possibility that sodium ions might influence the rate at which amino acids enter the free amino acid "pool" within the nucleus.

This approach has not only provided an explanation of the sodium ion effect but it has also revealed the existence of a mechanism, hitherto unknown, for amino acid transport and accumulation within the cell nucleus.

The penetration of free amino acids into the nuclear "pool" has been measured as follows: nuclei were suspended in a buffered sucrose medium containing sodium (or potassium ions) and a small, accurately measured amount of the radioactive amino acid. The mixture was incubated aerobically, with shaking. Aliquots of the suspension were removed at zero time and at appropriate time intervals thereafter. The nuclei were centrifuged down, washed with sucrose, and then extracted with cold 2% $HClO_4$. The radioactivity in each extract was measured and, after correcting for the small amount of amino acid adsorbed at zero time, the counts were plotted as a function of the time of incubation. The time course of $[1\text{-}^{14}C]$-alanine transport at $37°$ is shown in Fig. 5, which compares the radioactivity present in the nuclear "pool" after incubation in 0·04 M NaCl with that observed at an equivalent concentration of KCl. The transport of the amino acid into the acid-soluble "pool" is evidently sodium-dependent, and does not occur to any appreciable extent when equivalent amounts of potassium replace the sodium. There is good evidence that the radioactivity in the perchloric acid extract of the isolated nuclei occurs as free $[^{14}C]$-alanine. This was checked by chromatography of the concentrated extract on paper and subsequent elution of the alanine spot. A definite increase in the radioactivity of the isolated alanine is evident after only a few minutes' incubation. Other tests have shown that, after 30 min. at $10°C.$, the nuclei build up an alanine concentration that may exceed the alanine concentration of the surrounding medium [46].

It remains to be seen whether some transient derivative of alanine is formed in the course of this accumulation process.

Competition experiments using non-radioactive D-alanine and L-alanine before adding DL-[1-14C]-alanine have shown that only the naturally occurring L-isomer of the amino acid competes with radioactive alanine for transport. It follows that the D-isomer of the amino acid is not actively accumulated by the nucleus [29, 46]. The stereo-specificity of the reaction suggests that amino acid transport into the nucleus involves the operation of an enzymic mechanism.

The alanine transport reaction has a well-defined pH optimum at neutrality. This is shown in Fig. 6. A study of the temperature-dependence

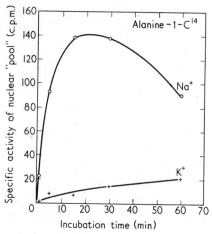

FIG. 5. The specific effect of sodium ions in promoting the transport of free [1-14C]-alanine into the amino acid "pool" of the isolated cell nucleus. The specific activity of the acid-soluble nuclear extracts (see text) is plotted against the time of incubation at 37°.

of the reaction reveals the optimum in the physiological temperature range (38°–40°) (Fig. 7). A comparison of the rates of alanine transport at 10° and 20° (0·83 and 1·6 mμmoles of L-alanine per 10 min. per 20 mg. nuclei) shows that the velocity of the reaction has doubled for a 10° rise in temperature. This temperature coefficient ($Q_{10} = 2$) indicates that amino acid transport into the nucleus involves a chemical reaction and is not simply a result of diffusion.

It has already been pointed out that even after short periods of incubation, the [14C]-alanine concentration within the nuclei may exceed that of the incubation medium. This transport and accumulation of an amino acid against a concentration gradient would be expected to require the expenditure of energy. In this connection there is some evidence

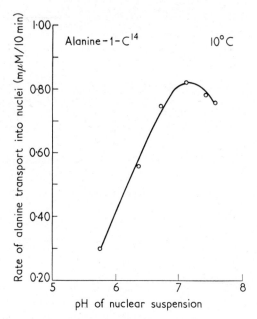

FIG. 6. The pH dependence of the nuclear alanine transport reaction. The rate of amino acid transport (in mμmoles of L-alanine per 10 min. at 10°) is plotted against the pH of the incubation medium.

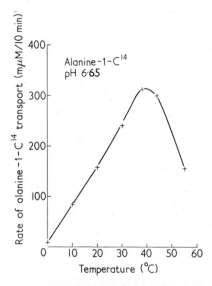

FIG. 7. The temperature dependence of the nuclear alanine transport reaction. The rate of amino acid transport (in mμmoles of L-alanine per 10 min. at pH 6·75) is plotted against the temperature of incubation.

which suggests that the transport of amino acids into the nucleus is an active process requiring the participation of ATP or some similar energy source. For example, the addition of 0·002 M cyanide or dinitrophenol (both of which suppress nuclear ATP synthesis) causes some inhibition of alanine transport. Similarly, the removal of nucleotides by selective extraction with acetate buffers [8] destroys the nuclear capacity for subsequent amino acid accumulation [46].

Other experiments have made it clear that the primary reason for the sodium dependence of amino acid incorporation into the proteins of intact nuclei is simply that sodium ions are needed for the transport of amino acids to the sites of synthesis. For example, we have found that thymus nuclei will synthesize ^{14}C-labelled protein even in an all-potassium medium, provided they are first exposed to a sodium-rich medium containing the radioactive amino acid. (Other tests have shown that isolated nuclei cannot retain sodium ions taken up during this preincubation.) Once transport has occurred, the continued presence of sodium ions in the medium is not necessary for the incorporation process [46].

Thus the sodium dependence of protein synthesis in the nucleus is due to the operation of a specific transport mechanism. This sodium ion requirement becomes a useful test for establishing the intranuclear localization of protein synthetic reactions, especially when one considers that many cytoplasmic systems display a specific requirement for potassium ions in amino acid transport [48] and incorporation [15].

Other synthetic processes in isolated nuclei may or may not show a sodium ion requirement. The range of the sodium ion requirement will not be discussed here, except to mention that a good correlation has been found between the ionic requirements for uptake and for transport of several isotopic precursors of ribo- and deoxyribo-nucleic acids [46].

DNA EFFECTS ON ISOLATED NUCLEAR RIBOSOMES

A useful test for the nuclear localization of a synthetic process is a measure of its DNA dependency. The addition of DNAase to suspensions of intact isolated nuclei leads to a cessation of nearly all synthetic activity [4, 5, 13]. As mentioned before, this is largely due to the fact that DNA plays a role in mediating nuclear ATP synthesis: removal of the DNA therefore has an indirect effect on all nuclear processes that require ATP.

However, some recent results suggest that DNA may play a more specific role in controlling the synthesis of nuclear proteins. These results were obtained in tracer experiments with isolated nuclear ribosomes. The incorporation of amino acids into ribosomes outside the nucleus is not affected by deoxyribonuclease [44] because the ATP needed for amino acid activation is supplied by an exogenous ATP-generating system. It was surprising therefore, to find that the addition of isolated thymus DNA to the ribosome suspension stimulates the uptake of [1-^{14}C]-leucine into ribosomal proteins. As shown in Fig. 8, the increase in specific activity of the protein is appreciable; DNA-supplemented ribosomes are 50% more active than the corresponding "controls". The figure also shows that the simultaneous addition of DNAase with the DNA abolishes the stimulatory effect [44].

There is, as yet, no evidence for the tissue- or species-specificity of DNA in promoting uptake. DNA preparations from calf thymus, calf

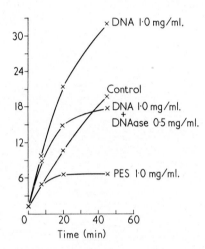

FIG. 8. Effects of added DNA, DNA + deoxyribonuclease, and polyethylene sulphonate on [1-^{14}C]-leucine incorporation into the proteins of isolated nuclear ribosomes. The specific activity of the ribosomal protein (in c.p.m./mg.) is plotted against the time of incubation at 37°.

kidney, and wheat germ are all equally effective in this test system. On the other hand, the results cannot be explained as simply a matter of adding large negatively-charged molecules (which could bind traces of ribonuclease in the preparations and so enhance their activity) because the addition of an equal amount of polyethylene sulphonate actually inhibits amino acid uptake by isolated nuclear ribosomes (Fig. 8).

The stimulatory effect of DNA takes on added interest in view of related findings that added histones inhibit amino acid uptake by nuclear ribosomes [44] (Fig. 9). The role of histones as repressors of nuclear synthetic activities was observed earlier in studies of amino acid uptake in intact nuclei (Fig. 10) [49].

The stimulation of protein synthesis in the ribosomes by DNA and the corresponding inhibition by histones suggest that the synthetic activity of ribosomes within the nucleus will vary depending on their proximity to

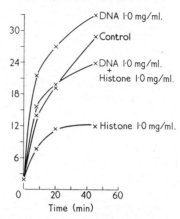

FIG. 9. Effects of added histone, DNA + histone, and DNA on [1-^{14}C]-leucine incorporation into the proteins of isolated nuclear ribosomes. The specific activity of the ribosomal protein (in c.p.m./mg.) is plotted against the time of incubation at 37°.

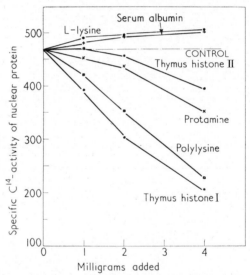

FIG. 10. Effects of added histone I (arginine-rich histone fraction), histone II (lysine-rich histone fraction which is less basic than histone I), protamine, and polylysine on [1-^{14}C]-alanine uptake into the proteins of isolated calf thymus nuclei. The specific activity of the nuclear protein after 60 min. incubation at 37° is plotted against the amount of material added to the nuclear suspension.

DNA or histone at different loci of the chromosome. This may prove to be a physiological mechanism for controlling the rates of synthesis of different proteins in the nucleus, and one may speculate that such control is part of the process of cell differentiation.

Summary

A study of isolated thymus nuclei and sub-nuclear fractions shows that the pathway of protein synthesis in the nucleus involves a sequence of reactions similar to that observed in cytoplasmic systems.

The nucleus contains amino-acid-activating enzymes which act on at least fifteen L-amino acids; D-amino acids are not activated.

Following activation, the amino acid is transferred to a nuclear RNA fraction. Neither DNA nor the high molecular weight RNA of the nucleolus takes part in this process.

Analysis of the nuclear leucyl-RNA complex shows that the receptor group in nuclear "carrier" RNA is a terminal adenylic acid.

Ribonucleoprotein particles in the nucleus are active sites of protein synthesis. These particles (termed nuclear ribosomes) can be isolated and fractionated by differential ultracentrifugation of nuclear extracts, and are capable of independent amino acid incorporation, provided they are isolated and tested under isotonic conditions.

Amino acid uptake into the isolated nuclear ribosomes requires the presence of ATP, amino-acid-activating enzymes, and GTP.

The addition of DNA promotes amino acid uptake in ribosome suspensions while added histones inhibit the process. This may prove to be one of the physiological mechanisms for the direction and control of nuclear protein synthesis.

The protein synthetic process in isolated nuclei responds to the addition of sodium ions because Na$^+$ is required in a specific amino acid transport mechanism. This transport of amino acids to the sites of nuclear protein synthesis is apparently an enzymic reaction that is specific for the L-form of the amino acid.

References

1. Bergstrand, A., Eliasson, N. A., Hammarsten, E., Norberg, B., Reichard, P., and von Ubisch, H., *Cold Spr. Harb. Symp. quant. Biol.* **13**, 22 (1948).
2. Daly, M. M., Allfrey, V. G., and Mirsky, A. E., *J. gen. Physiol.* **36**, 173 (1952).
3. Allfrey, V. G., Daly, M. M., and Mirsky, A. E., *J. gen. Physiol.* **38**, 415 (1955).
4. Allfrey, V. G., *Proc. nat. Acad. Sci., Wash.* **40**, 881 (1954).
5. Allfrey, V. G., Mirsky, A. E., and Osawa, S., *J. gen. Physiol.* **40**, 451 (1957).
6. Allfrey, V. G., and Mirsky, A. E., *Proc. nat. Acad. Sci., Wash.* **43**, 821 (1957).
7. Stern, H., and Mirsky, A. E., *J. gen. Physiol.* **37**, 177 (1953).
8. Osawa, S., Allfrey, V. G., and Mirsky, A. E., *J. gen. Physiol.* **40**, 491 (1957).
9. Allfrey, V. G., and Mirsky, A. E., *Proc. nat. Acad. Sci., Wash.* (in press).
10. Friedkin, M., and Wood, H., *J. biol. Chem.* **220**, 639 (1956).
11. Allfrey, V. G., and Mirsky, A. E., *Proc. nat. Acad. Sci., Wash.* **45**, 1325 (1959).
12. Breitman, T., and Webster, G. C., *Nature, Lond.* **184**, 637 (1959).
13. Allfrey, V. G., and Mirsky, A. E., *Proc. nat. Acad. Sci., Wash.* **43**, 589 (1957).
14. Allfrey, V. G., and Mirsky, A. E., *Proc. nat. Acad. Sci., Wash.* **44**, 981 (1958).

15. Sachs, H., *J. biol. Chem.*, **233**, 643 (1958).
16. Allfrey, V. G., Daly, M. M., and Mirsky, A. E., *J. gen. Physiol.* **37**, 157 (1953).
17. Hoagland, M. B., *Biochim. biophys. Acta* **16**, 288 (1955).
18. Crane, R. K., and Lipmann, F., *J. biol. Chem.* **201**, 235 (1953).
19. Hopkins, J. W., *Proc. nat. Acad. Sci.*, *Wash.* **45**, 1461 (1959).
20. Behrens, M., *Hoppe-Seyl. Z.* **209**, 59 (1932).
21. Allfrey, V. G., Stern, H., Mirsky, A. E., and Saetren, H., *J. gen. Physiol.* **35**, 529 (1952).
22. Chauveau, J., Moulé, Y., and Rouiller, C., *Exp. Cell Res.* **11**, 317 (1956).
23. Webster, G. C., *Biochem. Biophys. Res. Commun.* **2**, 56 (1960).
24. Hoagland, M. B., Keller, E. B., and Zamecnik, P. C., *J. biol. Chem.* **218**, 345 (1956).
25. Holley, R. W., *J. Amer. chem. Soc.* **79**, 658 (1957).
26. Ogata, K., and Nohara, H., *Biochim. biophys. Acta* **25**, 660 (1957).
27. Berg, P., and Ofengand, E. J., *Proc. nat. Acad. Sci.*, *Wash.* **44**, 78 (1958).
28. Weiss, S., Acs, G., and Lipmann, F., *Proc. nat. Acad. Sci.*, *Wash.* **44**, 189 (1958).
29. Allfrey, V. G., Hopkins, J. W., Frenster, J. H., and Mirsky, A. E., *Ann. N.Y. Acad. Sci.* **88**, 722 (1960).
30. Yarmolinsky, M. D., and de la Haba, G., *Proc. nat. Acad. Sci.*, *Wash.* **45**, 1721 (1959).
31. Schramm, G., and Kerejkarto, B., *Z. Naturf.* **76**, 589 (1952).
32. Kirby, K. S., *Biochem. J.* **64**, 405 (1956).
33. Breitman, T., and Webster, G. C., *Biochim. biophys. Acta* **27**, 409 (1958).
34. Hopkins, J. W., Allfrey, V. G., and Mirsky, A. E., *Biochim. biophys. Acta* **47**, 194 (1961).
35. Zachau, H. G., Acs, G., and Lipmann, F., *Proc. nat. Acad. Sci.*, *Wash.* **44**, 885 (1958).
36. Preiss, J., Berg, P., Ofengand, E. J., Bergmann, F. H., and Dieckmann, M., *Proc. nat. Acad. Sci.*, *Wash.* **45**, 319 (1959).
37. Frenster, J. H., Allfrey, V. G., and Mirsky, A. E., *Proc. nat. Acad. Sci.*, *Wash.* **46**, 432 (1960).
38. Porter, K. R., *J. Histochem. Cytochem.* **2**, 346 (1954).
39. Bernhard, W., Bauer, A., Gropp, A., Hagenau, F., and Oberling, C., *Exp. Cell Res.* **9**, 88 (1955).
40. LaFontaine, J. G., *J. biophys. biochem. Cytol.* **4**, 229 (1958).
41. Gall, J. G., *J. biophys. biochem. Cytol.* **2** (*Suppl.*), 393 (1956).
42. Beerman, W., and Bahr, G. F., *Exp. Cell Res.* **6**, 195 (1954).
43. Callan, H. G., *in* "Symposium on Fine Structure of Cells (Leiden)", I.U.B.S. publ. **B21**, 89 (1956).
44. Frenster, J. H. Allfrey, V. G., and Mirsky, A. E., *Biochim. biophys. Acta* **47**, 130 (1961).
45. Allfrey, V. G., Mirsky, A. E., and Osawa, S., *Nature, Lond.* **176**, 1042 (1955).
46. Allfrey, V. G., Mirsky, A. E., Hopkins, J. W., and Naora, H. *Proc. nat. Acad. Sci.*, *Wash.* (in press).
47. Lorente de No, R., *J. cell. comp. Physiol.* **33** (Suppl.), (1949).
48. Christensen, H. N., and Riggs, T. R., *J. biol. Chem.* **194**, 57 (1952).
49. Allfrey, V. G., and Mirsky, A. E., *Trans. N.Y. Acad. Sci.* Ser. II, **21**, 3 (1958).

Discussion

CANELLAKIS: Have you tried adding ribonucleic acid instead of deoxyribonucleic acid to your isolated ribosomes?

ALLFREY: Yes. In isolated ribosomes the addition of commercially prepared yeast RNA failed to stimulate the uptake of [1-^{14}C]-leucine.

CANELLAKIS: Was it a high molecular weight polymer?

ALLFREY: Yes. That is, it was non-dialyzable.

ARNON: When you speak of ATP synthesis by the nucleus do you imply that the nucleus is self-sufficient with respect to its ATP requirement for protein synthesis or does it still depend on ATP formation by mitochondria?

ALLFREY: I would say that for amino acid incorporation in isolated thymus nuclei it is not necessary to add mitochondria or some other ATP-generating system. Amino acid uptake into proteins by isolated nuclei is not as active as in whole cells (perhaps only one-third as active) but the process can continue actively for 8–9 hr. in the absence of mitochondria. Moreover, mitochondrial contamination is not a problem because we inhibit mitochondrial phosphorylation by adding Ca^{2+} ions. The nuclei are still able to carry out all of these synthetic reactions.

ARNON: What is the substrate for ATP formation? Is oxygen being consumed?

ALLFREY: Yes, oxygen is consumed. The $Q(O_2)$ usually lies between 1 and 2.

ARNON: But what is the chemical substrate?

ALLFREY: We don't know how the coupling of oxidation and ATP formation takes place. We are working on that, and know that glucose is metabolized in these nuclei.

SCHOFFENIELS: Did you find competition between the L and the D forms of the same amino acid in the process of transfer from the solution to the nuclei?

ALLFREY: There is no competition between the L and the D forms. It is only the L form of the non-radioactive amino acid which will compete with the radioactive amino acid; the D form does not.

SCHOFFENIELS: If you add both, will not the D form be inhibitory?

ALLFREY: It has no action at all at the concentrations we have tested.

HERBERT: I wonder if you have characterized the RNA, which I presume is much like soluble RNA, further than to establish that the amino acid complexes with adenylic acid, and whether you have characterized the activating enzymes to any extent. It has been reported that activating enzymes isolated from nuclei are different from the cytoplasmic enzymes with respect to certain amino acids.

ALLFREY: We have tried both specificity reactions, testing the nuclear amino acid-activating enzymes and cytoplasmic enzymes from guinea-pig liver, and ribonucleic acids from different types of nuclei. Now, the answer you get depends on the amino acid you use. If you use leucine, both Dr. Webster and I agree there is no sign of specificity, i.e. the nuclear enzyme will transfer to cytoplasmic RNA or the RNA of other nuclear types, and the cytoplasmic enzyme will transfer to nuclear RNA. But in Dr. Webster's experiments with alanine-activating enzymes there is evidence of specificity between liver nuclear enzymes and cytoplasmic enzymes. We haven't checked this with thymus nuclei. We have now started to characterize the amino acid "carrier"-RNA of the thymus nucleus. We do not call it "soluble"-RNA because in our system it occurs in association with the nuclear ribosomes. This may be because we flood the system with Ca^{2+} ions during the course of isolating the nuclei.

BERGERON: Would it be correct to say that DNA-ase has free access by diffusion into a compartment into which alanine does not diffuse freely but has to be moved by active transport ?

ALLFREY: I think that is right. It is not only true for DNA-ase, which has a molecular weight of 61 000, and for RNA-ase with a molecular weight of about 13 000, but also for some of the polyelectrolytes which we have used with molecular weights up to 200 000. However, an alternative explanation may be offered to the compartment hypothesis. Perhaps the apparent presence of alanine in a free "pool" is an instance of specific adsorption rather than membrane-limited compartmentalization.

BERGERON: Might it not be true that you have different pools in the one system you are dealing with, which you call the nucleus?

ALLFREY: I think it's true. Certainly the effect of sodium in stimulating amino acid entry into the "pool" differs greatly for different amino acids.

PORTER: Did you imply that the radioactive sodium is concentrated intra-nuclearly or in the perinuclear space ? This arrangement of channels bringing it to the perinuclear space would account for the increased density in the nuclear area in a radioautograph of a whole cell.

ALLFREY: The figure shown was a radioautograph of a section of the frog oocyte. The high grain density over the nuclear area indicates the presence of ^{22}Na within the nucleus. This result has been checked by direct isolation of these nuclei. Dr. H. Naora made a set of very small chopsticks out of wood and devised techniques for removing a single nucleus from frozen oocytes. Thus we were able to count the nuclei separately from the cytoplasm.

PORTER: It seemed to me that sodium ought really to be concentrated in the perinuclear space and that the migration of the sodium is through the pores in the nuclear envelope from the cytoplasm matrix.

ALLFREY: Well the sodium is freely diffusible in our system of isolated thymus nuclei.

MITCHELL: Could you tell us what evidence there is that the alanine which is accumulated is free inside the nucleus ? This is a difficult problem, and one that many people have encountered in trying to prove that a given process was active transport. How do you get the alanine out to show that it was free ?

ALLFREY: To put it as briefly as possible, we extract with cold trichloroacetic or preferably cold 2% perchloric acid. This leaves the proteins behind. Then we take the perchloric acid extract which is concentrated and chromatographed. We find a single spot corresponding in R_f to free alanine. Now this does not mean some other intermediate wasn't formed in the process, but we have not yet found evidence for any other radioactive product.

Effects of 8-Azaguanine on the Specificity of Protein Synthesis in *Bacillus cereus*

H. Chantrenne

Laboratory of Biological Chemistry, Faculty of Sciences, University of Brussels, Belgium

If 8-azaguanine is added to a growing population of *Bacillus cereus*, the rate of increase of the optical density of the bacterial suspension is reduced by about 50% [1, 2, 3]. Such an observation is usually expressed in the following way: "azaguanine reduces the rate of growth of the bacteria". This statement can be misleading; it depends what is meant by "growth". A closer study of the effects of 8-azaguanine revealed the following facts [3, 4, 5]. The analogue inhibits the increase of bacterial dry weight by 40 to 50%. Protein synthesis is almost completely suppressed, whereas the formation of cell wall material, including the peptides it contains, is practically untouched. The synthesis of ribonucleic acid can be stimulated, unaffected, or slightly depressed depending on experimental conditions, especially aeration. No effects are observed on the synthesis of DNA when low concentrations (4 μg./ml.) of azaguanine are used; a partial inhibition slowly establishes in the presence of higher concentrations (40 μg./ml.) of the drug.

The formation of various essential cell constituents is thus very differently affected by azaguanine, with the obvious result that the gross composition of the bacteria is progressively changed. On the other hand, the number of viable bacteria, i.e. the number of bacteria which are able to form a colony when plated on a normal medium, ceases to increase within 20 min. of the addition of azaguanine; it then stays constant for about 2 hr. before dropping sharply. Therefore, the changes in chemical composition of the bacteria which are caused by 8-azaguanine are not immediately lethal. Recovery of the bacteria from the toxic effects of the analogue is a slow and progressive process.

The inhibition of protein synthesis in *B. cereus* is fully expressed within about 10 min. of the addition of azaguanine (36 μg./ml.). If guanosine (135 μg./ml.) is added together with azaguanine, it completely protects the bacteria against the analogue. If added not later than 30 min. after azaguanine, guanosine rapidly restores the synthesis of proteins. But this restoration becomes more and more sluggish as guanosine is added later and later. Moreover, qualititative changes are observed among the protein produced during restoration.

Figure 1(*a*) shows how the synthesis of protein material—as measured by phenylalanine incorporation—is restored when guanosine is added 30, 45 and 60 min. after azaguanine. In the same experiment, the synthesis of

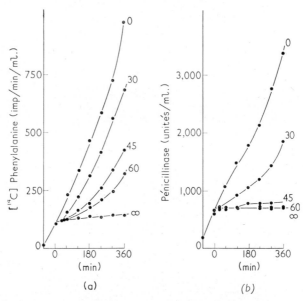

(a)   (b)

FIG. 1. Restoration of protein and penicillinase synthesis [7]. To five growing suspensions of *B. cereus* (penicillinase-constitutive mutant) containing 0·08 μC of L-[^{14}C]-phenylalanine per ml., 36 μg. of 8-azaguanine were added at time 0. Guanosine (135 μg./ml.) was added respectively 0, 30, 45 and 60 min. after azaguanine. No guanosine was added to the last suspension (∞).

(*a*): ^{14}C in protein material (c.p.m. per ml. suspension).
(*b*): penicillinase (units of activity per ml. suspension).

constitutive penicillinase—as measured by its enzymic activity—was determined; the results are shown in Fig. 1(*b*). Comparison of figures 1(*a*) and 1(*b*) indicates that when guanosine is added 45 or 60 min. after azaguanine, penicillinase production is still completely obliterated at a time when the synthesis of protein material was already restored to a considerable extent [7].

The damage caused by 8-azaguanine to the formation of the enzyme penicillinase is therefore more severe or more difficult to repair than the damage caused to the synthesis of protein material as a whole. Moreover, it becomes worse and worse as the time of action of azaguanine increases. All the enzymes, however, do not suffer as much as penicillinase. For instance, the synthesis of catalase is restored almost at the same time as the average protein material; for some time during restoration the rate of catalase formation per weight of newly formed protein material is even greater than in normal bacteria (Fig. 2).

Clearly, besides inhibiting protein synthesis in general, the purine analogue must jam some mechanism upon which the specificity of protein synthesis depends.

Cells or bacteria which are unable to incorporate azaguanine into ribonucleic acids and nucleotidic compounds are insensitive to the analogue

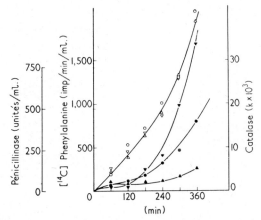

FIG. 2. Restoration of the synthesis of protein material, catalase and penicillinase [7]. Two growing suspensions of B. cereus (penicillinase-constitutive mutant) in a casein hydrolysate were shaken in a water bath at 30°. At time o, each suspension received o·08 μC L-[^{14}C]-phenylalanine and 36 μg. 8-azaguanine per ml. Guanosine (135 μg./ml.) was added respectively at the same time as 8-azaguanine (control, clear points) and 45 min. later (black points).

O, ● : ^{14}C in protein material per ml. suspension.
△, ▲ : Penicillinase activity (units per ml. suspension).
▽, ▼ : catalase activity, per ml. suspension.

[8, 9]. The inhibitory action of azaguanine therefore is probably due to some harmful synthesis of nucleotidic compounds containing the analogue instead of guanine. Since guanosine triphosphate is required for the passage of the amino acids from transfer RNA to the nascent polypeptides on the ribosomes [10, 11, 12, 13], an obvious possibility is that azaguanosine triphosphate might interfere at this stage. The degree of inhibition of growth is indeed more closely correlated with the concentration of azaguanine in acid soluble compounds than with the total amount of analogue in the nucleic acids [1]. On the other hand, in Tetrahymena geleii which requires exogenous uracil to make RNA, the degree of inhibition of growth by azaguanine depends on the level of uracil in the medium [14]

and it was observed in our laboratory (Allinckx, unpublished) that azaguanine inhibits amino acid incorporation into the proteins of this protozoan only when uracil is provided. This suggests that the harmful synthesis in which azaguanine is involved depends on uracil. One of the lesions caused by azaguanine thus probably concerns some RNA fraction undergoing a relatively rapid metabolism.

The possibility that 8-azaguanine might change the acceptor specificity of soluble transfer RNA for certain amino acids was investigated recently by Osawa (personal communication): in soluble RNA as isolated by the phenol method from azaguanine-inhibited *B. cereus*, about 25% of the guanine molecules were replaced by the analogue. In spite of this, no difference was observed between this abnormal soluble RNA and the normal compound in their ability to bind [^{14}C]-leucine or in the total amount of ^{14}C bound from a mixture of radioactive amino acids in the presence of a normal extract of bacteria.

According to these data, azaguanine does not seem to interfere with the activation of the amino acids, at least if the classical scheme of protein synthesis involving Hoagland's activation enzymes is valid for *B. cereus*. The possibility that the "incorporation enzymes" of Beljanski and Ochoa [15] is involved should also be investigated, for these enzymes require the participation of the four nucleoside triphosphates [16] and azaguanine might possibly interfere at this point.

If the activation steps are not disturbed by azaguanine, and if the acceptor specificity of transfer RNA is not changed, then azaguanine probably interferes with the passage of the amino acids from transfer RNA to the ribosomes or with their condensation into polypeptides in the genetically controlled structure. These are the most obscure steps of protein synthesis, and azaguanine might be a useful tool for the study of these steps. An important observation in this respect is that azaguanine, which is incorporated into both soluble and ribosomal RNA, disturbs the normal balance between these two groups of nucleic acids. The ratio of sedimentable to non-sedimentable RNA decreases considerably as azaguanine is being incorporated (Otaka, in press). In our laboratory, current research by J. Lahou indicates that azaguanine drastically reduces uracil incorporation into ribosomal RNA, while non-sedimentable RNA accumulates. The addition of guanosine, which restores protein synthesis, causes an increase of sedimentable RNA, and part of this originates from non-sedimentable RNA which was formed in the presence of azaguanine.

There is certainly a block at this stage. Unfortunately, it has not been possible to establish yet whether the inhibition of formation of ribosomal RNA is the cause or the consequence of the inhibition of protein synthesis. It is indeed conceivable that ribonucleic acids which would normally be bound into ribosomes remain in the non-sedimentable fraction for lack of protein with which they could combine. But this certainly does not completely explain what happens. When guanosine is added to intoxicated bacteria, a reorganization of RNA takes place: both non-sedimentable and ribosomal RNA lose the largest part of the azaguanine that they had incorporated, whereas all the pyrimidine residues that had been taken up during azaguanine action are retained as polynucleotides; part of the pyrimidines which were incorporated into soluble RNA are now found in the ribosomal sediment. It would seem that the presence of azaguanine in the ribonucleic acids prevents some normal interaction between soluble and ribosomal RNA which is important for protein synthesis.

In a discussion on the structure and function of transfer RNA [17] it was pointed out that the individual transfer ribonucleic acids must be recognized by the activation enzymes, and that in turn the transfer RNA must recognize the different sites on the template. In this perspective, it seems that transfer RNA's which have incorporated a considerable amount of azaguanine are still recognized by the activation enzymes; on the other hand, it is possible that they cannot recognize the template any more.

The differential effects of azaguanine on the synthesis of individual enzymes indicates an action of the analogue on RNA fractions which carry genetic information (messenger RNA or template RNA). To account for the differential susceptibility of various enzymes, one can imagine that certain templates are blocked, whereas others are not. This would result in the production of an abnormal assortment of proteins. It is also conceivable that the templates are all modified and that they produce abnormal proteins, the abnormalities being of such a nature that certain enzymes are more adversely affected than others. Incorporation of 2-thiouracil or of 5-fluorouracil into RNA of *Escherichia coli* indeed causes the production of proteins which differ from the normal ones in their serological properties, enzymic activity and amino acid composition [18, 19, 20].

These possibilities are presently being investigated in our laboratory in the case of catalase and penicillinase synthesis in *B. cereus*; the work is not advanced enough for results to be reported at present. A few data on catalase may be quoted. The catalase which forms during restoration of protein synthesis at a time when the production of active penicillinase is not yet restored (see Fig. 2) was compared to the enzyme of normal bacteria. No difference in sensitivity to azide or hydroxylamine inhibition was detected; the concentration of inhibitor required for 50% inhibition was the same for both the normal enzyme and the enzyme made during restoration by guanosine. However, the relative activities of the two samples of enzyme at different temperatures were markedly different, as shown in Fig. 3. These activities were measured on crude bacterial extracts prepared by sonication, and indirect effects cannot be completely excluded at present. As the protein content of the extracts differed, an excess of serum albumin was added to the bacterial extracts in certain experiments; this did not change the results appreciably.

These results suggest that the protein moiety of catalase made during the restoration period was abnormal, although the enzyme was active. Considerable change in the protein moiety of catalase can probably be brought about without changing much the catalytic properties of the haem; to the contrary, the active centre of penicillinase must be a region of the polypeptide, the catalytic properties of which are directly affected by

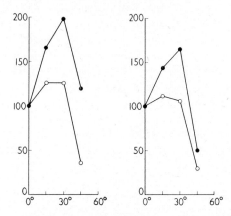

FIG. 3. Changes in catalase properties. Extracts were prepared by sonication from normal bacteria (●) and from bacteria which had been incubated with azaguanine for 45 min. before adding guanosine. These bacteria were collected 120 min. after the addition of guanosine (○). The catalase activity of the extracts was determined according to von Euler and Josephson [21] at four different temperatures: $0°$, $15°$, $30°$ and $45°$. In the second experiment, an excess bovine serum albumin was added to both extracts. The results are expressed as per cent of the activity measured at $0°$.

malformations of the chain. This may account for the greater sensitivity of penicillinase to the damages caused by azaguanine.

Our results suggest that 8-azaguanine, like 2-thiouracil and 5-fluorouracil, can affect the structure of the proteins produced by the bacteria which have incorporated the analogue into their nucleic acids. On the other hand, azaguanine exerts a general inhibition of protein synthesis, most probably by disturbing the normal interactions between some soluble and ribosomal ribonucleic acids.

References

1. Mandel, H. G., *J. biol. Chem.* **225,** 137 (1957).
2. Chantrenne, H., *Rec. Trav. chim. Pays-Bas* **77,** 586 (1958).
3. Chantrenne, H., and Devreux, S., *Exp. Cell Res. Suppl.* **6,** 152 (1958).
4. Chantrenne, H., and Devreux, S., *Nature, Lond.* **181,** 1737 (1958).
5. Chantrenne, H., and Devreux, S., *Biochim. biophys. Acta* **39,** 486 (1960).

6. Chantrenne, H., *Biochem. Pharmacol.* **1,** 233 (1959).
7. Chantrenne, H., and Devreux, S., *Biochim. biophys. Acta* **31,** 239 (1960).
8. Matthews, R. W., *in* "Ciba Foundation Symposium on the Chemistry and Biology of Purines", Churchill, London, 270 (1957).
9. Brockman, R. W., Hutchinson, D. J., and Skipper, H. E., *Fed. Proc.* **17,** 195 (1958).
10. Hoagland, M. B., Zamecnik, P. C., and Stephenson, M. L., *Biochim. biophys. Acta* **24,** 215 (1957).
11. Hoagland, M. B., Stephenson, M. L., Scott, J. F., Hecht, L. I., and Zamecnik, P. C., *J. biol. Chem.* **231,** 241 (1958).
12. Webster, G. C., *Arch. Biochem. Biophys.* **85,** 159 (1959).
13. Lamborg, M. R., and Zamecnik, P. C., *Biochim. biophys. Acta* **42,** 206 (1960).
14. Heinrich, M. R., Dewey, V. C., Parks, R. E., and Kidder, G. W., *J. biol. Chem.* **197,** 199 (1952).
15. Beljanski, M., and Ochoa, S., *Proc. nat. Acad. Sci., Wash.* **44,** 494, 1157 (1958).
16. Beljanski, M., *Biochim. biophys. Acta* **41,** 104 (1960).
17. Zamecnik, P. C. (communicated to the Symposium).
18. Hamers, R., and Hamers-Casterman, C., *Biochim. biophys. Acta* **33,** 269 (1959).
19. Horowitz, J., and Chargaff, E., *Nature, Lond.* **184,** 1213 (1959).
20. Gros, F., *in* "Dynamik des Eiweisses, 10. Colloquium Gesellschaft für Physiologischen Chemie". Springer, Berlin, 82 (1960).
21. Von Euler, H., and Josephson, K., *Ann.* **455,** 1 (1927).

Discussion

CAMPBELL: If I understand it right the incorporation of your azaguanine into the S-RNA makes your system rather different from that of Dr. F. Gros of the Institut Pasteur in which there was very little incorporation of fluorouracil into his S-RNA?

CHANTRENNE: These were very short experiments, a matter of 10 or 20 sec., if I remember correctly.

CAMPBELL: But later on the label moved to 70S and not S-RNA?

CHANTRENNE: Yes. In the case of azaguanine, there are two effects. The first is an inhibition of protein synthesis; it might be due to an action of the analogue on GTP or on S-RNA which prevents this from interacting normally with the ribosomes. The second effect bears on the specificity of protein synthesis, and in this respect it resembles very much that observed by Gros with fluorouracil; it might concern the genetic messenger or the ribosomes.

CHARGAFF: Fluorouracil goes very largely into the S-RNA; it actually replaces more uracil of the S-RNA than it does of the ribosomes.

HERBERT: In Dr. Gros's experiments fluorouracil inhibited DNA synthesis and he had to add thymine to restore it.

CHANTRENNE: Yes, that is right.

HERBERT: Does azaguanine affect DNA synthesis?

CHANTRENNE: With low concentrations of azaguanine, DNA synthesis is not inhibited. To get an inhibition, you must use rather large concentrations and even so the inhibition establishes only after about one or one and a half hours. The incorporation of azaguanine into DNA is very low, but it might possibly be sufficient to cause changes in specificity.

Purine and Pyrimidine Analogues and the Mucopeptide Biosynthesis in Staphylococci

H. J. Rogers and H. R. Perkins

*National Institute for Medical Research,
Mill Hill, London, England*

Both Gram positive and Gram negative micro-organisms are surrounded by a rigid layer or cell wall. The outer surface of this material is distinguished with some difficulty from capsular material; its inner surface is applied closely to the "membrane" which, among many other functions, controls the passage of smaller metabolites into and out of the cell. If this rigid outer layer of insoluble material, the so-called cell wall, be removed, the remainder of the cell will only remain whole, as a spherical protoplast, providing high concentrations of material which cannot readily penetrate the "membrane" are present in the external medium. If this condition is not met the cell bursts because the internal concentration of solutes in the cell produces an osmotic pressure equivalent to about twenty atmospheres for cocci and about ten atmospheres for some rod forms, too great a force for the weak membrane, unsupported by the cell wall, to withstand. A large proportion of this insoluble cell wall material, in Gram positive micro-organisms, consists of a limited number of amino acids, usually two amino sugars and in some species a few hexoses. Such complexes, we have suggested, should be called mucopeptides [1]. In the staphylococci, these mucopeptides contain only alanine, lysine, glycine and glutamic acid together with glucosamine and muramic acid (3-*O*-carboxyethylglucosamine); most of each of the amino sugars exists as the N-acetyl derivative; some of the alanine and probably all the glutamic acid are in the D configuration [2, 3]. Apart from mucopeptide the wall material of staphylococci also contains 40–60% of a teichoic acid [4, 5] consisting of a polymer of ribitolphosphate with N-acetylglucosamine and D-alanine attached. In some strains it has been suggested that this material may account for up to 70–80% of the weight of the isolated wall material [6].

The biosynthesis of mucopeptide is inhibited by penicillin, bacitracin and oxamycin [7, 8, 9] but not by chloramphenicol [10, 8]. It seems probable that the inhibition of this process represents a primary site of action of the former group of antibiotics. During inhibition caused by penicillin

L

a small nucleotide-linked mucopeptide accumulates which consists of uridine diphosphate linked to N-acetylmuramic acid, alanine, glutamic acid and lysine in the molar ratios of $1:1:3:1:1$ [11]. Fragments of the mucopeptide, namely uridine diphosphate-N-acetylmuramic acid and uridine diphosphate-N-acetylmuramic acid linked to one molecule of alanine, also occur. On the basis of the analytical similarity of the first of these mucopeptides (excluding the nucleotide) with the cell wall mucopeptide of their strain of staphylococcus, Strominger and Park [12] suggested that the nucleotide-mucopeptide was a precursor of cell wall.

The cell wall mucopeptide from our strain of organism [8, 13] prepared by the Cummins and Harris [14] method differed in quantitative composition from that examined by Park and Strominger [12] which had been prepared by the Salton and Horne [14a] method. Such differences prompted further investigation of the relationship between uridine nucleotide linked compounds and cell wall mucopeptide synthesis. Also the compounds isolated by Park [11] contained neither N-acetylglucosamine nor glycine both of which are prominent components of the cell wall material in all strains of staphylococci so far examined.

A possible general way of examining the role of uridine compounds in biosynthesis appeared to be to supply the cell with a pyrimidine analogue which behaved sufficiently like the natural compound to be incorporated into the small molecular weight compounds without these being able to polymerize to form the macromolecules. The uracil analogue which appeared most suitable for such a study was 5-fluorouracil. It had been shown by Heidelberger and his colleagues [15, 16] that this uracil analogue was converted by mouse tissues to the mono- di- and triphosphate nucleotides and probably to fluorouridine-diphosphoglucose. Also on structural grounds fluorouracil might be expected to behave more like uracil than other analogues such as 5-bromo- and 5-iodouracil or 6-azauracil.

The effect of 5-fluorouracil upon the synthesis of mucopeptides was therefore studied and its action compared with that of other purine and pyrimidine analogues. A full account of most of this work has already appeared [20].

The effect of the compounds upon the biosynthesis of cell wall mucopeptide was examined by measuring the rate of incorporation of [1-^{14}C]-alanine, glutamic acid and glycine or [G-^{14}C]-lysine into washed cells of *Staphylococcus aureus* strain 524/SC incubated in the presence of chloramphenicol under the conditions of Mandelstam and Rogers [8]. After incubation, the measurements of biosynthesis were made using material, prepared from the cells, which was insoluble in hot trichloroacetic acid. It was shown that incorporation into such material reflected cell wall mucopeptide synthesis by preparing the cell walls according to the method of Cummins and Harris [14]. Of the following compounds only 5-fluorouracil inhibited cell wall mucopeptide synthesis: 5-bromouracil, 5-fluorouracil, 6-azauracil, 6-azathymine, 8-azaguanine and its riboside, 2 : 6-diamino-purine, and 6-mercaptopurine. At a concentration of $0 \cdot 1$ μmole/ml. of 5-fluorouracil the biosynthesis of cell wall mucopeptide was inhibited 30–60%. The other compounds were tested in concentrations up to 1 μmole/ml. without effect upon biosynthesis. A separate section will be devoted to the examination of the effect of certain substituted benzimida-zoles which have also been examined.

The accumulation within the cells of compounds soluble in trichloroace-tic acid and which contain N-acetylhexosamine in a bound form, was examined by the technique previously used by Strominger [18] for penicil-lin-treated cells. It was found that a considerable accumulation of such compounds occurred. For example, in the presence of $0 \cdot 4$ μmole of 5-fluorouracil/ml. the cells accumulated 600 μg. of N-acetylhexosamine/100 mg. of bacterial dry wt. during 1 hr. incubation, whilst the control cells incubated without 5-fluorouracil had accumulated only 50–60 μg. of bound N-acetylhexosamine. The amino sugar concentration is expressed in terms of N-acetylglucosamine. The amount present in the cells increased accor-ding to the concentration of fluorouracil added to the incubation medium up to the highest concentration of inhibitor examined ($0 \cdot 4$ μmole/ml.). This accumulation could be prevented equally by the simultaneous presence of either uridine or uracil; thymidine was about a third as effective as these two compounds on a molar basis.

The nature of compounds containing N-acetylhexosamine

Washed cells of *Staphylococcus aureus* 524/SC were incubated at $35°$ in the solution used previously which contained the four cell wall amino acids, glucose, phosphate, and chloramphenicol. A concentration of $0 \cdot 4$ μmole/ml. of [2-^{14}C]-5-fluorouracil was included. Incubation was con-tinued for 1 hr. at $35°$ with aeration. At the end of this time the cells were removed by centrifugation and washed with cold $0 \cdot 1$ M sodium-potassium phosphate buffer at pH $7 \cdot 0$. They were then extracted with cold 10% trichloroacetic acid [18] as before. The extract was freed from trichloroacetic acid by ether extraction, the residual ether removed by aeration and the extract then chromatographed on a column of Dowex-1 (X2, chloride form, 50–100 mesh). The eluents used were those described by Strominger [18]. The emerging samples were examined for bound N-acetylhexosamine by the usual technique [18] and for radioactivity. Two peaks containing both N-acetylhexosamine and [2-^{14}C]-5-fluorouracil were found corresponding in position to the bound N-acetylhexosamine peaks obtained when extracts from penicillin-treated cells were examined in a similar manner. Both these peaks appeared likely to contain more than one substance. Consequently the materials from each peak after concentration by adsorption on to, and elution from charcoal [19], were re-chromatographed on columns of diethylaminoethyl-cellulose. The columns were developed with a gradient of ammonium acetate at pH 6·5. Material from the first peak from Dowex-1 yielded only one substance containing both N-acetylhexosamine and [2-¹⁴C]-5-fluorouracil when examined on the substituted cellulose column whilst the second yielded two such peaks, one of which was still heterogeneous. This latter peak was chromatographed once more on diethylaminoethyl cellulose, the column being developed this time with an increasing concentration of ammonium acetate at pH 5·0.

Table I shows the analysis of the compounds isolated. It will be seen that 1A, 2C$_1$ and 2C$_2$ are the fluorouridine analogues of the compounds previously isolated by Park [11] from penicillin-treated staphylococci. Fluorouridine-diphospho-N-acetylglucosamine (2B) was also isolated: no other compounds containing N-acetylhexosamine could be recognized.

TABLE I

ANALYSIS OF THE COMPOUNDS EXTRACTED FROM *Staphylococcus aureus* STRAIN 524 WITH TRICHLOROACETIC ACID AFTER THE CELLS HAD BEEN INCUBATED WITH 0·4 μMOLE OF [2–¹⁴C]-5-FLUOROURACIL

(The molar proportions are related to the concentration of [2–¹⁴C]-5-fluorouracil which is taken as 1·00.)

	Molar proportions						
	5-Fluoro-uracil	Phos-phorus	Glutamic acid	Lysine	Alanine	Muramic acid	Glucosa-mine
1A	1·00	2·21	0·99	1·05	2·83	1·12	0
2B	1·00	—*	0	0	0	0	0·97
2C$_1$	1·00	—*	0	0	0	1·0	0
2C$_2$	1·00	—*	0	0	1·3	1·0	0

* = Not estimated.

It will be noted that none of the compounds contained glycine. In earlier experiments in which lower concentrations (0·1 μmole/ml.) of 5-fluorouracil had been used, traces of glycine were found in hydrolysates from the materials in both peaks which emerged from the Dowex-1 columns [17]. Only very small amounts of a definite compound, however, were found containing glycine, glutamic acid, alanine, and muramic acid. This compound seemed no longer to be present when 5-fluorouracil was present at the higher concentration in the incubation medium.

From the above observations it seems reasonable to suppose that at least part of the cell wall mucopeptide in our strains of staphylococcus is synthesized via uridine diphospho-N-acetylglucosamine and a uridine diphospho-mucopeptide similar to that isolated by Park [11]. Equally it seemed possible that glycine which did not accumulate in any form associated with 5-fluorouridine might be incorporated into the wall mucopeptide via a co-enzyme other than uridine. If such a precursor also contained other amino acids besides glycine, the differences in molecular proportion between our cell wall mucopeptides and those of other strains [13] might be explained. Earlier work, already described, showed that some analogues of thymine, guanine, and adenine did not inhibit mucopeptide synthesis or lead to the accumulation of compounds containing bound N-acetylhexosamine which were soluble in trichloroacetic acid.

TABLE II

THE EFFECT OF SUBSTITUTED BENZIMIDAZOLES ON THE INCORPORATION OF [1-^{14}C]-GLYCINE AND [G-^{14}C] LYSINE INTO MATERIAL INSOLUBLE IN HOT TRICHLOROACETIC ACID

The organisms were incubated under conditions [8, 10] for cell wall synthesis such that little or no protein synthesis took place.

Compound	Concentration (μmoles/ml.)	% Inhibition of incorporation	
		[1–^{14}C]-glycine	[G–^{14}C]-lysine
5 : 6 dimethyl-	0·4	12	24
benzimidazole	1·0	15	32
5 : 6 dichloro-1-			
(β-ribofuranosyl)-	0·5	24	32
benzimidazole	1·0	62	63
5 : 6 dichloro-	0·5	12	15
benzimidazole	1·0	21	31
	2·0	64	59

Another group of analogues, the substituted benzimidazoles, have been shown to inhibit [8-^{14}C]-adenosine incorporation into ribonucleic acid of chorioallantoic membrane [21, 22] and to inhibit incorporation of amino acids into trichloroacetic acid insoluble material from staphylococci [23, 24, 25]. The effect of these substances upon cell wall formation under our conditions was examined. On the hypothesis that the small amount of material referred to above as having been isolated from cells treated with 0·1 μmole/ml. of fluorouracil, which contained glutamic acid, glycine, and alanine but not lysine, might be a cell-wall precursor, the effects of the substituted benzimidazoles on the incorporation of glycine and lysine were compared. It was found (see Table II) that two of the compounds inhibited incorporation of both amino acids when tested in the same system as used before, but that both amino acids were equally affected. The third, 5, 6-dimethylbenzimidazole, was only weakly inhibitory but rather more active in inhibiting lysine incorporation than that of glycine. No definite accumulation of glycine-containing compounds was found. Full analysis of the mechanism of the inhibition has not yet been attempted but it does not seem to be possible to inhibit differentially the two possible pathways of synthesis in an obvious manner by means of the substituted benzimidazoles. It may be, of course, that even if two such pathways exist, it is impossible to obtain a polymer principally made from only one set of precursors. If this were so, then one would not expect to be able to inhibit the incorporation of amino acids differentially, although earlier work with penicillin [8] held out promise of such possibilities.

References

1. Perkins, H. R. and Rogers, H. J., *Biochem. J.* **72,** 647 (1959).
2. Strominger, J. L., and Threnn, R. H., *Biochim. biophys. Acta* **33,** 280 (1959).
3. Salton, M. R. J., *Nature, Lond.* **180,** 338 (1957).
4. Armstrong, J. J., Baddiley, J., Buchanan, J. G., Carss, B., and Greenberg, G. R., *J. chem. Soc.* 4344 (1958).
5. Baddiley, J., *Proc. chem. Soc.* 177 (1959).
6. Hancock, R., *Biochim. biophys. Acta* **37,** 42 (1960).
7. Park, J. T., *Biochem. J.* **70,** 2P (1958).
8. Mandelstam, J., and Rogers, H. J., *Biochem. J.* **72,** 654 (1959).
9. Strominger, J. L., Ito, E., and Threnn, R. H., *J. Amer. chem. Soc.* **82,** 998 (1960).
10. Mandelstam, J., and Rogers, H. J., *Nature, Lond.* **181** 956 (1958).
11. Park, J. T., *J. biol. Chem.* **194,** 877, 885, 897 (1952).
12. Strominger, J. L., and Park, J. T. *Science* **125,** 99 (1957).
13. Rogers, H. J., and Perkins, H. R., *Nature, Lond.* **184,** 520 (1959).
14. Cummins, C. S., and Harris, H., *J. gen. Microbiol.* **14,** 583 (1956).
14a. Salton, M. R. J., and Horne, R. W., *Biochim. biophys. Acta* **7,** 177 (1951).
15. Chaudhuri, N. K., Montag, B. J., and Heidelberger C., *Cancer Res.* **18,** 318 (1956).
16. Harbers, E., Chaudhuri, N. K., and Heidelberger C., *J. biol. Chem.* **234,** 1255 (1959).
17. Rogers, H. J., and Perkins H. R., *Biochem. J.* **74,** 6P (1960).
18. Strominger, J. L., *J. biol. Chem.* **224,** 509 (1957).
19. Cabib, E., Leloir, L. F., and Cardini, C. E., *J. biol. Chem.* **203,** 1055 (1955).
20. Rogers, H. J., and Perkins H. R., *Biochem. J.* **77,** 449 (1960).
21. Tamm, I., *Science* **126,** 1235 (1957).
22. Tamm, I. "8th Symposium of the Society for General Microbiology", ed. S. T. Cowan and E. Rowatt. Cambridge University Press, 178 (1958).
23. Gale, E. F., and Folkes, J. P., *Biochem. J.* **64,** 4P (1956).
24. Gale, E. F., and Folkes, J. P., *Biochem. J.* **67,** 507 (1957).
25. Gale, E. F., "8th Symposium of the Society for General Microbiology", ed. S. T. Cowan and E. Rowatt. Cambridge University Press, 212 (1958).

Discussion

REICHARD: Do you believe that the fluoronucleotides are less effective as donors of the peptides, and connected with this question is the second question didn't you find any uracil in your fluorouracil nucleotides ?

ROGERS: In answer to the first question we have taken the cells in which we have accumulated the pyrimidine mucopeptide and have tried in all ways to obtain utilization of them. We get no utilization of the small mucopeptide even when the cells are incubated in the presence of a large excess of normal uridine. Our hypothesis is that the fluorine-substituted compounds inhibit the polymer formation by competitive inhibition of the final steps of condensation. We haven't any very good evidence, but one can specifically prevent the accumulation of these materials by adding uridine simultaneously with purines. The second question concerns uracil again; in preliminary experiments we have used half as much fluorouracil as those I have shown today and under these conditions we got approximately equal amounts of the uracil compound and the fluorouracil compound accumulating. When we doubled the amount of fluorouracil, the normal uracil compounds completely disappeared.

Studies on the Incorporation of Arginine into Acceptor RNA of *Escherichia coli**

H. G. BOMAN, I. A. BOMAN†

The Rockefeller Institute, New York, U.S.A.

and

W. K. MAAS‡

*New York University College of Medicine,
New York, U.S.A.*

Introduction

The activation of amino acids and their transfer to acceptor RNA (soluble RNA, sRNA) has been extensively investigated in several laboratories (for a review see Zamecnik [1]). Although it is generally assumed that these reactions are involved in the biosynthesis of proteins, relatively little experimental evidence from whole cell studies is available on the exact nature of their participation [2]. To characterize further the role of these reactions in cellular metabolism we began a study of the incorporation of arginine into acceptor RNA. It has been shown that in *E. coli* the intracellular concentration of this amino acid controls the formation of enzymes involved in its own biosynthesis [3]. When the concentration of arginine is high, such as in cultures growing in the presence of exogenously provided arginine, the formation of these enzymes is repressed; when it is low, as in an arginine-requiring mutant growing with limiting arginine in a chemostat, the level of enzymes rises to 500 times that of the repressed culture. In view of recent studies which have implicated RNA in the regulation of protein synthesis [4, 5] we felt that the arginine system, in which it is possible to vary the rate of formation of certain specific enzymes, would be suitable to elucidate a possible regulatory function of RNA.

The present paper is chiefly a description of a system for the *in vitro* incorporation of arginine into the acceptor RNA. Certain compounds

---

* This work was supported by grant no RG-6048 from the U.S. Public Health Service.
† Present address: *Institute of Biochemistry, Uppsala, Sweden.*
‡ Senior Research Fellow, U.S. Public Health Service.

L*

structurally related to arginine have been investigated and their effect on the rate of formation of arginine-RNA will be described. In addition cells obtained from different states of repression will be compared in regard to the arginine-activating enzyme and the arginine-RNA. In particular this comparison involves a mutant in which arginine no longer represses enzyme formation.

Methods and Materials

The strains used were *E. coli* Hfr $30S_0$ ("wild type") and Hfr $30S_0A5$, a canavanine-resistant mutant [6] in which arginine can no longer repress the synthesis of some enzymes involved in its own biosynthesis (in the following this mutant is designated arg.R−).

Growth of the cells was carried out aerobically in two types of minimal media, A and S-2, [7, 8] both supplemented with monosodium glutamate ($1 \cdot 67$ g./l.) and glucose (5 g./l.). The cells were harvested near the end of the logarithmic growth phase, collected by centrifugation in a Sharples centrifuge, and stored as a frozen paste.

The preparation of the acceptor RNA can be summarized as follows [9]: The procedure was designed to avoid large volumes and ultracentrifugations and is essentially a combination of steps taken from the methods of Crestfield *et al.* [10] and Kirby [11] to which a lanthanum precipitation [12] has been added. It consists of a heating step which breaks up the cells, a deproteinization with phenol, an alcohol precipitation to remove phenol and low molecular weight material, an extraction of the precipitate with 1 M sodium chloride to separate the acceptor RNA from the high molecular weight RNA, and a lanthanum precipitation to separate the acceptor RNA from polysaccharides.

The assay of the arginine-RNA* was carried out in a volume of $0 \cdot 5$ ml. at pH $7 \cdot 0$. The concentration of the components were $0 \cdot 1$ M tris-maleate buffer, $0 \cdot 002$ M ATP, $0 \cdot 004$ M Mg^{++} (added as MgO), $0 \cdot 002$ M glutathione, $0 \cdot 002$ M fructose diphosphate, $0 \cdot 28$ mM L-[^{14}C]-arginine with $5 \cdot 93 \times 10^6$ c.p.m./μmole, 15–20 μg. arginine-activating enzyme in $0 \cdot 5$ ml., and 5–25 optical units of RNA in $0 \cdot 5$ ml. The reaction mixture was incubated at $37°$ for 15 min. Mixing of reagents and termination of the reaction by the addition of 2 ml. of $0 \cdot 01$ M lanthanum nitrate in $0 \cdot 5$ M perchloric acid were done in an ice bath. After the reaction was stopped, $0 \cdot 2$ ml. of 5% commercial yeast RNA was added as carrier. The precipitate was washed twice with 2 ml. of cold 5% trichloroacetic acid containing

---

* The following abbreviations are used: RNA, ribonucleic acid; tris, tris-(hydroxymethyl)aminomethane; ATP, adenosine triphosphate; c.p.m., counts per min.; optical unit (o.u.), the amount of RNA which in 1 ml. gives an extinction of 1 at 260 mμ; U.S.P., United States Pharmacopoeia; DEAE, diethylaminoethyl.

1% casein hydrolysate, and once with 2 ml. of cold ethanol-ether (2 :1). It was dissolved by adding 0·3 ml. of 0·2 M triethylamine and heating to about 60° for 2 min. transferred to planchets, dried and counted with a windowless gasflow counter. A sample in which RNA was omitted was used as a blank except if otherwise stated. Correction for self absorption and geometry was read from a standard curve.

The large scale labelling of RNA with [14C]-arginine was carried out with the same reaction mixture as that used for the assay. The reaction was terminated by addition of an equal volume of 88% phenol in water and shaking for 2 min. After cooling to 4°, the phases were separated by centrifugation. The water layer (at the top) was removed and alcohol was added to it to a final concentration of 20% (to increase the solubility of the remaining phenol). The arginine-RNA was then precipitated with lanthanum nitrate [8], redissolved in a small volume of 0·2 M potassium ethylene diamine tetraacetic acid, pH 7, and finally dialysed for 15–20 hr. with several changes of water.

The protein and the nucleic acid contents were determined from the extinctions at 280 and 260 mμ [13].

Chemicals used: Nitroarginine was synthesized according to Kossel and Kennaway [14]. The melting-point was 248° d. and it was found to be homogeneous by paper electrophoresis at pH 6 and by chromatography in isopropanol: ammonia: water (7 : 1 : 2) ($R_f = 0·56$). The strong u.v. absorption of nitroarginine makes it convenient to observe it on paper by quenching of fluorescence in the same way as nucleotides. Sulphaguanidine (U.S.P.) was purchased from Amend Drug and Chem. Co., New York, New York, L-canavanine sulphate from Nutritional Biochemical Corp., Cleveland 28, Ohio; streptomycin sulphate (U.S.P.) from Ely Lilly and Co., Indianapolis, Indiana; L-[14C]-arginine with $5·93 \times 10^3$ c.p.m./m-μmole from Nuclear Chicago Corp., Des Plaines, Illinois; L-[14C]-arginine with $88·8 \times 10^3$ c.p.m./mμmole and [14C]-alga protein hydrolysate with $1·4 \times 10^5$ c.p.m./μg. were obtained from Volks Radiochemical Co., Chicago 40, Illinois.

Results

PARTIAL PURIFICATION OF THE ARGININE-ACTIVATING ENZYME

The frozen bacterial paste (about 11 g.) was placed in a temperature-insulated mortar. Liquid nitrogen was poured into it until the paste was well covered. As temperature equilibrium was approached the paste became brittle and was then ground to a fine powder by gently tapping with a pestle for 5–10 min. The liquid nitrogen was allowed to evaporate and the frozen powder was spread over the bottom surface of a plastic container. It was melted by dipping the container into water at 30° for 2–3 min., and cooled to 0°. It was suspended with stirring in about 4 ml.

of o·o2 M MgCl$_2$ in o·o2 M tris-HCl, pH 7·3 until a viscous but homogeneous mixture was obtained. This was centrifuged at 100 000 **g** for 1 hr.
The pellet (about one-third of the volume) was discarded and the clear
supernatant was dialyzed at 4° for 12–15 hr. against o·o4 M tris-HCl,
pH 7·4. The resulting solution (Fraction I) contains about 9·9 mg. of
protein and o·9 mg. of nucleic acid per ml. It was used as a general
source of all activating enzymes as well as for the further purification of
the arginine-activating enzyme.

For this further purification the extract was chromatographed on DEAE
cellulose [15]. A column containing a 100 ml. of absorbent was equilibrated
with o·o4 M tris-HCl, pH 7·4, and was then loaded with a volume of
Fraction I corresponding to 30 mg. of protein. The chromatogram was
developed by stepwise elution, using the following amounts of tris-HCl
buffers, pH 7·4: (a) 65 ml. of o·23 M; (b) 45 ml. of o·38 M, and (c) 100 ml.
of 1 M. Step (a) elutes a protein fraction with none or very little arginine-
activating enzyme; step (b) contains most of this activity; step (c) elutes a
fraction consisting mainly of nucleic acid. It was observed that the first use
of a batch of DEAE cellulose caused a considerable loss of enzyme activity.
Repeated use of the same column gave, however, satisfactory results.

The fractions containing the arginine-activating enzyme were pooled
and concentrated about twenty times using negative pressure dialysis with
1 cm. wide dialysis tubing. The concentrated solution (and also Fraction I)
were stored at −15° with 30–40% ethylene glycol as antifreeze because it
was found that repeated freezing and thawing results in marked loss of
activity. A typical concentrated solution of the arginine-activating enzyme,
including the ethylene glycol, had a protein content of 2·9 mg. per ml. and
a nucleic acid content of o·o2 mg. per ml.

LEVEL OF ACTIVATING ENZYMES UNDER DIFFERENT CONDITIONS OF GROWTH

As mentioned previously the addition of arginine to the growth medium
represses the formation of enzymes in its own biosynthesis. It was therefore
of interest to examine the effect of arginine on the formation of its activating
enzyme. For comparison a similar test was carried out for leucine, although
a corresponding repression by leucine has not yet been investigated.

Two cultures of strain 30S$_0$ were grown, one in medium A + L-
arginine (200 μg./ml.), the other in medium A + L-leucine (200 μg./ml.).
In the latter, L-isoleucine (100 μg./ml.) and L-valine (100 μg./ml.) were
added to counteract the slight inhibition of growth produced by L-leucine.

Fraction I was prepared from the harvested cells as described in the
preceding section and designated I$_a$ for the arginine-grown and I$_1$ for the
leucine-grown cells. The levels of the activating enzymes were determined
by following the formation of arginine- and leucine-RNA. In all tests the

same preparation of acceptor RNA was used. The initial reaction volume was 1·5 ml., and included 100 μl. of Fraction I. Aliquots of 0·5 ml. were removed at different times and assayed as described under Methods. The results are shown in Fig. 1 where the formation of arginine-RNA is represented by circles (open for Fraction I_a and filled for Fraction I_1) and the formation of leucine-RNA is denoted by triangles (open for Fraction I_a and filled for Fraction I_1). The figure includes an experiment with a twenty-times diluted sample of Fraction I_a (open squares) to show that this reaction like that with leucine procedes linearly with time. As Fig. 1

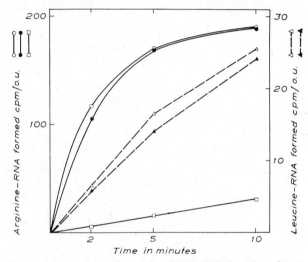

FIG. 1. Rate of formation of arginine-RNA (filled and unfilled circles) and leucine-RNA (filled and unfilled triangles). The enzyme sources were Fraction I_a obtained from cells grown in the presence of arginine (open circles and triangles), and Fraction I_1 from cells grown in the presence of leucine (filled circles and triangles). The open squares represent the formation of arginine-RNA with a twenty-times diluted sample of Fraction I_a.

shows, the addition of either amino acid to the growth medium is without effect on the formation of either activating enzyme.

EFFECT OF GUANIDINO DERIVATIVES ON THE ARGININE-ACTIVATING ENZYME

Certain guanidino derivatives were tested for their effect on the rate of formation of arginine-RNA. Purified arginine-activating enzyme (about 3 μg. per assay) was used in all experiments with arginine, and Fraction I was used in the experiments with the amino acid mixture (the alga protein hydrolysate). Table I shows that canavanine and streptomycin were found to be inhibitory whereas nitroarginine was slightly stimulatory and sulphaguanidine without a definite effect.

TABLE I

EFFECT OF GUANIDINO DERIVATIVES ON THE ARGININE-ACTIVATING ENZYME

Incorporation of	Addition	Activity	
		c.p.m.	per cent
All amino acids	—	6140	100
,,	Canavanine	5090	83
Arginine	—	2830	100
,,	Canavanine	1320	47
All amino acids	—	1550	100
,,	Streptomycin	1110	72
Arginine	—	3680	100
,,	Streptomycin	2270	62
Arginine	—	3390	100
,,	Sulphaguanidine	3480	103
,,	Nitroarginine	3860	114

The concentration of the compounds listed under "Addition" were 3 mM, and the [^{14}C]-arginine concentration was 0·28 mM in all experiments. The concentration of the [^{14}C]-alga protein hydrolysate was 3·4 μg./ml. in the experiment with streptomycin and 8·4 μg./ml. in the one with canavanine. Except for the use of an excess of RNA from 30S$_0$, the assay was carried out as described under Materials and Methods. The activity in c.p.m. is given without correction for self-absorption and geometry.

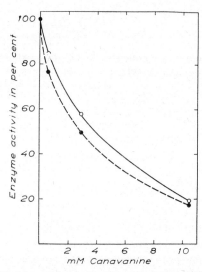

FIG. 2. Activity of the arginine-activating enzyme as a function of canavanine concentration. The concentration of [^{14}C]-arginine was 0·28 mM. Enzyme purified from strain 30S$_0$ represented by open circles; from strain 30S$_0$A5 by filled circles.

Since the arg.R⁻ strain 30S₀A5 was originally isolated as a canavanine-resistant mutant [5], a comparison was made of the canavanine inhibition of the arginine-activating enzymes isolated from 30S₀ and from 30S₀A5. About 3·3 μg. of purified activating enzyme was used in each assay and the canavanine concentration was varied over a twentyfold range. The results from these experiments (see Fig. 2) show no difference in the sensitivity between the enzymes from the two strains.

CHARACTERIZATION OF THE ARGININE-RNA

A comparison was made between the acceptor RNA from the wild type and the arg.R⁻ mutant, using 15 μg. of the same preparation of purified arginine-activating enzyme in each assay. Figure 3 shows the RNA-

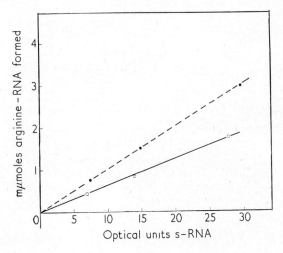

FIG. 3. RNA dependence for the formation of arginine-RNA. Acceptor RNA from strain 30S₀ (wild type) represented by open circles, from strain 30S₀A5 (the arg.R–mutant) denoted by filled circles.

dependence for the formation of arginine-RNA. The slopes of the lines correspond to an uptake of 1 arginine per 1900 nucleotides for the wild type and 1 arginine per 1200 nucleotides for the arg.R⁻ mutant. Figure 4 shows the enzyme dependence of the formation of arginine-RNA for a pair of RNA preparations other than those used for the experiments of Fig. 3. At all levels of enzyme, the amount of arginine-RNA formed in 15 min. is larger in the arg.R⁻ mutant than in the wild type. To test whether or not the difference observed in the two previous experiments was specific for arginine, the incorporation of arginine was compared to that of the amino acid mixture (which contains about 6% arginine). Table II shows

TABLE II

AMINO ACID INCORPORATION INTO ACCEPTOR RNA

Incorporation of	Type of RNA	Specific activity of RNA	
		c.p.m./o.u.	per cent
Arginine	Wild type ($30S_0$)	176	100
,,	Mutant ($30S_0A5$)	282	160
All amino acids	Wild type ($30S_0$)	568	100
,,	Mutant ($30S_0A5$)	675	119

The concentration of the [^{14}C]-alga protein hydrolysate was 3·4 μg./ml.; other conditions of the assay as described under Materials and Methods. The specific activity in c.p.m./o.u. is given without correction for self adsorption and geometry.

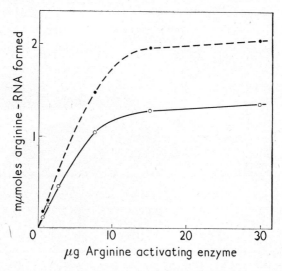

FIG. 4. Enzyme dependence for the formation of arginine-RNA. Purified arginine-activating enzyme from strain $30S_0$ (the wild type) was used with 24·0 optical units acceptor RNA from the same strain (open circles) and with 23·8 optical units acceptor RNA from the arg.R$^-$ mutant $30S_0A5$ (filled circles). The blanks used in this experiment were the c.p.m. obtained by extrapolation to zero μg. of enzyme.

that the incorporation of the amino acid mixture is 19% higher into the mutant RNA than into the wild type RNA, whereas the incorporation of arginine into the mutant RNA is 60% higher. However, it should be pointed out, that in all experiments in Tables I and II, the incorporation of the amino acid mixture is proportional to its concentration, while the formation of arginine-RNA is independent of arginine concentrations above 0·1 mM.

As a qualitative test of the product formed, a sample of acceptor RNA from $30S_0A5$ was labelled with the more active of the [^{14}C]-arginine preparations (see Methods and Materials). The labelled RNA obtained had a specific activity of 5730 c.p.m./o.u. It was subjected to mild alkaline treatment (0·05 M triethylamine for 3 min. at 60°) and analyzed by paper chromatography. Only the arginine spot could be detected, despite the fact that the arginine used for the incorporation experiment showed four spots of impurities.

The hydrolysis of arginine-RNA at pH 8·0 was studied at three temperatures. Samples of [^{14}C]-arginine-RNA with 160 c.p.m./o.u. were incubated at different temperatures; aliquots were removed at various

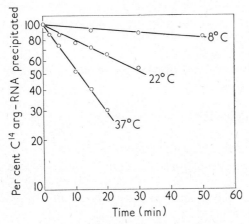

FIG. 5. Rate of hydrolysis of arginine-RNA at pH 8·0 and different temperatures.

times and added to 1 ml. of cold 0·01 M lanthanum nitrate in 0·5 M perchloric acid. The precipitate collected after centrifugation was counted. Figure 5 shows these data as a percentage of the counts of the zero time precipitate.

Discussion

THE ARGININE-ACTIVATING ENZYME

The chromatography of the arginine-activating enzyme described here removes nucleic acid rather well but gives on a protein basis only about a threefold increase in specific activity. However, the amount of protein required to label 1 mg. of RNA in 15 min. is only 15 μg. (see Fig. 4). The corresponding figure for a seven-times purified leucine-activating enzyme calculated from Fig. 3 in ref. [16] was found to be around 4·7 mg. A similar figure has been reported also for an isoleucine-activating protein fraction [17]. There may thus be considerable differences in turnover number between activating enzymes.

The experiments in Fig. 1 show a comparison of the incorporation of arginine and leucine when the enzyme fractions had been obtained from cells grown in the presence either of arginine or of leucine. The results show that the addition of the amino acids to the media had no effect on the level of the corresponding activating enzyme and that the repression mechanism found for the enzymes in the biosynthesis of arginine [18] does not operate on the arginine-activating enzyme. Further support for this conclusion is provided by the results of several experiments in which no appreciable difference was found between the quantities of arginine-activating enzyme obtained from the wild type and the arg. R⁻ mutant.

In vivo experiments have earlier shown that canavanine inhibits growth by interfering with the utilization of arginine in protein synthesis [19]. The present finding of the inhibition of the arginine-activating enzyme suggests this step as the site of action of canavanine. Since the enzyme from the mutant is as sensitive as that from the wild type, the mechanism of the resistance in the mutant does not involve an alteration of this enzyme (cf. ref. 20 and 21).

The experiments in Table I show that streptomycin inhibits the formation of arginine-RNA and that this inhibition is greater for arginine than for a mixture of all amino acids. Streptomycin is known to complex with nucleic acids [22] and it is difficult to exclude that this presumably non-specific effect contributes to the inhibition we have recorded here, although no precipitation occurred in the presence of the buffer used in our experiments. The increased sensitivity of the arginine incorporation compared to that of the mixture of all amino acids (including arginine), though rather slight, indicates some degree of specificity for the inhibition of the formation of arginine-RNA. Some further support for a relation between the utilization of arginine and the action of streptomycin is suggested by the fact that Gorini [23] has obtained a mutant which requires either arginine or streptomycin. It has also recently been found that the genes for streptomycin resistance, the arginine repressor and some of the arginine synthesizing enzymes are closely linked [6].

Davis and his co-workers [24] have recently shown that streptomycin damages the cell membrane but they have concluded that this action though necessary, may not be sufficient to account for the bactericidal effect. It may well be that both the specific action of streptomycin in the incorporation of arginine into acceptor RNA and its non-specific complex formation with nucleic acid contribute to the bactericidal action.

In vivo experiments with nitroarginine showed that it neither affects growth, nor does it replace arginine for the growth of an arginine-requiring mutant. The 14% increase in the rate of formation of arginine-RNA observed in the presence of this compound is obscure, although an inhibitor normally present in the cell and antagonized by nitroarginine could account for an effect like this.

When comparing the four guanidino derivatives tested in Table I it can be seen that those in which the electronegative character of the guanidino group has been decreased (nitroarginine and sulphaguanidine), have no inhibitory action on the arginine-activating enzyme. This is in agreement with the observation that the enzyme is relatively acidic and eluted from the DEAE cellulose column with $0 \cdot 38$ M tris-HCl pH $7 \cdot 4$ whereas the threonine-activating enzyme from calf liver was eluted by $0 \cdot 12$ M tris-HCl pH $7 \cdot 8$ during otherwise similar conditions [25].

Sharon and Lipman [26] have studied the influence of analogues on the tryptophan-activating enzyme and have compared their *in vitro* results with *in vivo* studies on the growth of *E. coli* [27, 28]. It was found that 5-methyltryptophan and 6-methyltryptophan, inhibited both growth and the tryptophan-activating enzyme. At a concentration ratio of analogue: tryptophan of 200 : 1 the inhibition was 70% for 5-methyltryptophan and 42% for 6-methyltryptophan in the *in vitro* experiments. In comparison we found at a concentration ratio of 10 : 1 (analogue: arginine) 47% inhibition for canavanine and 38% inhibition for streptomycin. The somewhat greater effect of the arginine analogues lends additional support to the suggestion that the *in vivo* action of these inhibitors are on the level of the activating enzymes.

THE ARGININE-RNA

The alkaline liability of the formed arginine-RNA as well as the other characteristics of the reaction are consistent with the general notion of an amino acid-acyl-RNA compound of the type previously described for other amino acids [29, 30].

The difference in the amount of arginine-RNA between the wild type and the arg.R⁻ mutant (see Figs. 3 and 4) has been observed in two independent pairs of RNA preparations. At present we do not know whether this difference is only a quantitative one or also a qualitative one. The physiological significance of the difference in relation to the mechanism of the arginine repression is also not clear. However, the observed difference supports our original notion that repression is linked with RNA metabolism and encourages us to continue studies along these lines.

Acknowledgments

We should like to express our thanks to Dr. F. Lipmann for much help and many stimulating discussions.

References

1. Zamecnik, P. C., "The Harvey Lectures" Series 54 (1958-9), Academic Press, New York (1960).
2. Lacks, S., and Gros, F., *J. mol. Biol.* **1,** 301 (1959).
3. Gorini, L., and Maas, W. K., *Biochim. biophys. Acta* **25,** 208 (1957).
4. Maaløe, O., in "Microbial Genetics". Cambridge University Press, 272 (1960).
5. Neidhardt, F. C., and Magasanik, B., *Biochim. biophys. Acta* **42,** 99 (1960).
6. Borgois, S., Lavallee, R., Maas, W. K., and Wiame, J., in preparation.
7. Davis, B. D., and Mingioli, E. S., *J. Bact.* **60,** 17 (1950).
8. Hager, L. P., Ph.D. Thesis, Univ. of Illinois (1954).
9. Method developed in the laboratory of Dr. F. Lipmann.
10. Crestfield, A. M., Smith, K. C., and Allen, F. W., *J. biol. Chem.* **216,** 185 (1955).
11. Kirby, K. S., *Biochem. J.* **64,** 405 (1956).
12. Hammarsten, E., Hammarsten, G., and Theorell, T., *Acta med. scand.* **68,** 219 (1928).
13. Warburg, O., and Christian, W., *Biochem. Z.* **310,** 384 (1941).
14. Kossel, A., and Kennaway, E. L., *Hoppe-Seyl Z.* **72,** 486 (1911).
15. Peterson, E. A., and Sober, H. E., *J. Amer. chem. Soc.* **78,** 751 (1956).
16. Allen, E. H., Glassman, E., Cordes, E., and Schweet, R. S., *J. biol. Chem.* **235,** 1068 (1960).
17. Hele, P., and Finch, L. R., *Biochem. J.* **75,** 352 (1960).
18. Gorini, L., and Maas, W. K., in "The Chemical Basis of Development", ed. McElroy and Glass. Johns Hopkins Press 489 (1958).
19. Schwartz, J., and Maas, W. K., *J. Bact.* **79,** 794 (1960).
20. Davis, B. D., and Maas, W. K., *Proc. nat. Acad. Sci., Wash.* **41,** 775 (1952).
21. Hotchkiss, R. D., and Evans, A. H., *Cold Spr. Harb. Symp. quant. Biol.* **23,** 85 (1958).
22. Cohen, S. S., *J. biol. Chem.* **168,** 511 (1947).
23. Gorini, L., personal communication.
24. Anand, N., Davis, B. D., and Armitage, A. K., *Nature, Lond.* **185,** 23 (1960).
25. Acs, G., Hartmann, G., Boman, H. G., and Lipmann, F., *Fed. Proc.* **18,** 178 (1959).
26. Sharon, N., and Lipmann, F., *Arch. Biochem. Biophys.* **69,** 219 (1957).
27. Halvorson, H., Spiegelman, S., and Hinman, R. L., *Arch. Biochem. Biophys.* **55,** 512 (1955).
28. Pardee, A. B., Shore, V. C., and Prestidge, L. S., *Biochim. biophys. Acta* **21,** 406 (1956).
29. Zachau, H. G., Acs, G., and Lipmann, F., *Proc. nat. Acad. Sci., Wash.* **44,** 885 (1958).
30. Preiss, J., Berg, P., Ofengand, E. Y., Bergmann, F. H., and Dieckmann, M., *Proc. nat. Acad. Sci., Wash.* **45,** 319 (1959).

POLYSACCHARIDES

Introduction

GUNNAR BLIX

Medicinsk-kemiska Institutionen, Uppsala, Sweden

In the present symposium problems related to polysaccharides occupy a relatively modest place, being dealt with only at this afternoon's session. This is perhaps a reasonable limitation in view of the general aim of the symposium. But polysaccharides undoubtedly play a very important role in "biological structures and functions" throughout the animal and plant kingdoms down to the bacteria. Since the lectures we shall listen to during the next few hours seem to be dealing mainly with metabolic and methodological aspects, it will perhaps be appropriate as an introduction to touch upon the arrangement and functions of the polysaccharides in the tissues. Because I have little personal experience of the conditions in plants I shall confine myself to some words about polysaccharides in animal tissues. In some regards they may have a wider application.

Bone, cartilage, skin, tendons, blood vessels, etc., all contain considerable amounts of acid mucopolysaccharides. As you know it has turned out during later years that there are many kinds of these substances: hyaluronic acid, chondroitin sulphuric acids of different types, keratosulphuric acid and others. Within each species minor modifications probably occur, at least as regards degree of polymerization. Certain general statements may be made about the arrangement of the mucopolysaccharides in the structural pattern of the connective tissues, and also about their physiological functions. They belong to the amorphous ground substance, they are present in the form of a sol or a gel in the pores of a collagenous network and they are loosely or more firmly associated with proteins. It also seems safe to say that they are in part responsible for the physical, and not least the mechanical properties of the connective tissues. But when we come to questions such as exact ultrastructural or molecular arrangements and precise mode of functions we are still very much in the dark.

The physiological function of a biological substance is in the first instance dependent on its chemical and physical properties. But these properties may in different biological structures or environments have very different physiological significance or consequences.

I should like to illustrate this point with an example. Hyaluronic acid, wherever it occurs, is a high-molecular, poly-anionic, highly hydrated, essentially unbranched polysaccharide, the molecules of which seem to be present in living tissues as randomly kinked coils. As might be expected, aqueous solutions of this substance are highly viscous. The viscous character of the joint fluids is due to hyaluronic acid, which occurs dissolved in the fluid together with some serum proteins. In this environment the properties of hyaluronic acid make it suitable to serve as a lubricant, protecting the cartilaginous surfaces in the joints against mechanical damage. This may be regarded as the main function of the hyaluronic acid of the joint fluid.

In the skin, subcutaneous, and other connective tissues the hyaluronic acid has quite other functions. The characteristic mechanical properties of these tissues, their rigidity, degree of compressibility, resistance to injected fluids and so on are no doubt due to the particular arrangement in which a sol or gel of hyaluronic acid (and of some other mucopolysaccharides) is included into the fine three-dimensional network of collagen fibres. Variation in pore-size, in fibre-width, fibre-length and orientation and in concentration, polymerization and ionization of the polysaccharides may of course influence and modify the mechanical and other properties of the tissues, but these fields are largely unexplored.

Karl Meyer and his collaborators have made the interesting observation that the ratio between hyaluronate and chondroitin sulphate and the ratio between different chondroitin sulphates vary with age. In pig's skin the ratio between chondroitin sulphate B and hyaluronate was found to be 1 : 5 in the new-born but a good 1 : 1 in the adult. In new-born infants the rib cartilage contains a high concentration of chondroitin-4-sulphate. This concentration decreases with increasing age, whereas the concentration of keratosulphate increases from the first year to adulthood and then remains constant. Furthermore chondroitin-4-sulphate is practically all replaced by the 6-sulphate. The physiological significance of these changes is unknown, but since they concern chemical substances with different properties they must undoubtedly influence the mechanical and other properties of the tissues. The mechanism by which these chemical changes are initiated may be something essential in the process of ageing.

There is evidently a long way to go before arriving at a clear understanding of the precise physiological significance of these and other structural polysaccharides. The work still to be done must comprise investigations of their primary and conformation structure, as well as studies on their interactions with fibre and globular proteins. It should also include a close inquiry into the physicochemical properties of the pure substances and of the complexes formed between them and proteins. It should of course involve direct studies on living tissues with optical and other methods. Investigation on artificial models may also be valuable.

The so-called structural polysaccharides should by no means be regarded as metabolically inert material. Already the relatively rapid metabolic turn-over of some of the acid mucopolysaccharides may be taken as evidence of that. It has been suggested that the architecture of the collagen bundles is determined by the type of polysaccharide formed by the cells in various types of connective tissues, and that the polysaccharide in some way or the other influences fibre formation. In embryonic development and wound healing the fibre formation is preceded by or concomitant with the formation of mucopolysaccharides. Of these, hyaluronic acid is usually the first produced, followed by sulphated forms. Some kind of template function of the polysaccharides bearing upon secondary or tertiary structure of connective tissue proteins might perhaps be conceivable.

In any event the problems pertaining to formation and metabolic turn-over of the polysaccharides must of course be of great interest in connection with biological structure and function. These problems have been very much to the fore during latter years and Prof. Dorfman and Prof. Hestrin have, as you all know, made outstanding contributions in these fields. We have learned that biosynthesis is not, as was earlier assumed, a simple reversal of the process of hydrolysis. The enzymic polysaccharidic syntheses work with donor substances, a common feature of which is that they consist of a sugar substituted on the anomeric carbon atom. The splitting of the bond between sugar and substituent supplies the energy required for the polymerization. The availability of suitable donors and appropriate enzymes (and perhaps other catalysts) will be the primary factors directing and guiding the formation of the polysaccharides. This field is as fascinating as it is complicated.

We await with great interest what Prof. Hestrin and Prof. Dorfman have to tell us about their work.

As with all other sciences progress in the polysaccharide field is very much dependent on the finding of new tools, principles, and methods of investigations. The separation of biological substances in unchanged state from the complex mixture in which they occur in living tissues, is one of the basic methodological problems of biochemistry. Dr. Flodin will give us a report of a new and promising device for the fractionation and separation of biological substances, which seems promising not least for the carbohydrate field, and I should not be surprised if it spread like an epidemic in biochemical laboratories.

The Growth of Saccharide Macromolecules

Shlomo Hestrin

*Department of Biological Chemistry, The Hebrew University,
Jerusalem, Israel*

In the context of a symposium on "Biological structure and function", it is surely appropriate to consider processes of polysaccharide synthesis which directly underlie striking morphological change in living organisms. Levan and dextran synthesis from sucrose and bacterial cellulose synthesis afford instructive examples of reactions in this class. The syntheses of these polymers proceed often to levels of product concentration at which a polymer-rich aqueous phase separates out in the surround of the cells. The ability for extracellular polymer synthesis appears to be so firmly established in the genetic make-up of widely different species, that one cannot but wonder whether some important biological function is not fulfilled by this property. Experiments reported in this symposium by P. A. Albertsson [1] are of interest in this connection. He has discovered that when phases arise in a mixed aqueous solution of appropriate species of macromolecules, particles dispersed in the system are often partitioned between the phases in a highly selective manner, and that particle size and shape affect this distribution very markedly. When phases separate out in a living system in the wake of polysaccharide synthesis, a similar specific partition pattern must occur. Thus a means may be afforded in the evolutionary process whereby potent macromolecular agents could be selectively concentrated or excluded from any separated phase. Such a phenomenon might have particular importance in the coacervate systems to which a prominent role has been assigned in a recent hypothesis concerning the nature of the primaeval milieu in which biological structure originated [2].

Size of the radical transferred from donor to the growing polymer chain in syntheses of levan and dextran

Reactions catalyzed by a range of carbohydrases are now known to consist in the transfer of a glycosyl rather of a glycosido group from the donor to an oxygen atom in the acceptor. If a change in substrate structure at an atom position close to that at which the bond breakage is to occur can be expected to exert a more profound effect on the reaction rate than a similar change effected at a relatively remote atom position, it might be possible on the basis of enzyme specificity studies in a family of substrate analogues to infer the position of the bond at which the enzymic cleavage occurs [3]. However, an attempt to derive this inference from a considera- tion of the substrate range of the polymer-synthesizing carbohydrases— levansucrase and dextransucrase—encounters the difficulty that in both these systems minor changes in glycose structure at atom positions on *both* sides of glycosidic oxygen in sucrose result in a complete suppression of the reactivity [4]. The question therefore arose whether these poly- merizing enzymes are glycosylases, as are the common hydrolases, or whether they are glycosidases and thus perhaps different in a salient aspect of structure from the common hydrolase group. An investigation which made it possible to select between these concepts was carried out in collaboration with Dr. Frank Eisenberg during a visit to the National Institute of Health at Bethesda.

Sucrose was synthesized enzymically by levansucrase-catalyzed trans- fer of fructose from raffinose (melibiosyl fructoside) to $[1\text{-}^{18}O]$-glucose. Sucrose formed was converted chemically first into its octoacetate and then, by transacetylation to methanol, was reconstituted in crystalline form. If a fructosido radical is transferred by the action of levansucrase, synthesized sucrose should have been devoid of any ^{18}O. If fructosyl rather than fructosido was the group transferred from raffinose to the added glucose acceptor, the atom excess of ^{18}O in the synthesized sucrose was expected, on the basis of the atom excess of ^{18}O in the glucose used, to be 0.65%. Experimentally the atom excess of ^{18}O in the recovered crystallized sucrose was found to be 0.64%, in close agreement with the calculated value. Hence it could be concluded that levansucrase, like the common hydrolyzing β-fructofuranosidase, is a glycosylase and not a glycosidase.

$[^{18}O]$-Sucrose which had been synthesized in the above manner was then incubated with dextransucrase of *Leuconostoc mesenteroides*. Dextran formed in this system and isolated from aqueous solution by repeated precipitation with ethanol proved to be devoid of ^{18}O. Hence we are able to draw the further conclusion that dextransucrase, like levansucrase, is a glycosylase and not a glycosidase.

It follows that levansucrase and dextransucrase attack sucrose each on a different side of the oxygen bridge. Should we be inclined, accordingly, to write the structure of sucrose with a Lipman wiggle ($\sim$) to indicate the site of the "high-energy-bond", we would be at a loss to decide the side of the oxygen bridge in which the symbol could properly be placed.

The results with dextransucrase further afford conclusive proof that the only site in enzymically synthesized sucrose at which ^{18}O occurred was the glycosidic oxygen. $[^{18}O]$-Sucrose synthesized as described by the action of levansucrase is easily available and can be expected to be a useful aid for the elucidation of the intimate mechanisms of reactions in which an interglycosidic oxygen bridge is concerned.

FIG. 1. An early reaction time in synthesis of cellulose by *Acetobacter xylinum*. Cells were incubated in a droplet of glucose solution on a collodion film for 2 min. Product was freed from non-polymeric solutes in the extracellular phase by flotation on water. A typical intercellular space is shown. There is an abundance of a polymeric material in the form of granules, rods and branched processes extending from slimelike regions. At zero time of reaction the space was optically empty. Pt shadow-cast (shadow ratio 1 : 5). Magnification × 50 000. (Electronmicrograph prepared by Dr. D. Danon and Mr. I. Ohad.)

Growth of cellulose fibre in an extracellular phase

Synthesis of cellulose in *Acetobacter* provides an example of a polymerization system in which, as in the case of the production of levan and dextran by cells, the accumulation of polymeric product occurs in the extracellular phase. In the case of cellulose production, unfortunately, even the general nature of the reaction mechanism remains obscure.

Greathouse [5] has reported that an ATP-fortified homogenate of *A. xylinum* cells readily synthesizes cellulose. Stacey [6] has reported, on the other hand, that attempts to duplicate this result have failed. Dr.

Z. Gromet-Elhanan in our laboratory likewise attempted to repeat the result described by Greathouse, and used for this purpose the same strain in conditions which resembled as closely as possible those used by the earlier workers. We have been unable in our laboratory to obtain any significant synthesis of cellulose in this homogenate system.

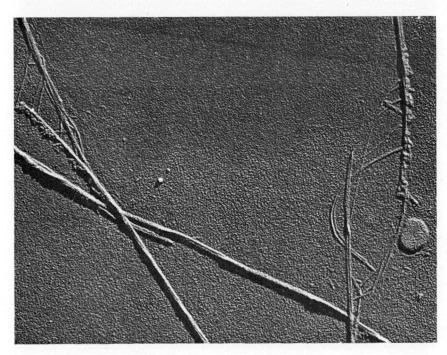

FIG. 2. Cellulose fibres formed from glucose in a dilute suspension of cells of *Acetobacter xylinum*. Fine filaments ("ultrastrands"), whose thickness as estimated by measurement of shadow length is about 15 Å, are seen both in solitary dispositions and in intertwisted bundles ("composite fibre"). Along the length of some of the latter, aggregations of rods and granules ("amorphous formations") are seen. Photograph was taken at a reaction time of 20 min. Intercellular space at zero time was free from polymer. Specimen is mounted on a collodion film and was freed from non-polymeric solutes by filtration over agar (Kellenberger's technique). Pt shadow-cast (shadow ratio, 1 :6). Magnification × 50 000. (Electronmicrograph prepared by Dr. D. Danon and Mr. I. Ohad.)

The work of Glaser [7] has demonstrated that UDPG labelled in the glucose moiety incorporates ^{14}C into cellulose in the presence of a subcellular particle prepared from *A. xylinum*. Mr. I. Ohad in our laboratory has successfully repeated this experiment. However, it should be noted that the cellulose-synthesizing activity manifested by this particle preparation is very poor. It has, moreover, not as yet been shown that the observed incorporation reaction involves a polyrepetitive process rather than the transfer of one or only a few glucose residues to the acceptor site. Hence, one cannot be confident that this system is indeed one of complete cellulose synthesis by a cell-free agent. Nor can it as yet be asserted with any confidence that the major donor system involved in cellulose synthesis by this bacteria is indeed UDPG itself rather than an analogue thereof.

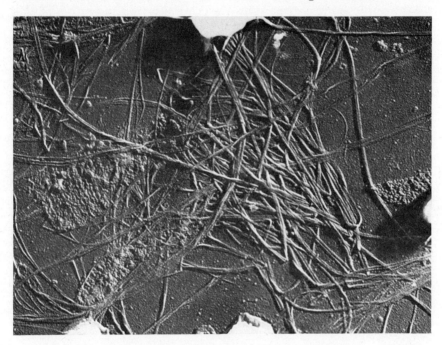

FIG. 3. Morphological elements in cellulose formed from glucose in a dilute suspension of cells of *Acetobacter xylinum*. In addition to the elements listed in the legend of Fig. 2, this field reveals characteristic arrangements ("mats") of polymer in parallel rows of granules or rods apparently patterned by an enclosed framework of ultrastrands. Technique as in Fig. 2, except for the use of a longer reaction time (about 2 hr.). Magnification × 25 000. (Electronmicrograph prepared by Dr. D. Danon and Mr. I. Ohad.)

A production of electron-microscopically demonstrable cellulosic fibre has been observed by Colvin [8] in *A. xylinum* homogenates incubated with glucose in presence of adenosine triphosphate. Colvin has also reported that an ethanol extract made from a suspension of cells incubated with glucose contains a solute which on transfer to water assumes a fibrillar form, is alkali-insoluble, and affords glucose on acid hydrolysis. When such an ethanol extract was heated and then supplemented with an ultrafiltered *Acetobacter* preparation (aqueous extract of a dried suspension of cells in a glucose solution), the yield of fibre, as judged on the basis of fibril incidence in an electron-microscope field, was significantly increased. However, in view of the complexity of design and the sparsity of quantitative information in these experiments, the chemical interpretation of these results remains still uncertain.

In a recent note, Klungsöyr [9] revealed the existence in *A. xylimun* of a disproportionating enzyme system which can catalyze a transfer of glucosyl units from soluble cellodextrins into an insoluble cellulose fraction. This may indeed prove an important clue towards the understanding of the intermediary mechanism in cellulose synthesis.

Although hexose phosphate (α- and β-glucose-1-phosphate and UDPG) supplied to the cell exogenously does not yield cellulose, the assumption that hexose phosphate is an intermediary of cellulose production can be strongly supported. In this connection it may be noted that these cells readily form cellulose both from hexonic acids (gluconate, 2-ketogluconate,

TABLE I

DISTRIBUTION OF RADIOACTIVITY IN CELLULOSE
FORMED FROM SPECIFICALLY-LABELLED FRUCTOSE

Substrate	Total radioactivity in cellulose monomer (% of that in fructose)	Distribution of radioactivity in cellulose monomer (total in monomer = 100)					
		C_1	C_2	C_3	C_4	C_5	C_6
[1-^{14}C]-fructose	37 to 42	—	—	—	—	—	—
[2-^{14}C]-fructose	76	17	63	11	2	4	1
[6-^{14}C]-fructose	103	6	0	0	0	0	4

5-ketogluconate) and from other compounds (glucose, fructose) which could readily be converted by an *Acetobacter* cell into hexose phosphate. Furthermore, the view that hexose phosphate is an intermediate is also supported by the observation that radioactivity recovered in cellulose formed from specifically-labelled glucoses presents a distribution pattern quite different from that in the original substance but which is similar in unique features to the pattern which would arise if the intermediate on the pathway between exogenous hexose and formed cellulose is hexose phosphate in pentose cycle [10]. An analysis of radioactive carbon distribution in the cellulose afforded from specifically-labelled fructose was carried out in our laboratory by Dr. Gromet-Elhanan with results shown in Table I. These findings have given additional support to the view that the cellulose arises from hexose phosphate in a pentose cycle. It should be noted, however, that a detailed examination of the results does reveal a quantitative deviation in some of the data from values that would be predicted on the basis of the conventional scheme of the pentose cycle. This implies, as indeed can readily be assumed, that hexose phosphate in the metabolic pools of this cell is probably involved also in additional and perhaps still undefined metabolic transformations.

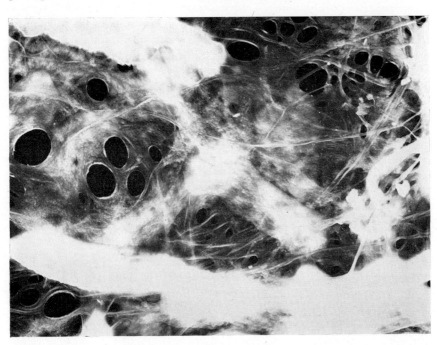

FIG. 4. Cellulose pellicle formed from glucose in a relatively concentrated suspension of cells of *Acetobacter xylinum*. Cells are enmeshed in a cellulosic film which consists of fibres running through relatively amorphous regions of polymer. Ultrastrands are resolvable in the fibre regions. Granular matter constitutes the amorphous phase. Specimen, which was freed from non-polymeric solutes by flotation in water, is mounted directly on a copper grid. Pt shadow-cast (shadow ratio 1 : 5). Magnification × 25 000. (Electronmicrograph prepared by Dr. D. Danon and Mr. I. Ohad.)

The *Acetobacter* enzyme-system which converts hexose phosphate into cellulose is known to be anchored to the cell. Since the formed cellulose fibre is observed in the extracellular medium as a free entity rather than as a physical appendage of the organism, we may assume that the morphological precursor of the fibre is a diffusible cellulose form—probably a lone cellulose molecule—which escapes from the cell into the medium wherein it finally enters into a crystalline fibrous habitat.

M

If the diffusible entity which enters into the extracellular phase and there serves as a precursor of the cellulose fibre is indeed itself *chemically* identical with the cellulose in fibre, it could be anticipated that when cells are incubated with glucose the point of time at which fibre appears might be preceded by an interval during which a relatively large fraction of cellulose molecules in the extracellular phase is still in a relatively disorganized state. Mühlethaler [11] has shown that, when *A. xylinum* grows in a complex medium, cellulose fibres arise in the vicinity of the cell within an amorphous "slime". Studies recently conducted in our laboratory by Mr. I. Ohad in collaboration with Dr. D. Danon at the Weizmann Institute have indicated that when washed cells of this organism are suspended in radioactive glucose solution the synthesis of cellulose proceeds linearly in time without any observable induction phase, but that deposition of fibre becomes apparent only after an initial interval during which electron-microscopically discernible material is accumulated in the extracellular phase within relatively amorphous formations which consist of an alkali-insoluble, radioactive macromolecular compound—presumably cellulose itself. Within a few minutes after contact of the cells with glucose, almost all cellulose in the extracellular phase assumed a well-defined crystalline habitat. Ribbons and ropes of cellulose arose by side-to-side aggregation and intertwisting of an element which presented a remarkably constant morphology—the cellulose "ultrastrand" The thickness of this element was estimated by means of measurements of the length of the shadow which it casts. On this basis, the thickness was shown to be in the range 15 Å. Width estimates were relatively more difficult to arrive at in view of the distortion imposed by metal-shadowing. Allowing about 80 Å for contribution made by metal to apparent width (cf. Hall [12]), the net width of the ultrastrand can be estimated to have been about two or three times the thickness. This would imply that the basic morphological element in bacterial cellulose fibre is a bundle which comprises about twelve glucose chains in its cross-section.

Celluloses from widely different sources including preparations of bacterial origin, have been generally supposed, on the basis of electron-microscope studies, to consist of fibrils $\geqslant$ 60 Å in diameter [13]. However, correction was not made in any of these earlier studies for the effect of metal on the apparent fibril width, nor was the thickness estimated on the basis of measurements of length of shadow. In view of the present findings on bacterial cellulose, a re-examination of the value which has been assigned to the thickness dimension of the cellulose fibril in celluloses of different sources may be desirable.

References

1. Albertsson, P. Å., these proceedings, Vol. 1, p. 33.
2. Oparin, A. I., *in* "The Origin of Life", First International IUBS Symposium. Pergamon Press, London, 428 (1959).
3. Koshland, D. E., Jr., *in* "The Enzymes", Vol. 1, ed. P. Boyer *et al*. Academic Press, New York, 305 (1959).
4. Hestrin, S., Feingold, D. S., and Avigad, G., *Biochem. J.* **64,** 340 (1956).
5. Greathouse, G. A., *J. Amer. chem. Soc.* **79,** 4503 (1957).
6. Stacey, M., *in* "Soc. Exp. Biol. Symposium XII". Cambridge University Press, Cambridge, 185 (1958).
7. Glaser, L., *J. biol. Chem.* **232,** 627 (1958).
8. Colvin, J., *Arch. Biochem. Biophys.* **7,** 294 (1957); Colvin, J., *Nature, Lond.* **183,** 1135 (1959).
9. Klungsöyr, S., *Nature, Lond.* **185,** 104 (1960)
10. Schramm, M., Gromet, Z., and Hestrin, S., *Nature, Lond.* **179,** 28 (1957).
11. Mühlethaler, K., *Biochim. biophys. Acta* **3,** 527 (1949).
12. Hall, C. E., *J. biophys. biochem. Cytol.* **2,** 625 (1960).
13. Cf. review by Frey-Wyssling, A. *in* "Symposium on Biocolloids", *J. cell. comp. Physiol.* **49,** (Supplement 1), 63 (1957).

Discussion

ROGERS: I wonder if Dr. Hestrin could tell us a little more about his comparison of the rate of synthesis of cellulose by the UPDG system and his system, because these comparisons are a little difficult to make especially when you are isolating particles from bacteria with rather tough cell walls. It is a little difficult to know what proportions of "particles" you have got out of the organisms, or how damaged or undamaged the preparation is. The second point I am not quite clear about, although I think you may have explained it already, is why you used fructose in these experiments, because if the UDPG system were functioning then presumably the fructose must get in, be reconstituted to the appropriate glucose-phosphate, the UDPG be made and this transferred back to the cellulose and during the process I would have thought there was an equal chance that endogenous supplies of glucose might be used in preference to fructose, in any case the penetration of cells by fructose is sometimes rather difficult.

HESTRIN: As in the work reported by Glaser, we were only able to recover about 1% or less of the cellulose-synthesizing activity of the cells in the equivalent amount of particle. Even on a weight per weight basis, the activity of the particle was less than that of the cell.

The advantage of using fructose as a substrate in the synthesis of radioactive cellulose relates to the circumstance that fructose does not appear to be subject to a direct oxidation, whereas glucose tends to be oxidized to gluconate and thence to ketogluconate isomers each of which in turn can give rise to cellulose. The existence of many alternate pathways by which glucose can form cellulose complicates the calculation of the distribution which ^{14}C supplied as glucose may be expected to assume in the synthesized cellulose. Using fructose, however, we have no gluconate, we have no ketogluconate, but we still have of course, all the intermediates of the pentose cycle to contend with. There existed a fairly close agreement between a pattern predicted on the basis of a schematic pentose cycle and the actual findings.

DORFMAN: The first part of your paper might be of interest in this question of specificity of the aglucone or glucone of glucosidase. Dr. Julio Ludowieg has recently studied this problem with Dr. Vennesland and myself using ^{18}O with the hyaluronidases. In the case of the streptococcal hyaluronidase, as some of you know, the product is an unsaturated compound. Presumable this is an elimination reaction and, as one might have guessed, no incorporation of ^{18}O from the medium occurs during this hydrolysis. The cleavage is thus of the ether rather than the glycoside link. With testicular hyaluronidase, which is a conventional glucosidase, ^{18}O incorporation apparently occurs, the cleavage is thus apparently of the glycoside bond. Testicular hyaluronidase does not act on chondroitin sulphuric acid B which contains L-iduronic acid instead of D-glucuronic acid but it does act on both hyaluronic acid and chondroitin sulphuric acid A, one of which has glucosamine and the other has galactosamine. Thus the specificity does not reside in the glycone portion of the molecule.

HESTRIN: Such cases encourage the consideration of the possibility that the interaction of enzyme and sugar does not exclusively involve one side of the sugar. Conceivably the substrate has to be fitted into a pit on the protein surface, or perhaps, as Wallenfels has conjectured, the protein winds itself around the substrate.

MITCHELL: I would like to ask Dr. Hestrin a question stemming from his last remarks. It seems as though the specificity of some of these enzymes implies that there may be a hole into which the precursor goes and out of which the polymer has to be extruded. Now, could I preface my question by saying that about five years ago, Dr. Moyle and I discovered that in certain micrococci there was an autolytic system that seemed to be capable of cutting a ribbon out of the spherical cell wall so that it would fall readily into two hemispherical parts; and this system seemed to be mechanically attached to the wall, for it centrifuged with the cell wall fraction of disintegrated cells and could not readily be washed off. We made the suggestion that this system might be a synthetic system, and we visualized the synthesis as though the enzymes were like the clasps on a set of zip fasteners fixed in the plasma membrane and the zips, representing the unpolymerized cell wall precursors, we imagined as being pushed through from the inside to become zipped together, forming a wall on the outside. Now, could I ask in that context, whether you know where the particles come from in your particulate preparations? Is it at all likely that they are originally part of the plasma membrane, and if so, do you think perhaps a precursor is being pushed out which is not actually visible yet as a fibre?

HESTRIN: The particles could be fragments of the cell wall; we don't know. If they are fragments of the cell wall we could be more confident that the observed incorporation activity truly represented a polymerization process leading to fibre production. If the particles are of an endocellular origin, it is difficult to see how they could have operated *in vivo* to give rise to extracellular deposition of fibre. Perhaps, in that case, the observed incorporation of radioactivity was only a manifestation of an oligorepetitive rather than of a polyrepetitive process of transglycosylation.

If we assume that the polyrepetitive step in synthesis occurs at the cell membrane and results in the liberation of a large cellulose molecule, we are attracted to suppose that such molecules diffuse into the medium and there crystallize to yield fibrils.

MITCHELL: Could I try to clarify my question a little ? In these organisms, one would presume that the cell wall, the outer stiff region, is a molecular sieve with holes in it that would be quite big enough to let through, say, sucrose molecules or an individual fibre, one sugar molecule in width, which is going to form a cellulose fibril. But, the plasma membrane, which is underneath the cell wall and is impermeable to glucose phosphates will also certainly be impermeable to glucose and fructose. We have never done permeability determinations on the organism that Dr. Hestrin has mainly been speaking about, but with many others, even when glucose is rapidly metabolized, the membrane is nevertheless quite impermeable to free glucose in the normal sense. You therefore have the problem of how the precursor comes through the plasma membrane and why it polymerizes outside and not inside the protoplast. We would like to imagine that the translocation and the polymerization of the precursor is controlled by a concerted catalytic process.

PORTER: As you may have guessed the other day I am fairly naïve in this area of wall formation but I have been impressed by the general facility with which cells seem to shed their outer layer and then form a plasma membrane under the shed cortex. I don't suppose this happens in the micro-organisms but I did want to ask you if you thought the proposals made the other day that elements of the ER might carry the catalysts for cellulose polymerization were at all feasible ?

HESTRIN: There does not appear to be any protoplasmic connection between cellulose in the medium and a cell. One might speculate that the cellulose molecules diffuse from the cell and crystallize in the medium at a distance from the cell. As to the polymerization step leading to the cellulose molecule, we still do not know whether it occurs in the cell wall, on the outer surface, or within the cell.

Mucopolysaccharides of Connective Tissue*

ALBERT DORFMAN AND SARA SCHILLER

The LaRabida-University of Chicago Institute and the Departments of Pediatrics and Biochemistry, University of Chicago, Chicago, Ill., U.S.A.

Polysaccharides, like other macromolecules, are generally classified on the basis of structure and composition. However, rapidly expanding research has made feasible an examination of the relationship between biological function and chemical structure. Consideration of the physiological role of polysaccharides suggests a distinction between energy-yielding and structural polysaccharides. In general, the former appear to be branched glucose polymers containing α glycoside linkages. Most typical of this group are starch and glycogen. In contrast, the structural polysaccharides are a more complex group of substances containing diverse monosaccharides. Many appear to be β-linked polymers. Examples of these are cellulose, chitin, and the acid mucopolysaccharides of mammalian tissues. Other polysaccharides, such as the hemi-celluloses, pectins, and bacterial capsular polysaccharides, may be regarded as structural, but chemical correlations have not been clearly established, particularly with regard to steric configuration of the glycoside bonds. It seems likely that with continuing investigation of chemical-biological correlations, a better understanding of the physiology of these substances may be reached.

Limitation of space does not permit an extensive review of the numerous structural polysaccharides. This presentation will be confined rather to a discussion of the acid mucopolysaccharides of mammalian connective tissues. These compounds are linear polyanions which contain alternating units of N-acetylated hexosamine and uronic acid (with one exception); and in some cases, sulphate. They exist in the ground substance, a complex mixture in which the formed elements of connective tissues are imbedded.

Figure 1 illustrates a portion of the chain of chondroitin sulphuric acid-A, present in high concentration in mammalian cartilage. Alternating glucuronic acid and N-acetylgalactosamine units are linked glycosidically to form linear molecules. The galactosaminidic bond is $1 \rightarrow 4$ while the

* Original investigations reported in this communication were supported by grants from The National Heart Institute of the United States Public Health Service (No. H 311), The National Foundation, and The Chicago Heart Association.

glucuronidic bond is $1 \rightarrow 3$, a pattern which is followed in the three chondroitin sulphuric acids and hyaluronic acid [1]. The sulphate in chondroitin sulphuric acid-A is esterified at C-4 of the acetylhexosamine residue [2, 3]. The studies of Mathews and Lozaityte [4] indicate that in cartilage

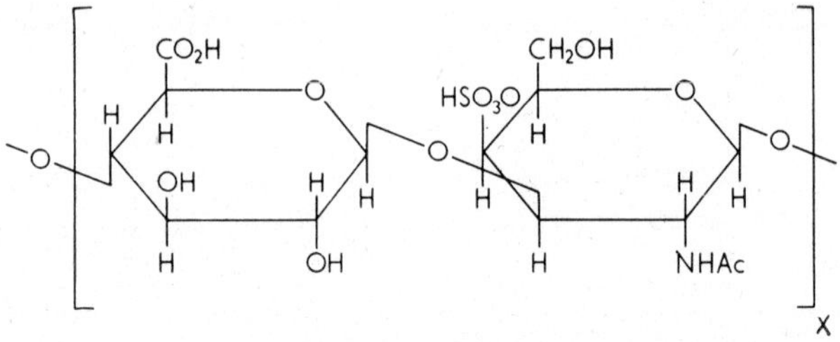

FIG. 1. The structure of the disaccharide unit of chondroitin sulphuric acid-A.

chondroitin sulphuric acid-A exists as coiled linear chains of molecular weight 50 000 attached to a protein core forming a macromolecule with a minimum molecular weight of 4 000 000. The state of other mucopolysaccharides is less well known although there is evidence that hyaluronic

TABLE I

MUCOPOLYSACCHARIDES OF CONNECTIVE TISSUES

	Amino sugar	Uronic acid	Sulphate
Hyaluronic acid	N-acetylglucosamine	Glucuronic acid	—
Chondroitin sulphuric acid-A	N-acetylgalactosamine	Glucuronic acid	+
Chondroitin sulphuric acid-B (β-heparin)	N-acetylgalactosamine	Iduronic acid	+
Chondroitin sulphuric acid-C	N-acetylgalactosamine	Glucuronic acid	+
Chondroitin	N-acetylgalactosamine	Glucuronic acid	—
Keratosulphate	N-acetylglucosamine	(Galactose)	+
Heparin	Glucosamine (N-sulphated)	Glucuronic acid (?)	+
Heparin monosulphuric acid	Glucosamine	(?)	+

acid may exist in chains of considerably greater molecular weight [5]. The presence of anionic groups along the chain imparts the capacity to bind small cations in a manner similar to other polyanionic macromolecules such as resins.

The known acid mucopolysaccharides, together with their component sugars, are listed in Table I. Hyaluronic acid consists of alternating units of N-acetylglucosamine and glucuronic acid and contains no sulphate. Although the extent and nature of the linkage between hyaluronic acid and protein is not yet established, it appears unlikely that a covalent bond exists [6]. Hyaluronic acid occurs in a large number of mammalian tissues. The presence of hyaluronic acid in the capsule of Group A streptococci is unique. Polysaccharides of similar structure are found in capsules of other microorganisms, but in no other authenticated case is the capsular substance identical with a mammalian polysaccharide. The biological function of hyaluronic acid is not clearly delineated; it is neither antithrombic nor anticoagulant. Hyaluronic acid appears together with other mucopolysaccharides in a number of connective tissues, but seems to be characteristic of tissues with high water content. It is the principal polysaccharide of vitreous humour, synovial fluid, Wharton's jelly of umbilical cord, cock's comb, and sex skin of certain primates. As will be demonstrated below, thyroid deficiency with its concomitant oedema is characterized by an increase in hyaluronic acid. While this association is highly suggestive, its significance is not entirely clear. The specific association of tissue hydration with hyaluronic acid rather than with the sulphated polysaccharides is not readily explained on the basis of osmotic considerations. Reinits [7], in a study of the rate of accumulation of hyaluronic acid and water in the sex skin of certain primates found that hydration precedes the peak of hyaluronic acid accumulation. He suggests that hyaluronic acid serves to induce an accumulation of protein in the extracellular space by hindering the access of protein to the lymph capillaries, with the consequent increase in osmotic pressure due to the proteins. Reinits's experiments may be open to criticism on the basis of the inadequacy of the methods for estimation of hyaluronic acid. Fessler [8] has emphasized the role of hyaluronic acid in forming a system of relative non-compressibility as a result of the interaction of a viscous solution with intermingled collagen fibres. However, this study establishes no specificity for hyaluronic acid in contradistinction to other acid mucopolysaccharides. That hyaluronic acid does afford a mechanical barrier is attested by the action of hyaluronidase in promoting the spread of particulates.

The association of hyaluronic acid with tissue hydration may be attributed to the fact that hyaluronic acid is bound less avidly with protein than are the sulphated polysaccharides. Insufficient data are available for localizing individual polysaccharides in tissues which contain mixtures. It is possible that the sulphated polysaccharides are more closely associated with structural elements while hyaluronic acid is present in higher concentration in the amorphous gel between these elements. Mathews [9] has demonstrated a strong affinity of the chondroitin sulphuric acid protein complex for collagen.

Chondroitin sulphuric acids-A and -C are present in largest concentration in cartilage and appear to be responsible to a considerable degree for the unique physical characteristics of this tissue. The possible role of chondroitin sulphuric acids in calcification has been considered but no mechanism has been clarified [10]. Chondroitin sulphuric acid-A differs from chondroitin sulphuric acid-C only in that the sulphate group is esterified at carbon 4 of the galactosamine rather than at position 6. The relationship of the sulphate position to the calcification process merits further consideration. It is of interest to note that chondroitin sulphuric acid-C predominates in elasmobranch cartilage which is not converted into bone [11]. The interrelationships of chondroitin sulphuric acids and collagen are not entirely clarified. Jackson [12] found that treatment of tendon with hyaluronidase increased the solubility of collagen.

Chondroitin sulphuric acid-B is distinguished from chondroitin sulphuric acids-A and -C by the presence of L-iduronic acid instead of D-glucuronic acid [13, 14]. The sulphate group occupies the same position as is characteristic of chondroitin sulphuric acid-A [2]. Figure 2 shows the

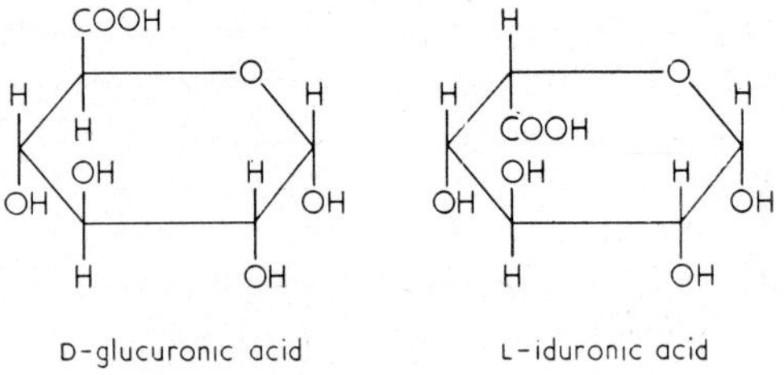

D-glucuronic acid   L-iduronic acid

FIG. 2. The structures of D-glucuronic acid and L-iduronic acid.

structure of L-iduronic acid compared with that of D-glucuronic acid. The two uronic acids are epimers differing only with respect to the stereisomerism at C-5. L-idose has not been identified in natural materials, but L-iditol has been found in mountain ash berry by de Bertrand [15] in 1905.

Chondroitin sulphuric acid-B (β-heparin) was isolated by Marbet and Winterstein [16] from a commercial preparation of heparin and because of its anticoagulant properties was believed to be an isomer of heparin. It was found to be more potent as an antithrombic substance than as a whole blood anticoagulant. Grossman and Dorfman [17] found that the antithrombic activity of chondroitin sulphuric acid-B varied with the concentration of thrombin. At low thrombin concentrations it is more active than heparin, but at high thrombin concentrations it is inactive. Like heparin, chondroitin sulphuric acid-B requires for activity a plasma cofactor, the natural plasma antithrombin. In the absence of plasma it is completely inactive. On whole blood the anticoagulant activity is only 5% that of heparin. The physiological importance of the antithrombic activity of chondroitin sulphuric acid-B is obscure. The relatively high concentration in certain tissues may permit a significant homeostatic role in the regulation of fibrinogen-fibrin conversion within tissues.

The contrast between the anticoagulant properties of chondroitin sulphuric acids-A and -B suggests that the substitution of L-iduronic acid for D-glucuronic acid alters biological properties. It is possible that anti-thrombic activity is related to some molecular characteristics which also confers an increased capacity to bind certain ions [18]. Hoffman et al. [13] suggested that chondroitin sulphuric acid-B is associated with coarser collagen bundles. This polysaccharide has been found in a variety of sites. It was identified in gastric mucosa by Smith and Gallop [19] and has been found in rabbit skin by Schiller et al. [20]. Of particular interest is the fact that chondroitin sulphuric acid-B and heparin monosulphuric acid are excreted in the urine and found in the tissues of patients afflicted with the Hurler syndrome [21]. The enzymic defect in this heritable disorder of connective tissue is unknown.

Davidson and Meyer [22] isolated from cornea a fraction composed of D-glucuronic acid and N-acetylgalactosamine and less than one mole of sulphate per disaccharide repeating unit. It was suggested that this compound, chondroitin, is a metabolic intermediate in the biosynthesis of chondroitin sulphuric acids-A and -C. Suzuki and Strominger [23] have recently demonstrated the transfer of radioactive sulphate from PAPS* to a chemically desulphated chondroitin sulphate by an enzyme isolated from chicken oviducts, suggesting that sulphation of chondroitin sulphate occurs at the macromolecular stage. This pathway cannot be considered as established since the amount of sulphate incorporated was extremely low, and biosynthesis of chondroitin has not yet been achieved. The physiological and metabolic role of chondroitin must yet be considered uncertain.

Unlike other mucopolysaccharides, keratosulphate lacks a uronic acid component. Instead, a galactose group is substituted. Hirano et al. [24] have indicated that the galactosyl bond is 1→4 and the glucosaminidic bond is 1→3 with sulphate substituted on carbon 6 of the amino sugar. Keratosulphate has been isolated from the nucleus pulposus [25]. Shetlar and Masters [26] and Kuhn and Leppelmann [27] demonstrated an increase in the ratio of glucosamine to galactosamine in cartilage with advancing age. This observation has found explanation in the demonstration by Kaplan and Meyer [28], that rib cartilage of the human adult contains a large proportion of keratosulphate in contrast to the absence of this substance in rib cartilage of newborns. Even larger amounts of keratosulphate were reported in patients with the Marfan syndrome, although it is dubious whether the difference was significant. Hallén [29] similarly found that the relative concentration of glucosamine in nucleus pulposus increased with advancing age. This was interpreted as an increase of keratosulphate/chondroitin sulphate ratio. Davidson and Woodhall [30]

---

* '3-phosphoadenosine 5'-phosphosulphate.

made similar observations. The difference between the physical-chemical properties of keratosulphate and chondroitinsulphuric acids-A and -C may be responsible for changes in the physical properties of cartilage and nucleus pulposus observed with increased age. These facts have obvious implications with respect to the pathogenesis of collapse of intervertebral discs.

Heparin monosulphuric acid was isolated by Jorpes and Gardell [31] in 1948 from a commercial preparation of heparin. Like heparin, it was found to contain glucosamine and to demonstrate a positive optical rotation. In contrast to heparin, N-acetyl groups and approximately one mole of sulphate per disaccharide were found. Subsequently, Linker *et al.* [32] isolated a similar compound from the liver of a patient with amyloidosis and from aorta. They named the substance heparitin sulphate. Large amounts of a similar compound have been isolated from the urine and tissues of patients with the Hurler syndrome by Brown [33], Dorfman, and Lorincz [21], and Meyer *et al.* [34]. Hen oviducts [35] and a mast cell tumour [36] have also been shown to contain a similar substance.

Heparin monosulphuric acid is characterized by a high colour yield in the Dische carbazole reaction for uronic acid, a positive optical rotation, less than one mole of acetyl per disaccharide unit, and variable sulphate content. In a recent study, Cifonelli and Dorfman [37] have shown that a number of compounds can be separated from a crude preparation, obtained as a by-product of heparin by the Upjohn Company. These materials all exhibited a positive optical rotation and contained both N- and O-sulphate as well as N-acetyl. The total of N-acetyl and N-sulphate was approximately 1. The N-acetyl content of most fractions approximated 0·7 mole per disaccharide unit. Preparations which manifested high N-acetyl values contained virtually no N-sulphate. Preliminary studies of the structure of these compounds suggest that they are not linked through the 3 position of the hexosamine as are the chondroitin sulphates and hyaluronic acid, but are probably linked through the 6 position of hexosamine [38]. These substances have little, if any, antithrombic or anticoagulant properties. Their origin and metabolic importance have not been clarified but chemical properties suggest a relationship to heparin. They may represent intermediates in the biosynthesis of heparin.

Heparin has been studied intensively from a biological point of view but its chemistry is yet poorly understood. It contains more than 2 sulphate groups per disaccharide unit and demonstrates a positive optical rotation. Unlike other acid mucopolysaccharides it has an N-sulphate group but no N-acetyl group. In addition, one to two sulphate groups per disaccharide repeating unit are present in other parts of the molecule.

The striking anticoagulant properties of heparin are well known. However, its role in the homeostasis of blood coagulation is not clear.

Heparin has not been isolated from blood but there is no doubt that it is present in mast cells. The possible physiological role of heparin assumed increased importance with the discovery that injection of heparin induced the release of a lipase responsible for "clearing" of blood [39]. The relation of these observations to fat metabolism and arteriosclerosis is obvious.

The foregoing discussion reviews briefly the status of knowledge regarding chemical structure and biological function of the acid mucopolysaccharides of connective tissues. Alterations in tissue functions may be a reflection of changes in metabolism of these substances. Clarification of the metabolism of acid mucopolysaccharides required first a delineation of the pathways of biosynthesis. These have been reviewed extensively elsewhere [40].

Briefly, Markovitz *et al.* [41] have shown that the acid mucopolysaccharide, hyaluronic acid, is formed from uridine diphosphoglucuronic acid and uridine diphospho-N-acetylglucosamine by an enzyme isolated from a strain of Group A streptococci. Although attempts to solubilize this enzyme have not been successful, it has been possible to show that the enzyme resides on the protoplast membrane [41]. Of interest, is the recent report by Smith *et al.* [43] that Type III pneumococcal capsular polysaccharide is synthesized from uridinediphosphoglucuronic acid and uridinediphosphoglucose.

Early studies on the metabolism of the acid mucopolysaccharides were concerned with rates of turnover in mammalian connective tissue. Skin was used as a source of connective tissue since it contains acid mucopolysaccharides in sufficient quantity for isolation and degradation [20]. The rate of turnover of hyaluronic acid and a chondroitin sulphuric acid fraction was determined in both rats and rabbits by utilizing [^{14}C]-glucose and -acetate as well as $^{35}SO_4^=$, as precursors [44]. Glucose is a precursor of the uronic acid and hexosamine moieties of the mucopolysaccharides; acetate is a precursor of the acetyl groups; and $^{35}SO_4^=$ is incorporated as ester sulphate. These experiments showed that hyaluronic acid, with a half-life of approximately $2 \cdot 5$ days, was metabolized at a rate comparable to other metabolically active substances [45]. Chondroitin sulphuric acid was metabolized more slowly. The rate of turnover was found to be similar when measured with acetate, glucose, or sulphate, indicating complete turnover of the entire molecule. Sulphate has been used by many investigators to label acid polysaccharides in diverse tissues.

Having determined these parameters of normal metabolism it was possible to utilize similar techniques for a study of the effects of hormones. Cortisone and hydrocortisone were found to decrease the rate of turnover of both the sulphated and non-sulphated mucopolysaccharides of skin [46]. This inhibition is time-dependent. Although the mechanism of action of the adrenal hormones is unknown, this metabolic effect may be responsible

N

for the delayed wound healings and demineralization of bone typical of Cushing's disease.

Investigation of the metabolism of acid mucopolysaccharides in alloxan diabetes indicated a decreased capacity to metabolize mucopolysaccharides and a restoration of the defect toward normal by the administration of insulin [47]. The rate of turnover of polysaccharides of partly fasted animals, which served as controls for the weight loss of the diabetic rats, was not different from that found in normal rat skin.

The influence of hypophysectomy [48], growth hormone, and thyroxine have also been investigated but these studies are difficult to interpret since changes in pool size occurred during the course of the experiments. Turnover studies depend upon the maintenance of a steady state or constant pool size; differences in rates of synthesis are difficult to define if a reasonably constant pool size does not obtain.

The information derived from turnover experiments suggested that marked variations in the concentrations of mucopolysaccharides might occur. It therefore became important to devise methods for the quantitative determination of acid mucopolysaccharides in tissues.

By the application of relatively simple procedures it is now possible to perform such analyses. The method, which is published elsewhere in detail [49], depends upon the solubilization of tissues with papain, followed by further deproteinization with trypsin and trichloroacetic acid. The partly purified polysaccharide preparation is separated on the basis of the differential solubility of complexes formed with cetyl pyridinium chloride (CPC). In the presence of $0 \cdot 035$–$0 \cdot 040$ M NaCl all the polysaccharides are quantitatively precipitated by CPC providing Celite is added. When the resultant precipitate is extracted with varying concentrations of NaCl sharp separation of three fractions is obtained. The CPC-hyaluronic acid complex is solubilized by $0 \cdot 4$ M NaCl in $0 \cdot 1\%$ CPC, while the complexes of chondroitin-sulphuric acids-A, -B, -C, and heparin monosulphuric acids are solubilized by $1 \cdot 2$ M NaCl in $0 \cdot 1\%$ CPC. Least soluble is the complex of heparin which is solubilized in $2 \cdot 1$ M NaCl. Further separation of these fractions can be achieved by subsequent chromatography on Dowex 1×2, chloride.

Table II illustrates a typical separation of a preparation of rat skin. The small amount of colour found in tubes 1 and 2 is due to interference by protein with the carbazole reaction and does not indicate significant loss of mucopolysaccharide. In the case of rat skin the fraction obtained with $1 \cdot 2$ M NaCl contains chondroitin sulphuric acids, but in other tissues heparin monosulphuric acid may be obtained in this fraction.

The validity of this method has now been established by a variety of prodedures. Table III indicates the recovery of polysaccharides added to rat skin in duplicate experiments. Excellent recovery and reproducibility

TABLE II

THE SEPARATION OF ACID MUCOPOLYSACCHARIDES FROM
AN EXTRACT OF RAT SKIN*

Flask No.	Solvent	Volume	Uronic acid
		ml.	μg.
1	Supernatant	9·5	317 (brown)
2	0·03 M NaCl in 0·1% CPC	15·0	95 (yellow)
			412
3	0·4 M NaCl in 0·1% CPC	30·0	1620
4		29·8	1091
5		30·0	612
6		29·8	122
7		30·0	24
8		30·0	0
			3469
9	1·2 M NaCl in 0·1% CPC	30·5	885
10		30·0	297
11		30·3	127
12		30·0	30
13		30·5	0
			1339
14	2·1 M NaCl	30·0	716
15		30·0	38
16		29·8	0
			754

* The uronic acid content was 5·89 mg. in a volume of 9·5 ml. To this were added 0·38 ml. of 1 M NaCl and 0·32 ml. of a 10% solution of CPC, bringing the total volume to 10·2 ml. The mixture was incubated for 1 hr. at 37°. Approximately 200 mg. of Celite were added prior to centrifugation as described in the text. 0·2 to 1·0 ml. aliquots were removed from each flask for uronic acid determinations. The recovery was 5·97 mg. uronic acid or 101%.

was achieved. The procedure has now been successfully adapted to analysis of human skin, human aorta, human lung, and basement membranes of dog and human kidney.

Table IV illustrates a series of analyses on rat skin [50]. A surprisingly large amount of heparin was found. Variation of polysaccharide content with age was noted. Particularly striking was the decrease in concentration of heparin beyond 44 days. Little or no heparin was found in hog, guinea-pig, rabbit, foetal calf, camel or human skin. The physiological significance

TABLE III

RECOVERY OF ACID MUCOPOLYSACCHARIDES ADDED TO SKIN

Substance added	Amount	Recovery of total mucopolysaccharides			Recovery of added mucopolysaccharides
		0·4 M NaCl	1·2 M NaCl	2·1 M NaCl	
	mg.*	mg. uronic acid per 5 g. acetone-dry skin			%
	—	2·96	1·40	0·57	—
Hyaluronic acid	2·53	5·08	1·36	0·45	93
		4·42	1·05	0·47	77
Chondroitinsulphuric acid-B	0·95	3·11	2·40	0·62	102
		3·20	2·33	0·62	99
Heparin	0·71	2·88	1·44	1·12	87
		2·72	1·13	1·16	90

* As uronic acid.

of this reduction in polysaccharide content, particularly with respect to hyaluronic acid and heparin, is not entirely clear. Previous claims [51] that with advancing age there is a shift from hyaluronic acid to chondroitin sulphuric acid are not substantiated by these data although a relative shift

TABLE IV

EFFECT OF AGE ON CONCENTRATION OF MUCOPOLYSACCHARIDES IN RAT SKIN

Age (days)	Hyaluronic acid	Chondroitin sulphuric acid	Heparin
	μg. uronic acid/g. dry rat skin		
21*	979	385	421
23*	894	406	562
44*	1232	337	388
57*	439	218	100
74*	540	197	92
217*	578	273	111
406	320	140	70
473	540	200	110
561	480	257	68
893	380	135	35
951	538	256	100

* These data were obtained from pools of eight to ten rat skins for each age group. In the older age groups, the results represent values from individual animals.

does occur. As noted, however, hyaluronic acid does appear to be correlated with the higher water content of the skin of young rats [52]. Further study is necessary to appreciate fully the effect of this shift on physical structure of ground substance and the consequent influence on the metabolism of cells imbedded therein.

This method of analysis has been used to study further the effect of insulin on the synthesis of acid mucopolysaccharides. The turnover studies discussed previously indicated that alloxan diabetes effects a decrease in turnover rate of both hyaluronic acid and the chondroitin sulphuric acid fraction. Analysis of skin from these animals confirmed a suspected decrease in concentration of these substances. Table V indicates

TABLE V

EFFECT OF INSULIN ON MUCOPOLYSACCHARIDE
CONTENT OF RAT SKIN

Type of rat	Age	Body weight	Distribution of mucopolysaccharides of skin		
			HA	CSA	Heparin
	days	g.	μg. U.A. per g. dry skin		
Normal	74	340	720	319	158
Restricted food	74	200	730	282	159
Diabetic	74	185	448	234	196
Normal	81	317	624	274	101
Restricted food	81	189	701	260	156
Diabetic	81	182	371	190	205
Diabetic + insulin	81	273	506	225	175

the results of these experiments. Noteworthy is the marked decrease in hyaluronic acid concentration and a less striking decrease of chondroitin sulphuric acid in contrast to heparin. The latter compound is actually increased in the diabetic animals. This may be due to a relative decrease in total ground substance. As in the turnover experiments, these effects were reversed by insulin. It seems possible that this defect of mucopolysaccharide metabolism in diabetes may play a role in the delayed wound healing, decreased resistance to infection and accelerated degenerative changes which occur in diabetes melitus.

Of particular interest has been the study of the effects of thyroid hormone on mucopolysaccharide metabolism. For this purpose propylthiouracil was employed to inhibit synthesis of thyroid hormones in rats. Table VI illustrates the results of such experiments. In contrast to previous

TABLE VI

EFFECT OF THYROID HORMONE ON CONCENTRATION OF
MUCOPOLYSACCHARIDES IN RAT SKIN

Treatment	Age	Weight	Thyroid weight	Distribution of mucopolysaccharides		
				HA	CSA	Heparin
	days	av. in g.	av. in g.	μg. U.A. per g. dry skin		
Normal	88	334	19·1	785	290	158
Normal	86	333	19·4	704	264	147
PTU	78	194	77·5	852	182	93
PTU	86	190	90·7	976	220	115
PTU	88	192	96·4	1024	204	87
PTU+T$_4$	78	254	13·7	778	249	117
PTU+T$_4$	86	279	25·1	748	234	94
PTU+T$_4$	88	273	18·5	809	271	137

experiments a striking differential effect was observed. Concomitant with
a decrease in the concentration of chondroitin sulphuric acid, there was
marked increase in hyaluronic acid. Administration of thyroxine reversed
these effects toward normal. The biochemical or endocrinological
mechanisms are not clear. Nevertheless, these findings may afford an
explanation for the mechanism of myxoedema.

Summary

The information presented in this paper indicates that the connective
tissues represent not only a mechanical support for parenchymal cells, but
a controlled and controlling environment. The acid mucopolysaccharides
are a family of compounds with a chemical unity. Nevertheless, the
chemical variations within the group are mirrored by differences in
biological activity. Various tissues exhibit variations in polysaccharide
composition. Furthermore, it is apparent that under physiological and
pathological influences, this composition may be altered both qualitatively
and quantitatively. Such variation results in a change in the milieu in
immediate contact with parenchymal cells.

Acknowledgment

The authors are grateful to Dr. Martin B. Mathews for many valuable
discussions of ideas presented in this paper.

References

1. Meyer, K., "The Harvey Lectures", Series 51 (1955-56), Academic Press, New York, 88 (1957).
2. Mathews, M. B., *Nature, Lond.* **181,** 421 (1958).
3. Hoffman, P., Linker, A., and Meyer, K., *Biochim. biophys. Acta* **30,** 184 (1958).
4. Mathews, M. B., and Lozaityte, I., *Arch. Biochem. Biophys.* **74,** 158 (1958).
5. Laurent, T. C., *Ark. Kemi* **11,** 487 (1957).
6. Ogston, A. G., and Sherman, T. F., *Biochem. J.* **72,** 301 (1959).
7. Reinits, K. G., *Biochem. J.* **74,** 27 (1960).
8. Fessler, J. H., *Biochem. J.* **76,** 124 (1960).
9. Mathews, M. B., *Circulation* **14,** 972 (1956).
10. Sobel, A. E., Burger, M., Samachson, J., and Slovik, N., "Resumés Commns. 3rd Intern. Congr. Biochim., Brussels", 48 (1955).
11. Nakanishi, K., Takahashi, N., and Egami, F., *Bull. chem. Soc., Japan* **29,** 434 (1956).
12. Jackson, D. S., *Biochem. J.* **54,** 638 (1953).
13. Hoffman, P., Linker, A., and Meyer, K., *Biochim. biophys. Acta* **69,** 435 (1957).
14. Cifonelli, J. A., Ludowieg, J., and Dorfman, A., *J. biol. Chem.* **233,** 541 (1958).
15. de Bertrand, G., *Bull. Soc. chim. Fr.* **33,** 264 (1905).
16. Marbet, R., and Winterstein, A., *Helv. chim. Acta* **34,** 2311 (1951).
17. Grossman, B. J., and Dorfman, A., *Pediatrics* **20,** 506 (1957).
18. Mathews, M. B., *Biochim. biophys. Acta* **37,** 288 (1960).
19. Smith, H., and Gallop, R. C., *Biochem. J.* **53,** 666 (1953).
20. Schiller, S., Mathews, M. B., Jefferson, H., Ludowieg, J., and Dorfman, A., *J. biol. Chem.* **211,** 717 (1954).
21. Dorfman, A., and Lorincz, A. E., *Proc. nat. Acad. Sci., Wash.* **43,** 443 (1957).
22. Davidson, E. A., and Meyer, K., *J. biol. Chem.* **211,** 605 (1954).
23. Suzuki, S., and Strominger, J. L., *J. biol. Chem.* **235,** 274 (1960).
24. Hirano, S., Hoffman, P., and Meyer, K., *Fed. Proc.* **19,** 146 (1960).
25. Gardell, S., *Acta chem. scand.* **9,** 1035 (1955).
26. Shetlar, M. R., and Masters, Y. F., *Proc. Soc. exp. Biol.* **90,** 31 (1955).
27. Kuhn, R., and Leppelmann, J., *Leibigs Ann. Chem.* **611,** 254 (1958).
28. Kaplan, D., and Meyer, K., *Nature, Lond.* **183,** 1267 (1959).
29. Hallén, A., *Acta chem. scand.* **12,** 1869 (1958).
30. Davidson, E. A., and Woodhall, B., *J. biol. Chem.* **234,** 2951 (1958).
31. Jorpes, E. A., and Gardell, S., *J. biol. Chem.* **176,** 267 (1948).
32. Linker, A., Hoffman, P., Sampson, P., and Meyer, K., *Biochim. biophys. Acta* **29,** 443 (1958).
33. Brown, D. H., *Proc. nat. Acad. Sci., Wash.* **43,** 783 (1957).
34. Meyer, K., Grumbach, M., Linker, A., and Hoffman, P., *Proc. Soc. exp. Biol. Med.* **91,** 275 (1958).
35. Schiller, S., *Biochim. biophys. Acta* **32,** 315 (1959).
36. Roden, L., and Dorfman, A., *Acta chem. scand.* **13,** 2121 (1960).
37. Cifonelli, J. A., and Dorfman, A., *J. biol. Chem.* **235,** 3283 (1960).
38. Cifonelli, J. A., and Dorfman, A., *Fed. Proc.* **18,** 204 (1959).
39. Korn, E. D., *J. biol. Chem.* **215,** 1 (1955).
40. Dorfman, A., Markovitz, A., and Cifonelli, J. A., *Fed. Proc.* **17,** 1093 (1958).
41. Markovitz, A., Cifonelli, J. A., and Dorfman, A., *J. biol. Chem.* **234,** 2343 (1959).
42. Markovitz, A., and Dorfman, A., *Fed. Proc.* **19,** 146 (1960).

43. Smith, E. B., Mills, G. T., Bernheimer, H. P., and Austrian, R., *J. biol. Chem.* **235**, 1876 (1960).
44. Schiller, S., Mathews, M. B., Goldfaber, L., Ludowieg, J. and Dorfman, A., *J. biol. Chem.* **212**, 531 (1955).
45. Schiller, S., Mathews, M. B., Cifonelli, J. A., and Dorfman, A., *J. biol. Chem.* **218**, 139 (1956).
46. Schiller, S., and Dorfman, A., *Endocrinology* **60**, 376 (1957).
47. Schiller, S., and Dorfman, A., *J. biol. Chem.* **227**, 625 (1957).
48. Schiller, S., and Dorfman, A., *Fed. Proc.* **16**, 242 (1957).
49. Schiller, S., Slover, G. A. and Dorfman, A., *J. biol. Chem.* **236**, 983 (1961).
50. Schiller, S., and Dorfman, A., *Nature, Lond.* **185**, 111 (1960).
51. Loewi, G., and Meyer, K., *Biochim. biophys. Acta* **27**, 453 (1958).
52. Lowrey, G., *Anat. Rec.* **7**, 143 (1913).

Discussion

DISCHE: I think that the findings of Dr. Mathews in your laboratory about this combination between the chrondroitin sulphate and proteins are of particular interest because there appears here a possibility to introduce the factor of specificity into the field of hexuronic acid-containing polysaccharides. The specificity cannot be related in these compounds solely to the composition of the carbohydrate but where proteins enter also into the structure and there is a multiplicity of poly-saccharide molecules on every protein, there is also a possibility of variations, which can be associated with changes in specificity; this is a very interesting development in this respect. I should like to make one remark on changes with age. I think we must be very cautious in establishing any such correlations. Dr. Karl Meyer who found such changes in the ratio between chrondroitin sulphate and keratin sulphate told me that this finding is not valid for the rat.

ROGERS: Just two points, one of which might be of possible interest to Dr. Dorfman, he just touched on the question of the β-linkage. Recently we have been examining cell wall preparations of *Bacillus subtilis* for a different reason altogether and we had cause to make a trichloroacetic extract of the walls and found there, rather to our surprise, a polysaccharide which we isolated in a homogeneous state. It had exactly the same composition as chondroitin but had positive rotation instead of a negative rotation and was hydrolyzed very readily with acid. We could not separate a disaccharide from it after mild acid hydrolysis as you can with chon-droitin. Finally, following very beautiful work of Barker and his colleagues, we examined the infra-red spectrum at low wave numbers and this showed the expected band at about 850 cm^{-1} which these authors found to be very typical of α-linkages and indeed this band was not present in chondroitin, thus it rather looks as though in this organism there is an α-linked substance which so far as we can see at the moment has the same composition as chondroitin; but we have no evidence that it behaves as a linear polyelectrolyte like chondroitin; it may be a highly branched chain compound. We have also looked at several species of micro-organisms during the last few years for the distribution of hexosamine-containing compounds and found that over 95% of materials which contain amino sugars appear to be outside the permeability membrane. We took the soluble protein con-stituents and we could never find more than about 5% of the total hexosamine of the cells there and we could always account for the other 95% either in the capsular material or in the cell wall. I wonder if you would like to speculate as to why hexosamine-containing substances seem to occur principally outside the permeability membrane.

DORFMAN: With regard to Dr. Dische's comments I am glad that he did mention this point because there wasn't time to expand on it. As a matter of fact we are at present reinvestigating the question of antigenicity of these substances with the protein complexes which are quite different compounds from alkali-degraded material. We have been able to show in work that I didn't cover (Gross, J. I., Mathews, M. B., and Dorfman, A., *J. biol. Chem.* **235**, 2889, (1960)) that *in vivo* the entire protein-polysaccharide complex appears to turn over as a unit. We have measured the metabolism of protein and carbohydrate separately and simultaneously in the same animals and have shown that the rates of turnover are identical for the protein part and the carbohydrate part. This raises some important implications on carbohydrate biosynthesis. With regard to Dr. Rogers' comment, I was careful not to make an absolute correlation between α- and β-linkages because I don't think that it would hold up. I think that there are other exceptions. β-Linkages arise more readily from linear compounds.

As far as my speculating as to why hexosamine compounds are outside the membrane, I suppose I should quote a very famous Swedish teacher I had, Prof. Anton J. Carlson who, whenever asked a question of that kind, said he wasn't there when they made it. I don't know what it is about the chemical properties of hexosamine which is desirable for Nature to incorporate it into structural polysaccharides. Chitin for instance in the insects and fungi, is also a β-linked glucosamine.

MITCHELL: I wonder if I might speculate a little on why these compounds appear outside, because I am afraid that my remarks earlier about the zip fastener idea were not very clear and were not really understood. Consider a piece of protoplast membrane as shown in the diagram. It is creating a growing cell wall on the outside and one believes that the precursors are inside, in the cytoplasm and one knows that the cell wall is outside the plasma membrane. The most interesting question is why is the wall made outside and not inside the plasma membrane? This is a directional matter: why should there be a vector component of the chemical process, seen as a whole? The simplest way of explaining this would be to say that an enzyme (*A*) (Fig. 1), rather like the ones which Dr. Hestrin is imagining with a sort of hole through it, is accepting the precursors on the inner surface of the plasma membrane and polymerizing them as they pass through to the outside—the polymerized chain becoming extruded as it forms. Such as enzyme, catalyzing a vectorial metabolic process would, of course, have to be specifically located to some substratum in the plasma membrane complex by means of primary or residual bonds.

As the cell wall is fairly porous, the externally secreted polysaccharides, such as the capsular polysaccharides and the cellulose of *Acetobacter xylinum*, could be produced and positioned by a similar mechanism. An enzyme polymerizing an extracellular polymer is depicted at B, and the fine chains of the polysaccharide are supposed to be thin enough to go through the holes in the substance of the wall, so that again we would have a vector component of the metabolic process playing a morphogenetic role. This conception is of interest to those trying to relate structure

N*

to function, I think, because it suggests a connection between morphogenesis and the unique asymmetry of protein molecules.

DORFMAN: I like this very much and there isn't time to expand on it. Last year we proposed a mechanism for polysaccharide synthesis which envisaged a mechanism of this kind. One of the difficulties is that we find no low-molecular weight intermediates. We have to think of an enzyme which somehow or other forms hyaluronic acid on the enzyme while the chain keeps getting longer until it is large enough and then is detached from the enzyme.

HESTRIN: In our laboratory Schramm and Zelinger have found that β-glucose-1-phosphate can be condensed in the presence of maltose phosphorylase with glucosamine to afford in good yield the α-glucosyl-1,4-glucosamine. They have also obtained similarly the acetylglucosamine derivative. These materials are thus

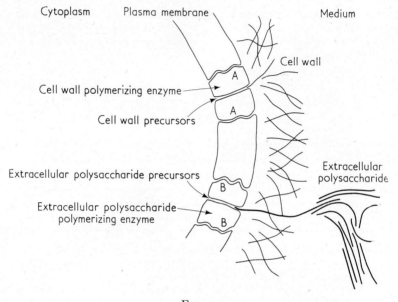

FIG. 1.

now readily available and may be useful for studies designed to elucidate the effect of an α-linkage on the properties of glucosamine-containing polymers.

A general comment concerning the interpretation of data obtained in enzyme solution on a substrate of a saccharide synthesis might perhaps be appropriate. There is a tendency to take the view that a demonstration of synthesis in an enzyme solution suffices to demonstrate that the substrate in question is also the physiological substrate. However, especially if the reaction observed in a solution is sluggish, an observed reaction may be only an artifact. Some of the uridine diphosphoglycoses, for example, can still conceivably merely be analogues of unidentified physiological substrates. Before accepting a particular polymer synthesis reaction as having been demonstrated, we should insist on a realization of the reaction under conditions in which there occurs a *net* increase of the mass of the polymer, with attendant increase either in the number of the polymer molecules present and/or large increase in their molecular weight.

DORFMAN: I should point out that we have shown net synthesis of hyaluronic acid.

MARSHALL: Dr. Dorfman's work is tremendously stimulating to some of us concerned with very different problems in cell physiology. May I add to Dr. Porter's comment a remark based on experience with amoebae ? We have come to view the amoeba surface as a combined structure, with an inner membrane and an outer mucoid coat. Both components must be thought of in dynamic terms, because in amoebae we observe new formation and expansion of surface without the appearance of successive layers, such as Dr. Porter has just described in chondrocytes. Rather there appears to occur some sort of interstitial formation of new membrane and new coat material. I don't know whether the amoeba surface is unusually labile, or unusually rapid in turnover compared to that of other cells, but it suggests an even more dynamic way to conceive of the passage of substances in or out of a cell, without there being at any time a stable structure in which holes must appear.

Separation of Oligosaccharides with Gel Filtration

PER FLODIN AND KÅRE ASPBERG

*Research Laboratory, AB Pharmacia and the Institute of Biochemistry,
Uppsala, Sweden*

In a series of oligosaccharides the individual members differ very
little in properties and the preparation of them requires highly selective
methods. Dickey and Wolfrom [1] succeeded in separating the acetylated
cellodextrins up to the cellohexaose chromatographically in magnesium
and calcium silicate columns. The acetates were adsorbed from a chloro-
form solution and the chromatogram was developed with a benzene-
ethanol mixture. The most commonly used procedure is to adsorb the
oligosaccharide mixture on charcoal from a water solution and then elute
them with a gradient of increasing ethanol concentration [2]. With minor
modifications the method has been applied to cellodextrins, maltodextrins
and isomaltodextrins. The selectivity is large enough to give a complete
separation up to the hexaoses. The higher members are generally obtained
as fairly pure substances containing the neighbouring oligosaccharides as
contaminants.

In an ion exchange resin sucrose and glucose move at different rates
when conditions are chosen so that no adsorption takes place. Similarly,
in swollen starch the retardation is smaller the higher the degree of
polymerization [3].

In columns packed with particular gels formed by cross-linking
dextran, large molecules were observed to emerge first from the column
while small molecules were retarded [4]. The same phenomenon was
observed when low molecular weight dextrans were fractionated [5]. It
should be mentioned that all operations were made in the same solvent.
The behaviour is in contrast to what occurs in the adsorption chromatographic techniques, where adsorption is stronger the higher the molecular
weight. It is consistent with a molecular sieve mechanism according to
which a larger part of the gel particle is available the smaller the molecular
size. The object of this communication is to show that the method, which
has been named gel filtration, may be used to separate cellodextrins.

Experimental

The dextran gel used was Sephadex G-25 (Pharmacia, Uppsala,
Sweden) 200–400 mesh dry sieved. It was swollen in water and sedi-

mented, and the fines remaining in the supernate was removed by decantation. It was then packed into a glass column with the dimensions 4·5 by 150 cm. The packing procedure was that described by Flodin [6]. When all the material (300 g.) had packed, a filter paper was put on top of the bed. The height of the bed was 126 cm. and its volume 2000 ml.

By passing a zone of indian ink through the bed the void space was determined and found to be 515 ml. and simultaneously a check of the packing was obtained.

The oligosaccharide mixture was obtained by acetolysis of cellulose followed by hydrolysis as described by Whittaker [2]. The product was extracted with water and the solution obtained contained about 10% oligosaccharides. 20 ml. were applied to the column and eluted with water

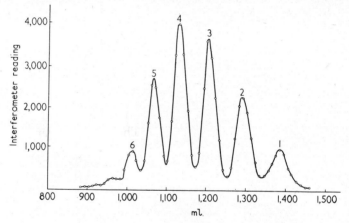

FIG. 1. Elution curve for a cellodextrin mixture. Numbers above the peak indicate the degree of polymerization.

at a rate of 30 ml. per hour. The effluent was collected in 10 ml. fractions and the concentrations were measured in a Rayleigh interferometer. The resulting curve is shown in Fig. 1. The numbers above the peaks indicate the degree of polymerization.

The material in each peak was identified by paper chromatography. The cellohexaose, cellopentaose, cellotetraose and cellotriose peaks from three almost identical experiments were pooled, dried by lyophilization and crystallized twice from water-ethanol solvents. The molecular weight was determined with the sodium borohydride-anthrone method of Peat et al. [7] (Table I).

The specific optical rotations were difficult to measure with sufficient accuracy for the higher cellodextrines because of the limited amounts available and their low solubility. The results obtained (Table I) are of the same order of magnitude as those given in the literature.

TABLE I

| Oligosaccharide | Molecular weight | | $[\alpha]_D^{25}$ |
	Theor.	Found	
Cellotriose	504	524	22·4
Cellotetraose	667	704	17·0
Cellopentaose	829	852	11·4
Cellohexaose	991	920	9·5

In collaboration with Dr. Bengt Nygård an X-ray diffraction analysis of the cellodextrins was made in a Guinier camera with Cu K_α radiation, and an exposure time of 1 hr. The films obtained were analyzed photometrically and the values for $\sin^2\theta$ calculated. In Table II the number of

TABLE II

| Oligo-saccharide | Number of reflections | $\sin^2\theta$ | | |
		I	II	III
Cellobiose	38	0·0308	0·0367	0·1044
Cellotriose	28	0·0298	0·0361	0·1065
Cellotetraose	21	0·0296	0·0363	0·1069
Cellopentaose	15	0·0296	0·0367	0·1075
Cellohexaose	10	0·0298	0·0367	0·1082

definitely identified reflections and the $\sin^2\theta$ values are given for the three strongest and most significant ones. The reflexions obtained from cellohexaose were diffuse indicating heterogeneity. Likewise the molecular weight was lower than the theoretical value, whereas the tendency for the other oligosaccharides was towards somewhat too high values.

Discussion

Preliminary experiments to separate cellodextrins were made with a 50–100 mesh sieve fraction of Sephadex. A high flow rate could be used and an experiment in a 2500 ml. column was made in 7 hr. The analysis of the effluent fractions gave a smooth curve. Paper chromatography of the material in the fractions showed, however, that the fractions contained only two and sometimes three components.

The results were so encouraging that it was decided to try more efficient columns in order to obtain a complete separation of the oligosaccharides. Earlier investigations had shown that the best way to increase the efficiency was to use smaller dextran gel particles, and consequently this approach was chosen. A sieve fraction passing through 200 mesh proved satisfactory.

As seen from Fig. 1 the volume between the peaks is only between 50 and 100 ml. compared with a total bed volume of 2000 ml. Thus, it was necessary to pack the column very carefully, but once packed it could be used for a long time. For example, in three experiments made with the same cellodextrin material the elution patterns were practically identical. There was a slight variation in the positions of the maxima but the form of the peaks and the resolution was the same. As seen in Fig. 1 the zones overlapped slightly indicating that a complete separation was not obtained. The amount of contamination in the peaks was so small that it was eliminated in the crystallizations. This was evidently not the case for the cellohexaose which showed inhomogeneity by some of the criteria used.

The volume of the sample must not be larger than $V_i(K_D'' - K_D')$ where V_i is the volume of water inside the gel grains and K_D'' and K_D' are the distribution coefficients of the solutes to be separated. For the oligosaccharides in the column used the sample volume must be less than 80 ml. and in practice considerably less. On the other hand the process itself is insensitive to the solute concentration if the viscosity is low. Thus, an optimal amount is separated if the concentration is high and the volume about one-fourth of the calculated value. To isolate a large amount of one of the oligosaccharides a two-step procedure may be preferable in which a preliminary rapid separation is made in a short column packed with, say, the 50–100 mesh sieve fraction. A further fractionation is then made in a high-efficiency column.

The outlined procedure is in principle applicable to any separation within a series of homologues in which the molecular size difference is at least as large as for the oligosaccharides. With ionized solutes, however, it is necessary to take the effect of the charges into consideration. This means that separations often have to be made in the presence of strong electrolytes. High-efficiency separations may also be made in higher molecular weight ranges. Dextrans on molecular weights up to about 40 000 have been fractionated with excellent results in dextran gels with different degrees of cross-linking.

References

1. Dickey, E. E., and Wolfrom, M. L., *J. Amer. chem. Soc.* **71,** 825 (1949).
2. Whittaker, D. R., *Arch. Biochem. Biophys.* **53,** 439 (1954).
3. Lathe, G. H., and Ruthven, C. R. J., *Biochem. J.* **62,** 665 (1956).
4. Porath, J., and Flodin, P., *Nature, Lond.* **183,** 1657 (1959).
5. Flodin, P., and Granath, K., *in* "Symposium über Makromolekyle", Wiesbaden, Oct. 1959.
6. Flodin, P., *J. Chromatography* **5,** 103 (1961).
7. Peat, S., Whelan, W. J., and Roberts, J. G., *J. chem. Soc.* 2258 (1956).

Discussion

HESTRIN: Would it be possible with the help of this method to separate linear from branched oligosaccharides when they have the same molecular weight?

FLODIN: It might be possible. There is, however, no experimental evidence as yet.

SMITH: Does this maximum molecular weight hold for proteins also?

FLODIN: Roughly. The size is probably the determining factor in the separations and therefore the molecular weight, though more convenient to use, is an inadequate measure.

SMITH: If you have a molecule which is the size of, say, 100 Å could you do anything with that?

FLODIN: Molecules larger than about 50 000 in molecular weight can be separated from smaller ones on the loosest gels. Even haemoglobin, however, is somewhat retarded in relation to gamma globulin and serum albumin.

AUTHOR INDEX

Numbers in brackets are reference numbers and are included to assist in locating references in which the authors' names are not mentioned in the text. Numbers in italics indicate the page on which the reference is listed.

SUBJECT INDEX

A

Acceptor-RNA (see s-RNA)

Acetobacter xylinum, cellulose synthesis by, 317–322

N-Acetylhexosamine, compounds in mucopeptide, 290–293

Adenosine monophosphate (AMP), incorporation into s-RNA, 114, 119

Adipose tissue, pinocytosis in, 158

Alanine, incorporation into mucopeptide, 290–292
  incorporation into proteins of thymus nuclei, 270–274, 276

Albumin (serum), formation in microsomes in rat liver, 255–258

Alloxan diabetes, effect on mucopolysaccharide metabolism, 344, 337

Amino acid activation, in cell nuclei, 263–265

Amino acid incorporation, effect of histones on, 275–276
  into ribosomes of cell nuclei, 268–269

Amino acid transfer, to RNA in cell nuclei, 265–267

Amino acid transport to nucleus, 270–274

Amino acid uptake, by isolated cell nuclei, 261–263

2-Aminofluorene, effect on liver glycogen, 230–231
  effect on protein synthesis, 226, 229–233

2-Aminonaphthalene, effect on protein synthesis, 229–231

Amoeba, defaecation in, 165
  pinocytosis in, 157–161, 163–166

Amylase, release from RNP particles, 241–242

Antigens, incorporation of isotopes into, 213–218
  in microsomes, 209–218
  transitory antigens of microsomes, 212–213, 218

Apurinic acid, 73

Arginine, incorporation into acceptor-RNA, 297–307

Arginine-activating enzyme, 305–307
  effect of guanidino derivatives on, 301–303
  levels during different growth conditions, 300–301
  purification from *Escherichia* 299–300

Arginine-RNA, 300–301, 306–307
  assay of, 298–299
  properties of, 303–305

8-Azaguanine, effect on protein synthesis, 281–286

B

Bacillus cereus, DNA synthesis in, 281
  protein synthesis in, 281–286

Benzimidazole compounds, effects on cell wall mucopeptide synthesis, 293–294

"Bunched" nucleotides, definition of, 71

C

Calf thymus, DNA biosynthesis in, 95
  DNA from, isolation of, 69–70
  nucleotide arrangement in, 77, 89

Caspersson's and Santesson's cells, "A", 182–190, 194
  "B", 181–188, 189–190

Catalase, synthesis in *Bacillus cereus*, 283–286

Cellodextrin (Sephadex), in gel filtration, 345–348

Cellulose, extracellular synthesis of, 317–322

Cellulose "Ultrastrand", 322

Ceruloplasmin, partition of, 37–39

Chicken embryos, enzymes for DNA synthesis from, 103–110

Chondroitin sulphuric acids (A, B and C), 327–322

Chymotrypsin, effect of urea and guanidine hydrochloride on, 60

Cluster analysis, 83–84

Coenzymes, synthesis of, 104

Cortisone, and amino acid incorporation in liver systems, 229–233
  effect on turnover of skin mucopolysaccharides, 333–334

Counter-current distribution, 33, 38, 39

Cytidine monophosphate (CMP), incorporation into DNA, 104–109
  incorporation into s-RNA, 117–118, 120

Cytidine triphosphate (CTP), incorporation into s-RNA, 118–119

D

Deoxycytidine monophosphate (deoxy-CMP), incorporation into DNA, 104, 106, 108

Deoxyguanosine monophosphate (deoxy-GMP), incorporation into DNA, 104, 109

Deoxyribonuclease (DNA-ase), micrococcal, 105–106
  pancreatic, 72–73, 105

Deoxyribonucleic acid (DNA), acid degradation of, 73–75